EGON RONAY'S
Jameso ... 094

Ireland

**Over 500 of the best hotels, restaurants & pubs
in the Republic of Ireland and Northern Ireland**

**Egon Ronay's Guides
35 Tadema Road
London SW10 0SW**

Consultant **Egon Ronay**
Editorial Director **Bernard Branco**
Managing Editor **Andrew Eliel**
Publishing Director **Angela Nicholson**
Sales & Marketing Director **Stephen Prendergast**

**First published 1994 by Pan Macmillan
Publishers Ltd, Cavaye Place,
London SW10 9PG**

987654321

Cover Design © **Elizabeth Ayer**

Cover Concept and Illustration
© **Chris Ackerman-Eveleigh**

TX 907
.5
.I73 E36

1994

**The contents of this book are believed correct at
the time of printing. Nevertheless, the publisher
can accept no responsibility for errors or
omissions or changes in the details given.**

ISBN 0333 62206 5

Printed and bound in Great Britain by
BPC Hazell Books Ltd
A member of
The British Printing Company Ltd

*All restaurant and hotel inspections are
anonymous and carried out by Egon Ronay's
Guides' team of professional inspectors.
Inspectors may reveal their identities at hotels
in order to check all the rooms and other facilities.
The Guide is independent in its editorial selection
and does not accept advertising, payment or
hospitality from listed establishments.*

Contents

Message from Jameson   4

Foreword from the Minister for Tourism and Trade, Ireland   6

Introduction from Managing Editor Andrew Eliel   7

How to Use This Guide   10

De Luxe Hotels, Starred Restaurants & Map   13

Ireland 1994 Awards

Ireland 1994 Awards	Hotel of the Year	19
	Restaurant of the Year	23
	Host of the Year	27
	Chef of the Year	31
	Food Pub of the Year	33
	Best Table Presentation	37
	Best Irish Brown Bread	39
	Wine Cellar of the Year	43
	Cheese Dish of the Year	47
	Seafood Restaurant of the Year	50
	Seafood Dish of the Year	51
	Irish Meat Restaurant of the Year	57
	Desserts of the Year	61
	Irish Cheeseboard of the Year	65
	Coffee Award of Excellence	69
	Oriental Restaurant of the Year	73
	Business Hotel of the Year	77
	Pub of the Year	81
	Newcomers of the Year	85
	International Hospitality Award	89

The Attraction of the Emerald Isle by Georgina Campbell   90

Useful Information   96

Development of Irish Food and Hospitality
by Georgina Campbell   97

Main Entries	Republic of Ireland	103
	Northern Ireland	259

Quick Reference Lists   275

Entries listed in county order, featuring conference,
banqueting and leisure facilities   295

Maps	Ireland map & Dublin town plans	316

Index   323

Advertisers Index and Acknowledgements   329

Readers' Comments tear-out Pages   331

A word of welcome from the distillers of Jameson Irish Whiskey.

Jameson, the world's most popular

Irish Whiskey is part of the renowned welcome and hospitality to be found in Ireland. So it is fitting that Jameson be associated with this Guide.

Whiskey is an intrinsic part of Irish life and whether you are enjoying the warmth of an Irish pub, relaxing in a hotel, or sitting back after a memorable meal, there is always an

occasion to savour a glass of Jameson Irish Whiskey.

We take great pride in the quality of Jameson. From the rich countryside of Ireland come nature's finest barley and crystal clear water. These natural ingredients are carefully distilled three times and then slowly matured for years in oak casks to produce an exceptionally smooth whiskey.

I hope you will enjoy using this Guide as you sample some of the best of Irish hospitality, food and – of course – Whiskey!

Richard Burrows
Chairman
Irish Distillers Group

JAMESON The Spirit of Ireland

FOREWORD
from the
Minister for Tourism and Trade, Ireland

Egon Ronay's Jameson Guide to Ireland is an exercise in the pursuit of excellence. It is this spirit of seeking out and rewarding the best that helps raise standards and inspires others to follow the same path. We must cultivate it in all aspects of our enterprises, regardless of the market area in which we operate.

The publication in 1994 within this highly regarded international range of titles of a guide specifically for Ireland is a recognition of the high standards being achieved in Irish hotels, restaurants and pubs. It will give a big boost to confidence and create greater awareness of our products and services. This will, ultimately, lead to employment creation.

My congratulations to all the establishments listed and recommended in the Guide. Particular congratulations to those establishments that have been chosen to receive the special awards.

I hope that Irish people as well as our international visitors will use and enjoy the establishments listed in the Guide.

Charlie McCreevy, TD

Introduction by Managing Editor Andrew Eliel

My long affection for Ireland, and particularly County Kerry, started almost exactly 30 years ago when I spent the occasional holiday visiting an Irish friend (at that time we were both students at the Swiss Hotel School in Lausanne). The family's house was in Dublin, and it was a real treat being taken to either *Jammet* or the *Russell Hotel Restaurant*, the latter then among Europe's finest; there was also a holiday home just outside Sneem, and I remember, as fresh-faced exponents of the skilled art of waiting, being often asked to help out at tables at *Parknasilla*, then a Great Southern Hotel favoured by sports lovers. I'm told we spent more time pioneering the hotel's speedboat for water-skiing trips and jaunts around the bay – purely to solicit tips from guests – than we actually did in the dining room, though I find this hard to believe!

Moving on ten years, my friend was by now a restaurateur of some note with a splendid restaurant in Co Wicklow (included in the Guide), and my visits increased, as did my geographical knowledge, touring in Donegal, Galway, Tipperary and the North; so, by the time I joined Egon Ronay's Guides in the early 80s, I had a high opinion of the quality of catering and renowned hospitality, and needed no second invitation to carry out further inspections, sometimes touring for a month or more at a time. Our UK *Hotels & Restaurants Guide* has always featured Ireland prominently – the only national guide to do so comprehensively – thus my only surprise is that it has taken us so long to bring out this new Guide, entirely devoted to Ireland, and which I hope will be the first of many. As the bush telegraph reverberates and more people (not least hoteliers and restaurateurs unknown to us) become aware of the Guide, I am confident that it will expand.

This Guide covers the full spectrum of establishments from hotels and restaurants through to pubs, brasseries, cafés and the like, and as with all Egon Ronay's Guides the criteria for an establishment's inclusion remain the same: our inspectors must be satisfied that the standards of accommodation, cooking or both meet or exceed our exacting requirements. All inspections are anonymous and are carried out by our own team of professional inspectors, who may reveal their identities *after* their meals or visits. The Guide is independent in its editorial selection and does not accept advertising, payment or hospitality from listed establishments.

In addition to recommending establishments for inclusion in a guide, Egon Ronay's Guides work in several other ways to promote higher standards in the hospitality industry. Establishments can receive coveted stars for exceptionally high standards of cooking achieved on a consistent basis, and there is also a wide selection of awards recognising excellence in all the major categories. The importance of these awards should not be underestimated since they reward in a tangible way those who have reached the pinnacle in their field through their hard work, dedication and creativity. Egon Ronay's Guides and the companies supporting these awards are delighted to give due recognition to the winners chosen by the Guide's inspectorate.

Continuity

These consistent standards of excellence are best illustrated by those indefatigable professionals who have been dispensing hospitality, sometimes for fifty years or more (and in the case of Joe McCollam at P J McCollam, Cushendall, Co Antrim an incredible 73 years!). Others at the forefront are: Constance Aldridge at *Mount Falcon Castle*, Ballina; the Allens at *Ballymaloe,* Shanagarry; the Ryans at *Arbutus Lodge*, Cork; the Thompsons at *Newport House*, Newport; Aidan MacManus at the *King Sitric*, Howth; and Rory Murphy at *Ashford Castle*, Cong – to name but a few. There are, of course, many others and indeed some of the pubs recommended in this Guide have been in the same family for several generations.

Welcome

Inveterate travellers themselves, the Irish have always been the most welcoming of hosts in return, and with a way and pace of life that is perhaps more relaxed than anywhere else in the world it is not surprising that the country appeals to many so visitors – Americans, especially, return to their roots time and time again, but also increasingly French, Germans and Italians. With tourism playing such an essential role in the country's economy, which in turn builds up employment levels, it's important that the hotel and catering industry leads by example. There is no doubt that it does, and when these high standards are accompanied by a smile, you have a winning combination. Furthermore, it is estimated that given a successful peace initiative, visitors to the North could increase within three to five years by 40% and thousands of new jobs could be created in the tourist industry.

Service charges

To tip or not to tip? how much do you add? is service included? optional service charge; compulsory service charge; service left to your discretion etc. Over the years we have addressed the subject of the service charge many times in our Guides, and it's one that in the UK a Conservative MP sought to ban, with the backing of several associations. Under a 10-minute rule bill the matter was debated earlier in the year, but that's probably as far as it will go under the present government. In Ireland the situation is equally unclear – some hotels and restaurants automatically add service, others don't, and you could be in for a nasty shock since several hotels add up to 15% on a hotel bill, as well as on restaurant bills. Though we include service in the prices we quote (see How to Use this Guide) always ask at the time of booking what's included. You might justifiably question whether one should be expected to pay 15% service charge for someone to take the cork out of a wine bottle – in effect a £20 wine becomes £23!

Wine lists

There are indeed some marvellous lists throughout the country, with of course fine clarets featuring prominently, since historically there has long been an Irish involvement in Bordeaux (Barton, Kirwan, Lynch, MacCarthy and others). But when our panel assesses these lists we encounter so many misspellings that we believe purists may be put off. Most common mistakes can be found among champagnes (Tattinger, Pol Roget and Hiedseick) with Gewurtztraminer, Muscat de Riversaltes and Nappa in close pursuit! So we make a heartfelt plea – if in doubt please read the labels. Tasting notes written alongside wines can sometimes be helpful, but not, we suggest, when they make spurious claims such as "rated as one of the top 20 buys" – by whom?

In this Guide we encourage restaurants to serve a variety of quality wines by the glass (those that do receive the appropriate symbol), since we believe that customers are no longer content just to be offered a glass of house white or red, especially when there is a variety of gadgets to preserve the quality of opened bottles. Finally, peculiarly to Irish wine lists you may encounter a *snipe* – a glass of champagne, a large one we hope, since we have noted prices up to £11.50.

Punts and pounds

At the time of going to press (March 1994) the Irish punt and the British pound were almost at parity, but it's as well to remind readers that the prices for establishments in the Republic of Ireland are quoted in punts, and those in Northern Ireland in pounds.

Acknowledgements

Getting a new Egon Ronay's Guide off the ground is never an easy task, and we are indebted to all the companies who have supported the Guide and its awards, thereby demonstrating their commitment to the industry and the economy in general. We would also particularly like to thank the following people for all their hard work: (in alphabetical order) our own resident Irish colleague Georgina Campbell, who was instrumental in setting the wagon rolling and has written the features on the history of Irish food and a portrait of Ireland; John Duffy of Aer Lingus; Betty Griffin for introducing us to a host of charming and influential people and keeping our diary; and finally to Matt McNulty and his team at Bord Fáilte who have lent us their support at every turn.

How to Use This Guide

This Guide includes not only our recommended establishments but many other interesting features and a wealth of useful quick reference lists designed to help you select the hotel, restaurant or pub that best suits your requirements. A list of all establishments in county order, with key statistics and prices, lets you see at a glance what is available in the area where you intend to stay or eat. Conference and banqueting capacities are included – a boon to organisers of business meetings or functions. Places of interest are listed under the nearest relevant location throughout the Guide. For details of all listings consult the contents page.

Order of Entries

Republic of Ireland appears first, in alphabetical order by **location**; Northern Ireland locations come after those in the Republic. See contents page for specific page numbers, and the index at the back of the Guide for individual entries by establishment name.

Map References

Map references alongside each hotel, restaurant or pub entry are to the maps at the back of the book. Use this section in conjunction with the county listings to select establishments in areas you wish to visit. Dublin has its own city maps and references alongside Dublin entries refer to those maps. Entries under Blackrock, Dun Laoghaire, Monkstown and Stillorgan are also plotted on the Dublin maps.

Accommodation

Hotel entries are identified by the letter '**H**' or '**HR**'. The former includes several superior guest houses where the public rooms are limited (apart, perhaps, from a drawing room) and the restaurant is only open to residents; these 'Private House Hotels' are ungraded. '**HR**' indicates a hotel with a recommended restaurant; Private House Hotels that offer good food will still be categorised as '**H**' if their restaurant is not open to the public; the entry will indicate where this is the case. '**A**' denotes accommodation classified by Bord Fáilte as a Private House or Irish Home. '**AR**' denotes '**A**' classified accommodation with a recommended restaurant.

Prices

These are based on current high-season rates at the time of going to press and include VAT, for a *double room for two occupants with private bath and cooked breakfast*. Wherever possible we have included the service charge that many Irish hotels add on to accommodation as well as food bills; this can be up to 15%.

The Percentage shown on a hotel entry is an individual rating arrived at after careful testing, inspection and calculation according to our unique grading system. **We assess** hotels on 23 factors, which include the quality of service and the public rooms – their cleanliness, comfort, state of repair and general impression. Bedrooms are looked at for size, comfort, cleanliness and decor. The exterior of the building, efficiency of reception, conduct and appearance of the staff, room service and leisure facilities are among other factors. The percentage is arrived at by comparing the total marks given for the 23 factors with the maximum the hotel could have achieved.

Percentage ratings

Hotels rated at 80% or over are classified 'De Luxe'. A map of these hotels is on page 13.

The Size of a hotel and the prices charged are not considered in the grading, but the food is, and **if we recommend meals in a hotel a separate entry is made for its restaurant.**

Certain accommodation is ungraded. Lodge-style chain hotels offer cheap, practical accommodation, usually in convenient locations for one-night stop-overs. Private House Hotels are de luxe 'bed and breakfast' establishments offering comfortable (often luxurious) accommodation and personal service. Inns are distinguished from hotels proper by their more modest nature, usually with respect to the day rooms. For our purposes an inn is normally either a pub with hotel-style accommodation or a small hotel with a bar and the atmosphere of a pub. Any hotel undergoing major construction or refurbishment programme at the time of research is also ungraded.

Bargain breaks. Almost all hotels now offer bargain breaks of some kind. Specific details regarding the availability and price of such breaks should be checked with individual establishments. In addition to bargain breaks many hotels regularly offer price reductions across their range; seasonal changes, late availability, single rooms, room upgrades – remember the price quoted in this guide is for high season. Phone the hotels in the area you're visiting and see what they have to offer.

Restaurants

Restaurants open to the public are identified by the letter '**R**'.

★★★   ★★   ★

We award one to three stars for excellence of cooking. One star represents cooking much above average, two outstanding cooking, and three the best in the British Isles. A map of Irish starred restaurants is on page 13.

↑ beside stars indicates a restaurant at the top of its star range.

↑ by itself indicates a restaurant approaching star status.

The category '**RR**' denotes a restaurant with rooms, a category based on *restaurants avec chambres* in France. Food is the main attraction, but overnight accommodation is also available. A list of these restaurants appears at the back of the Guide.

We only include restaurants where the cooking comes up to our minimum standards, however attractive the place may be in other respects. We take into account how well the restaurant achieves what it sets out to do as reflected in the menu, decor, prices, publicity, atmosphere – factors that add up to some sort of expectation.

Symbols

All symbols are judged and awarded by Egon Ronay's Guides' inspection team. Crowns are awarded to restaurants offering a degree of traditional luxury ⚜ or some striking modern features ▮ They have nothing to do with the quality of the cooking.

- ♪⟩⟩ **Outstanding table presentation** – sponsored by The National Dairy Council
- ♡ **Good home-made bread** – sponsored by Bord Fáilte
- ⌂ **Outstanding wine list**
- ♒ **Good range of wines by the glass**
- 🍲 **Good dishes using cooked cheese** – sponsored by The National Dairy Council
- ◉ **Quality seafood** – sponsored by Bord Iacscaigh Mhara
- 🐄 **Good Irish meat dishes** – sponsored by CBF Irish Livestock & Meat Board
- 🍧 **Notable desserts** – sponsored by Fyffes
- ⌂ **Good selection of Irish cheeses** – sponsored by The Traditional Cheese Company Ltd
- ♡ **Good quality coffee** – sponsored by Robt Roberts Ltd
- ▦ **Family-friendly establishments**

Restaurant prices, correct at the time of going to press, are for a **three-course meal for two including one of the least expensive bottles of wine, coffee, VAT and service.**

Set-price menus. Prices quoted will often not include service and usually exclude wine. They are not necessarily of three courses. Where two prices are given thus – £14.50/£17.75 – it indicates that there is a 2 or 3-course option; prices given thus – £17.95 & £24.95 – indicates that there are two different set-price menus. A great number of restaurants around the country now *only* offer a set-price menu (although this will usually include a choice).

Many restaurants offer at least one main course for vegetarians; tell them your requirements when you book. There are lists of no-smoking restaurants and those offering a serious vegetarian menu in the Quick Reference List section, as well as those establishments that we consider to be family-friendly.

Pubs

Pubs, identified by the letter '**P**', are recommended for their food and/or atmosphere. They vary from establishments that are more 'Inn' or modest restaurant to much simpler local bars that not only serve a good pint of stout but might also act as the village shop and general meeting place. Only where food is specifically mentioned in the entry is it positively recommended. Gaming machines are forbidden by law in the Republic.

De Luxe Hotels

Republic of Ireland

88%   **Cong** Ashford Castle
87%   **Kenmare** Park Hotel
     Kenmare Sheen Falls Lodge
     Straffan Kildare Hotel
84%   **Thomastown** Mount Juliet Hotel
81%   **Adare** Adare Manor
     Gorey Marlfield House

□ Hotel
● Restaurant

Starred Restaurants

Republic of Ireland * ↑

Dublin Patrick Guilbaud

Republic of Ireland *

Ahakista Shiro
Boyle Cromleach Lodge
Cork Arbutus Lodge
Cork Clifford's
Dublin Le Coq Hardi
Dublin Le Mistral
Kanturk Assolas Country House
Kenmare Park Hotel
Kenmare Sheen Falls Lodge
Moycullen Drimcong House
Shanagarry Ballymaloe House

Northern Ireland *

Belfast Roscoff
Portrush Ramore

Republic of Ireland ↑

Adare Adare Manor
Adare The Mustard Seed
Blackrock Clarets
Cong Ashford Castle
Dublin Cooke's Café
Dublin Zen
Killarney Aghadoe Heights Hotel
Kinsale Chez Jean-Marc
Newmarket-on-Fergus
  Dromoland Castle
Mallow Longueville House

Northern Ireland ↑

Helen's Bay Deanes on the Square
Londonderry Beech Hill House

DRINKING THE BEST OF IRISH

BY JOHN CLEMENT RYAN
AUTHOR OF "IRISH WHISKEY"

Health and long life to you
Land without rent to you
The woman (or man) of your choice to you
A child every year to you
and may you be half an hour in heaven before
the devil knows you're dead!

*Soldiers of Henry II and Elizabeth I
appreciated Irish Whiskey*

The art of distilling whisk(e)y has been around almost as long as people have enjoyed fine food, and Irish Whiskey is the world's oldest whisk(e)y

Finest barley

type. Nobody really knows where the story of whisk(e)y began or who began it. However we do know that the secret of distillation was brought to Ireland, probably from the Middle East, by missionary monks around the 6th century AD. They discovered the *alembic* being used for distilling perfume – they invented *whiskey* and called their version of the alembic a *Pot Still*.

Even the word whiskey comes from the Irish words *Uisce Beatha* (phonetically "isk'ke-ba'ha"). How the name came into the English language was when the soldiers of King Henry II paid what turned out to be the first of several uninvited visits to Ireland in 1170, they found the native Irish consuming their *Uisce Beatha*. Henry's soldiers soon got the hang of it, but never learned to pronounce the word *Uisce Beatha* and so, during the following centuries, the word was gradually anglicised, first to *Uisce*, then to *Fuisce*, and then finally to the word *Whiskey* that we know today.

The Old Bushmills Distillery, the world's oldest licensed whiskey distillery is located in Co. Antrim. They first received their license to distil in 1608 and so have nearly 400 years of tradition behind them. Look for Black Bush as a digestif or with a little plain water, and for Bushmills Malt, the only single malt brand of Irish whiskey.

Purest water

John Jameson founded his distillery in Dublin in 1780 and Jameson

Triple Distillation

soon became the best-known Irish Whiskey in the world, a position it still holds today. A glass of Jameson is particularly appreciated as an aperitif, either on the rocks with a little plain water, and as an accompaniment to a raw or smoked fish dish, and as a digestif try twelve year old *Jameson 1780.*

Matured in Oak Casks

The taste difference between Scotch and Irish is not something that words can convey, and stems largely from the difference in production methods. Both Scotch and Irish are based on barley, part of which is malted, and here comes the first difference: Malt for Irish is dried in a closed kiln, and not over open peat fires which gives the smoky flavour that is typical of Scotch – that smoky flavour is deliberately absent from Irish, and some of the subtleties and delicacies of taste can be appreciated because of the absence of the smoky taste.

Secondly, Irish Whiskey is distilled three times in the old-fashioned copper Pot Stills to ensure the maximum purity of the spirit, and no other whisk(e)y category in the world is distilled more than twice.

Finally, Irish is matured in oak casks for a minimum of three years by law, but in practice between five and eight years, and in the case of some of the premium brands ten, and twelve years. As well as the brands from the Jameson and Bushmills stables, other brands that will be encountered are Powers Gold Label, the favourite in Ireland.

John Jameson Distillery, founded in 1780

If you are travelling around Ireland, be sure to call in to learn the Story of Irish Whiskey. If you are in the North, visit the Bushmills Distillery, located in the village of Bushmills in Co. Antrim. This is open to visitors throughout the year (Mondays to Thursdays 9.00-12.00, 13.30-15.30 and Fridays 9.00-11.45, no reservations necessary). When in Dublin, go to the old Jameson distillery at Bow Street to see the *Irish Whiskey Corner* a museum to the history of Irish Whiskey where visitors are welcome. Here there is a tour daily (Mon-Fri) at 15.30 sharp. Finally *The Jameson Heritage Centre* in Midleton, Co. Cork, just 13 miles east of Cork City, is open to visitors throughout the

summer months during each day including weekends from 10.00-16.00. Visitors enjoy a guided tour through the Old Distillery, a whisk(e)y tasting, an audio-visual show, coffee shop, souvenir shop, and craft shops on the site.

After a fine meal, lift your glass of Jameson or Bushmills and wish an old Irish Toast to your companions:

> *May the road rise to meet you*
> *May the wind be always at your back*
> *May the sun shine warm upon your face*
> *And the rain fall soft upon your fields*
> *And until we meet again*
> *May God hold you in the hollow*
> *of His Hand.*

Matured to Perfection

THE IRISH WHISKEY TRAIL

Irish Whiskey is part of the rich heritage of Ireland and its people. Visitors can relive this fascinating story by visiting the historic distilleries that have made Irish Whiskey famous throughout the world.

In Dublin, at the old Jameson distillery at Bow Street, is *The Irish Whiskey Corner*, a museum to the history of Irish Whiskey where visitors are welcome. Here there is a tour

daily (Mon to Fri) at 15h30 sharp, and in summer an extra tour at 11h00 May-Oct. There is a charge of £3 per person, and the tour includes an audio-visual film, the opportunity to do a whisk(e)y tasting and to visit the museum. There is a very fine gift shop at the Irish Whiskey Corner, where souvenirs, including bottles of all brands of Irish Whiskey are

available for sale. The *Midleton Very Rare* Book which records the name and signature of the owner of each bottle of Ireland's finest whiskey is kept there.

At the Old Distillery in Midleton, Co. Cork, just 13 miles east of Cork City, the buildings on the 10 acre site have been refurbished

and opened as a major new tourist attraction called *The Jameson Heritage Centre*. Here we tell the story of Irish Whiskey to visitors with the aid of some magnificent artefacts, including a 40' Water Wheel, an original stationary Steam Engine, a charming steam-powered fire engine, and best of all the largest Pot Still in the world!

Open every day from 17 March to end October including weekends from 10h00 to 18h00 (last tour commences at 16h00), the entrance fee is £3.50 (£1.50 for children, and group & family rates are also available), which will permit visitors to enjoy an audio-visual show, a guided tour through the Old Distillery, a whisk(e)y tasting, a coffee shop, a large gift shop selling all brands of Irish Whiskey, and craft shops on the site. During winter, groups can visit by prior arrangement.

Bushmills Distillery, located in the village of Bushmills in Co. Antrim, is open to visitors throughout the year on Mondays to Thursdays 9h-12h, 13h30-15h30, and Fridays 9h-11h45, and Friday and Saturday opening 15h in summer (July-Sept), Bushmills is a jewel on the Tourist Trail known as the "Causeway Coast", which includes

the Giant's Causeway, one of the great natural wonders of the world. Visitors are welcome (£2 entry), and have a guided tour of the distillery, a 'dram' of Bushmills, and the opportunity to shop in two delightful souvenir shops, one of which sells whiskey!

JAMESON

Established ⚓ *Since 1780*

· SINE METU ·

IRISH WHISKEY

CONGRATULATIONS
TO
THE HOTEL OF THE YEAR

If travel broadens the mind then it also
tires the body. One step inside an Irish
hotel however, and your rest is completely
assured. There's something about our
friendly atmosphere that puts people at
their ease straight away.

Jameson Irish Whiskey is another
welcoming feature of Irish hotels. A taste of
its warmth is like tasting the authentic spirit
of Ireland and her people. Sláinte.

John Jameson&Son

JAMESON The Spirit of Ireland

Ireland 1994
Hotel of the Year

Ashford Castle
Cong, Co Mayo

The tingle of expectation as guests arrive at this part-13th-century castle, part-French-style chateau in spectacular surroundings, is fulfilled by a hotel that is both supremely elegant and perfectly managed. Standards of excellence are evident at every turn, whether you are relaxing in the grand and sophisticated splendour, or enjoying impeccable service from courteous and committed staff.

Sponsored by

LEGEND has it that Irish monks invented whiskey, learning of distillation from the perfumers of the Orient. They called their discovery *Uisce Beatha* (the water of life) and to this day the finest of whiskey is distilled by the Irish.

A visit to the Jameson Heritage Centre in Midleton, Co.

Cork will take you right to the heart of this cherished tradition. You are invited to take a two-hour tour of the Centre – it's a beautifully restored 18th century, self-contained industrial complex, unique in Britain and Ireland. Delight in the fully-operational water wheel and be amazed by the copper pot still of 32,000 gallons, the largest in the world.

An audio-visual presentation, available in six languages, breathes life into the Irish whiskey legend.

After the history comes the tasting. Relax in the atmosphere of a traditional Irish pub and sample Ireland's finest whiskey. *Sláinte.*

Lose yourself in the charm of another age – the Jameson Heritage Centre with its craft and coffee shops is located on the main Cork-Waterford road which links the ferry terminals of Rosslare and Ringaskiddy. We're open from 10.00am to 4.00pm, May to October. Telephone John Callely at 021-613594 or fax 021-613642 for information.

JAMESON The Spirit of Ireland

"Serve good food,

and your dinner guests will finish

every mouthful.

Open a good brandy and, regrettably,

the same is true."

ARNOLD SORENSON,
VEGAN FOOD CRITIC, CALIFORNIA.

INTRODUCE SOME CALIFORNIAN INTO
THE CONVERSATION.

SINGLE CASK MATURED BRANDY.

Ireland 1994
Restaurant of the Year

Cliffords
Cork, Co Cork

There has been something of a renaissance in Irish cooking in recent times, and one of the newer stars is Michael Clifford. His regularly-changing menus are both creative and inventive, and rely very much on local produce (Clonakilty black pudding, spring lamb, free-range duck and seafood). Service, led by Deirdre Clifford, is excellent and the end result is the equal of any top restaurant. The hard-working couple deserve their success, for this is an establishment of which Cork and Ireland can be justly proud.

The city he loved. The cafe she remembered. California's best loved wine.

Memories await. The Wines of Ernest & Julio Gallo, California.

WINE MAKER'S NOTES: Aged in oak, cork matured. Very dry and well balanced. Classic

Across the bay to San Francisco.

THE WINE CELLARS OF
Ernest & Julio Gallo
CABERNET SAUVIGNON
CALIFORNIA
RED WINE/VIN ROUGE

…bernet character with hints of berry, plum and spice. Superb with red meat and pasta.

JAMESON

Established · *Since 1780*

· SINE METU ·

IRISH WHISKEY

CONGRATULATIONS
TO
THE HOST OF THE YEAR

*"May the roof above us never fall in and may
we friends below never fall out."*

Only in Ireland are there so many old
sayings to greet a new friend. When a smile
and a handshake come as naturally as the
next breath, you know you've arrived in
good company.

Jameson Irish Whiskey is part of this great
welcome. Sip it slowly and you'll realise
you're tasting the spirit of Ireland – smooth
and friendly and always inviting.

John Jameson & Son

Ireland 1994
Host of the Year

Francis Brennan
Park Hotel Kenmare, Co Kerry

A more genial and warm-hearted host than Francis Brennan you're unlikely to meet. If he were a cricketer (perhaps he is?) he would surely open the batting for Ireland; when abroad there can be no finer ambassador to champion Ireland's cause than he. He has presided over the hotel, which is at the very top of the tree, for many years, and his infectious and charming personality (transmitted to the rest of the staff) ensures the well-being of guests.

Sponsored by

Out of Africa...

The Father of
South African Wine

Wine making in the Cape began over 350 years ago when, soon after the thirty year war, an expedition under the command of Jan Van Riebeeck (pronounced Ree-bee-ek) ended their four month voyage from Holland to South Africa.

The small fleet of three ships, led by the 200-ton Drommedaris, was sent by the Dutch East India Company to set up a food supplies station and arrived at their destination on 6th April, 1652.

On a four month sea journey at that time, a death rate of up to forty percent was not unusual, but this small fleet had just lost 2 of their company.

The 33 year old Van Riebeeck had been a ship's surgeon and noted that the Portuguese and Spanish losses at sea were less than those of the Dutch. The only difference seemed to be in their diet, the Mediterranean based fleets included wine in their on-board rations.

On arrival, Van Riebeeck quickly determined that the Cape had a Mediterranean climate and soon convinced his council of seventeen back home in Holland to send him some vine cuttings.

There are few countries that have been growing grapes as long as South Africa that can pin-point their exact winemaking beginnings.

Jan Van Riebeeck, however, kept a meticulous diary and on the 2nd of February 1659 he wrote;

**"Today, God be Praised, Wine was
pressed for the first time from Cape Grapes."**

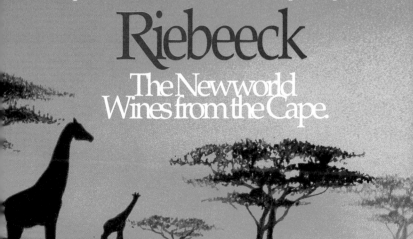

Riebeeck
The Newworld
Wines from the Cape.

Ireland 1994
Chef of the Year

Gerry Galvin
Drimcong House, Moycullen, Co Galway

Gerry and Marie Galvin opened their small country house restaurant some ten years ago. Gerry's style of cooking, from a French base, has an emphasis on the best ingredients with a dependence on organically produced vegetables, free-range chickens (plus their own eggs, of course), seasonal game, Connemara meat and local seafood (oysters, Galway Bay fish and pike from the lake). Daily, he bakes the bread, prepares the soup and makes the ice creams (a feature on the children's menu – youngsters are positively encouraged to eat at Drimcong) and his short, eclectic and frequently-changing menus always have a wide appeal. Gerry's cooking is joyful and professional, and the lovely surroundings add to the delight.

In the rolling hills of Tipperary,
nature has created this
Natural Mineral Water of unique character.
In recognition of its quality, Tipperary
has been awarded the supreme accolade
of the B.B.I Gold Medal for Excellence.

SPARKLING

TIPPERARY

Irish

NATURAL MINERAL WATER

Ireland 1994
Food Pub of the Year

Moone High Cross Inn
Bolton Hill, Moone, Co Kildare

In their rambling 18th-century pub the Clynch family are generous with both hospitality and home cooking. The fine pub food can be enjoyed throughout, either at a seat by the fire in the back bar or in the more formal dining room, or perhaps in an airy spot in the new beer garden. It's open all day for food, so you can pop in for morning coffee or help a pint of stout down with a freshly-made brown bread sandwich or a traditional dish such as bacon and cabbage, Irish stew at lunchtime, plus more involved à la carte evening meals. Don't leave without trying the grandmother of apple pies.

Sponsored by

TIPPERARY
— Irish —
NATURAL
MINERAL WATER

TO THE

connoisseur

IT'S THE

purist

WATER

IT'S NOT WHAT IS IN A MINERAL WATER

THAT DETERMINES ITS QUALITY,

IT'S WHAT IS ABSENT. IN THAT RESPECT,

TIPPERARY NATURAL MINERAL WATER

IS OF THE HIGHEST QUALITY.

IT HAS THE LOWEST MINERALISATION

OF ANY IRISH MINERAL WATER

AND A PERFECT PH BALANCE.

—

FROM THE PUREST ENVIRONMENT,

THE PURIST'S WATER.

TIPPERARY
= Irish =
NATURAL
MINERAL WATER

BY APPOINTMENT TO MOTHER NATURE

How long does it take to read the ingredients on a butter wrapper?

As long as it takes to say 100% natural.

Butter.
Often copied, never equalled.

ndc
THIS ADVERTISEMENT IS FUNDED
THROUGH THE EC COMMISSION

Ireland 1994
Best Table Presentation

The Motte
Inistioge, Co Kilkenny

Everything about Tom Reade-Duncan's and Alan Walton's intimate, characterful little restaurant is 'just right' – from the warm, welcoming atmosphere created with antiques and artistic candle-lit table settings to the carefully honed, seasonally-changing menu. Attention to detail is evident throughout: three kinds of olives to nibble over aperitifs and three kinds of bread, served with nice little chunks of butter in a pottery bowl, good choice of imaginatively presented vegetables, farmhouse cheese selection, delicious gimmick-free desserts and aromatic coffee.

Sponsored by

Just a flavour

It's impossible to show all the appeal of Ireland in one picture.

The freshness of the food ... the friendliness of the people ... the variety of places to stay and things to do.

Explore a different restaurant round every corner – no matter how simple or how gastronomic your taste.

Contact your nearest Irish Tourist Board office or travel agent and whet your appetite for the real Ireland.

Bord Fáilte
Irish Tourist Board

Bord Fáilte – Irish Tourist Board. Baggot Street Bridge, Dublin 2.
Tel: 01 6765871

Irish Tourist Board, 150 New Bond Street,
London W1Y 0AQ. Tel: 071 493 3201.

Irish Tourist Board, 345 Park Avenue, New York NY 10154.
Tel: 212 418 0800.

Ireland 1994
Best Irish Brown Bread

Strawberry Tree
Killarney, Co Kerry

Evan Doyle's total commitment to using only wild, free-range and organic produce extends to the brown and white flours for the wonderful home-made breads that he lovingly nurtures to fruition every day. Typically, a daily selection might include a traditional nutty brown loaf and white, round soda cake (both made to traditional recipes using buttermilk, bread soda, flour, salt and a little sugar) and a yeast bread with poppy seed. When the mood takes him, the selection of breads can rise to eight, using interesting ingredients like dill, wild garlic (in season), chestnuts and fruit for variety; flat soda breads are sometimes cooked in a bastable oven in front of the open fire in the bar. Elegantly appointed tables and carefully hand-scripted menus give an indication of the serious intent in Evan's kitchen.

Sponsored by

Enjoy the colour and beauty of Ireland six times a year...

Meet the Irish people and listen to their stories.

Share in the mouth-watering recipes.

Be entranced by the cream of Irish literature and poetry.

Learn of our culture and history.

Delight in the craftsmanship of traditional arts and crafts.

Read of family history and genealogy.

All this by simply subscribing to 'Ireland of the Welcomes'.

Ireland

VOL. 43 NO. 1   JANUARY-FEBRUARY 1994

OF THE WELCOMES

Ireland
OF THE WELCOMES

VOL 42 NO 6 NOVEMBER/DECEMBER 1993

RATES	1 year	2 years	3 years
	6 issues	12 issues	18 issues
Ireland:	Ir£11.00	Ir£19.00	Ir£26.00
Britain:	Stg£11.00	Stg£19.00	Stg£26.00
USA:	US$21.00	US$37.00	US$49.00

Send your name, address and cheque or credit card details to:
Ireland of the Welcomes, PO Box 84, Limerick, Ireland.
North American orders to:
Ireland of the Welcomes, PO Box 54161, Boulder,
CO 80322-4161

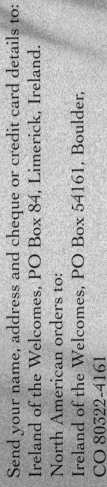

Ireland of the Welcomes, is a bi-monthly magazine published by Bord Fáilte - Irish Tourist Board.
Please allow six weeks for delivery.

JACOB'S CREEK®

"The wine is loaded with fruit, brilliantly drinkable and so easy to enjoy... This is what food and wine is all about; simple tastes, good quality; and with the wine the Australians tend to do it better than anyone else"

SANDY O'BYRNE
The Irish Times

"The rich chardonnay nose and layers of subtle fruit have a zingy freshness and a complexity that you expect from a much dearer wine. It's a revelation and I would expect it to have the same appeal as the red"

RONAN FARREN
The Sunday Independent

"It is clean, deliciously fruity with lovely tropical fruit nuances and offers remarkable value"

T.P. WHELEHAN
The Sunday Press

DISCOVER AUSTRALIA'S AWARD WINNING WINES

Ireland 1994
Wine Cellar of the Year

Arbutus Lodge
Cork, Co Cork

The perfect wine list may not exist, but what we look for is a well-balanced selection of exciting wines. The choice of vintages counts for more than length; there should be few or no duds, and a sprinkling of the best shippers and growers. Declan Ryan's cellar fulfils all the above criteria, and you will not encounter a more passionate and charming oenophile .

Sponsored by

Orlando. Australia's Award Winning Wines.

In 1847 Johann Gramp, a German immigrant and founder of Orlando Wines, planted his first vineyards at Jacob's Creek in South Australia's Barossa Valley. Within three years Johann had crushed his first grapes and made around eight gallons (36 litres) of white wine.

He later became the Barossa Valley's first commercial winemaker and named the company 'Orlando' a German derivation of the name Roland (now Rowland) Flat, the site of his first winery. Orlando expanded rapidly and by 1971 had become one of the leaders of the Australian wine industry.

Since then Orlando have carefully grown and selected premium grapes from a wide variety of cooler climate vineyard areas throughout South East Australia often many miles from their original vineyards in the Barossa Valley.

These areas such as Coonawarra and Padthaway, south of Adelaide, are becoming internationally famous for the production of some of Australia's finest wines.

BAROSSA VALLEY
EDEN VALLEY
ADELAIDE
COONAWARRA
PADTHAWAY
SYDNEY
MELBOURNE

Carrington.

CARRINGTON EXTRA BRUT AND CARRINGTON ROSE

Carrington Extra Brut is produced from early-harvested fruit to ensure delicacy and elegance. A small amount of carefully selected red wine is added to produce the Rosé. Complex in aroma and delicate fruit flavour, extended yeast contact adds richness to these top quality sparkling wines.

ORLANDO "RF" CABERNET SAUVIGNON

An excellent example of a premium, full-flavoured Cabernet Sauvignon. A rich, medium-bodied wine with minty Cabernet characters balanced by integrated soft oak flavours from 12 months maturation in French and American oak.

ORLANDO "RF" CHARDONNAY

This full-flavoured premium white is a complex blend of grapes from a large spectrum of warm and cooler regions. Aged in French and American casks this Chardonnay has distinctive oak character.

JACOB'S CREEK

With its first vintage in 1973 Jacob's Creek broke new ground in establishing a benchmark for quality Australian red wine and became the most popular brand in Australia. With 1992 being celebrated as the twentieth vintage of Jacob's Creek, it is now one of Australia's most successful wine exports being shipped to over forty international markets.

ST. HUGO COONAWARRA CABERNET SAUVIGNON

Coonawarra is regarded as the best region for Australian red wines. St. Hugo is traditionally vinified using selected premium fruit and is matured in oak for up to two years giving depth of colour and excellent fruit structure.

ST.HILARY PADTHAWAY CHARDONNAY

From Padthaway in South Australia, the components are fermented and aged in new and one year old oak for a period of six months. It is a fine elegant Chardonnay with attractive complexity on the nose and rich, round fruit flavours.

CRISPY CAMEMBERT
CHEESE MAKES MORE OF IT!

The National **ndc** Dairy Council

THIS ADVERTISEMENT IS FUNDED THROUGH THE EU COMMISSION

Ireland 1994
Cheese Dish of the Year

Truffles Restaurant
The Mall, Sligo, Co Sligo

The once-humble pizza is transformed into a gourmet attraction at Bernadette O'Shea's 'new age pizza' restaurant. From a range of eclectic ingredients some most unusual toppings are created, not least of which is 'the Irish Cheese Board', a surprisingly light taste experience adding melting goat's cheese, Cashel blue, smoked Brie, cream cheese, cottage cheese, Irish mozzarella and fresh herbs to a crisp base and fresh tomato sauce. Sounds over the top, almost indigestible? Not in the least – it's a clever example of balancing flavours that, quite simply, works. The cheeses mix and match interestingly and most unusually.

Sponsored by

**The National
Dairy Council**

It's easy to recognise a good place when you see one.

American Express Cardmembers have been doing it for years.

The secret? Instead of just relying on what they see in the window they look at the door. If there's an American Express Blue Box on it, they know they've found an establishment that cares about high standards.

Whether it's a place to eat, to sleep, to shop, or simply meet, they know they will be warmly welcomed.

So much so, they're rarely taken in by anything else.

Always a good sign.

Ireland 1994
Seafood Restaurant
of the Year

Chez Youen
Baltimore, Co Cork

Youen Jacob's long-established restaurant overlooking the harbour deals in all manner of simply prepared and zingy fresh seafood. If you want to push the boat out you order the pièce de résistance – the mighty shellfish platter with prawns, oysters, crab, velvet crab and lobster – all served in the shell and a sight to behold.

Sponsored by

Ireland 1994
Seafood Dish of the Year

Aherne's Seafood Restaurant
Youghal, Co Cork

Three generations of the FitzGibbon family have maintained the reputation of this renowned bar and seafood restaurant, which also offers accommodation. Local seafood is the speciality, appearing famously in chowder, moules marinière, a hot potato and smoked salmon gratin and Youghal Bay lobster.

Sponsored by

BIM
An Bord Iascaigh Mhara
Irish Sea Fisheries Board
is responsible for
developing and expanding
markets at home
and abroad
for Irish Seafood

For information contact:

Market Development Division,
BIM/Irish Sea Fisheries Board/
An Bord Iascaigh Mhara,
Crofton Road,
Dun Laoghaire,
Co.Dublin,
Ireland.

Tel: 353 1 2841544
Fax: 353 1 2841123

IRISH SEAFOOD
...Nature's Best

IRELAND'S

NUMBER 1

BUSINESS

PUBLICATION

CBF
congratulates the
Irish Meat Restaurant of the Year
The Dunraven Arms Hotel

and the
Irish Meat Restaurant Award Winners

Assolas Country House
Cromleach Lodge Country House
Le Coq Hardi
Rathsallagh House

Irish Meat Restaurant of the Year Regional Winners

Dunraven Arms Adare, Co Limerick

see facing page

Le Coq Hardi Ballsbridge, Dublin

John and Catherine Howard give due recognition to the small producers who deliver daily to their club-like restaurant, happy to demonstrate support for excellent 'cottage' industries who help to maintain their fine standards. Tender fillet of best Irish lamb may be encased in puff pastry with duxelles and served with thyme-spiked jus; prime beef steaks may be served with a red wine sauce, glazed shallots and beef marrow. The renowned wine list is as fine as the meat they serve.

Cromleach Lodge Boyle, Co Sligo

Beautiful views over Lough Arrow vie for the attention of diners in the restaurant, where owner/chef Moira Tighe's menu includes well-presented meat dishes like loin of lamb scented with Irish Mist and rosemary (or garlic and Madeira), beef fillet served with Roquefort sauce or marinated beef stuffed with vegetables.

Rathsallagh House Dunlavin, Co Wicklow

Freshness and quality are bywords in the kitchen at Joe and Kay O'Flynn's Rathsallagh House, where roast rib of beef with fresh horseradish sauce, sirloin steaks, herb-stuffed rack of lamb and barbecued leg of Wicklow lamb often feature on the short menu of sound home-cooked dishes.

Assolas Country House Kanturk, Co Cork

Hazel Bourke is well supplied in the kitchen at elegant Assolas House, with vegetables, soft fruits and herbs from a walled kitchen garden and quality meat from trusted local suppliers. She conjures up magical dishes like roast loin of local lamb with a rosemary-scented jus and her own mint jelly.

IRISH MEAT BOARD

Ireland 1994
Irish Meat Restaurant
of the Year

Dunraven Arms
Adare, Co Limerick

Surrounded by thatched cottages in one of Ireland's prettiest villages, the Dunraven Arms lists hunting, fishing and shooting as its main sporting attractions, but the superb local beef is an equally alluring draw. 'Today's prime roast joint' appears on the bar menu, while 'prime rib of beef carved (on the trolley at dinner) to your liking' may be the further enticement on the restaurant à la carte. Impeccable local butchers source the fine beef and provide the prime cuts, which are roasted to perfection and served with individual Dunraven Yorkshire puddings, crisp vegetables and a light red wine and peppercorn jus. One needs look no further for tip-top Irish beef, served unadulterated and in fine fashion.

Sponsored by

IRISH MEAT BOARD

The Natural Choice

...Irish Meat

Ireland, a land where tradition and

the most exacting standards combine

to produce the finest

meat in the world,

where fine food and

superb culinary skills serve

up memorable eating experiences.

CBF is delighted to sponsor

the Irish Meat

Restaurant of the

Year Awards and to

be associated with the development

of the Irish Catering Industry.

CBF

IRISH MEAT BOARD

Fyffes fresh produce fyffes

Ireland 1994
Desserts of the Year

MacNean Bistro
Blacklion, Co Cavan

Since keen young chef Nevan Maguire joined Vera, his mum, in the kitchen
of her most unusual little bistro the desserts have moved up a gear or two.
Nevan's time at *Roscoff* in Belfast has paid dividends from the pudding club,
and he now invests huge enthusiasm and time (along with an undoubted
talent) in the preparation of all things sweet. The pictured dish – "layered
sheets of meringue with strawberries, passion fruit ice cream and passion
vanilla anglaise" – is typical of the superb execution.

MacDuff's Restaurant, Blackheath House
Garvagh, Co Londonderry

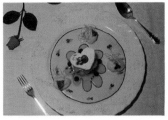

A characterful, comfortable and convivial restaurant set in the basement of an
immaculately kept Georgian house. Margaret Erwin's menu features
particularly good desserts that might include hazelnut meringue with
raspberries or simple Jamaican banana, split and grilled with rum and sugar.

Sponsored by

FYFFES FABULOUS FLAVOURS

Fyffes bananas have long featured on gourmet menus in restaurants all over Europe – as the traditional accompaniment to curries, or deep fried to enhance the flavours of meat and game and as mouth-watering desserts. Fyffes are the best selling brand of bananas in Ireland and as the provider of the highest quality bananas, are the brand chosen by top chefs and housewives nationwide.

However, Fyffes bananas have more than great taste and versatility in their favour. In many ways Fyffes bananas point the way to good health as an energy provider and as an excellent source of quality fibre. They are also rich in vitamins, minerals and especially potassium. Fyffes bananas are widely recognised as a wonderful tasty contribution to that all important balanced diet.

Fyffes bananas are highly versatile and can be used in a wide range of recipes. Most Fyffes bananas are eaten raw out of the hand. However, as they are so easy to use and add such a distinctive and appetising flavour, it is rewarding to experiment using Fyffes bananas in different dishes, both sweet and savoury.

These Fyffes fabulous recipes show just how delicious Fyffes really are.

ROAST MALLARD WITH FYFFES BANANAS, KIWI AND GIN SAUCE

INGREDIENTS
1 Wild duck
1 Kiwi
1 Fyffes banana
2 Tablespoons of gin
1/4pt Game juice (or stock)
1 knob of butter

METHOD
Roast the duck in a hot oven for 20 minutes until pink. Heat game juice (or stock) and add sliced Fyffes banana and segmented kiwi and gin. Cook for 2 minutes and pass through a sieve and stir until smooth. Add butter and season to taste. Garnish with kiwi and Fyffes bananas.

SERVES 2

COMPOTE OF FYFFES BANANAS IN LIGHT LIME SYRUP

INGREDIENTS
6 Fyffes bananas
1 Lime
4oz Sugar
1/2pt Water

METHOD
Place sugar and water plus the lime juice in a saucepan; grate small amount of lime zest and add into syrup. Bring to the boil and simmer for 2 minutes.
Slice Fyffes bananas; place in serving dish and pour syrup over.

SERVES 4

PANCAKES FILLED WITH FYFFES BANANAS, CREAM AND FRESH FRUIT

INGREDIENTS
2 Pancakes
3 Fyffes bananas
Selection of fresh fruit as desired
1/4pt Whipped cream

METHOD
Prepare fruit and slice 2 Fyffes bananas. Whip cream and puree 1 Fyffes banana to mixture. Place pancake on plate. Add cream filling and neatly arrange fruit around pancake.   SERVES 2

TRADITIONAL CHEESE
COMPANY
CONGRATULATES
THE WINNER OF THE
1994
IRISH CHEESEBOARD
OF THE YEAR
AWARD

Traditional Cheese Company Ltd.
Robinhood Industrial Estate
Clondalkin
Dublin 22
Phone: (01) 450 94 94
Fax: (01) 450 62 61

Ireland 1994
Irish Cheeseboard
of the Year

Blairs Cove Hotel Restaurant
Durrus, Co Cork

Farmhouse cheeses, mainly from West Cork, share the top of the grand piano with the dessert buffet at Sabine and Philippe De May's delightful restaurant. The starters in this lovely waterside location also take the form of a buffet, while many of the main courses are prepared on the wood-fired grill.

Sponsored by

Traditional Cheese Company's
Guide to
FINE IRISH CHEESES

Semi-soft **GUBBEEN** is made by Tom and Giana Ferguson at their farm at Schull, County Cork - exclusively from the milk of the Gubbeen herd. It is a creamy cheese which comes in both plain and oak-smoked varieties.

Full cream milk from the Friesian herd of Ann and Pat O'Farrell of Carrigaline, County Cork is used to make CARRIGA-LINE, a semi-hard gouda-style cheese containing no artificial flavouring or additives.

Handmade to a traditional recipe in the Irish speaking area of County Waterford, **RING** is an entirely natural product, with a full, nutty flavour and firm, close texture.

Norman and Veronica Steele make the longest established Irish farmhouse cheese - the award-winning **MILLEENS** - at their farm in West Cork. A soft, washed-rind cheese made from unpasteurised cow's milk, Milleens should be ripe and runny beneath it's natural, edible skin and is the perfect accompaniment to a fine claret or a good port.

COOLEENEY Camembert is handmade by Jim and Breda Maher at Moyne, Thurles, County Tipperary using only best quality milk from their Friesian herd. Their cheese is made using traditional skills and contains no added colouring or preservatives. When allowed to ripen Cooleeney develops a semi-liquid interior and strong flavour.

CHETWYND BLUE, a semi-soft mild blue cheese, is made by Jerry Beechinor at his Castlewhite Farmhouse at Chetwynd, County Cork.

Made from fresh cow's milk, **DURRUS** is a tangy, semi-soft cheese made by Jeffa Gill in Coomkeen, Durrus, West Cork. It is usually sold young having been stored for 3 to 5 weeks.

Right in the heart of one of the finest dairying areas in Ireland, Mary and Eugene Burns produce their distinctive **ARDRAHAN** cheese with milk from their herd of pedigree Friesians at Kanturk, County Cork. Ardrahan is a semi-soft washed rind cheese with a strong flavour and distinctive aroma.

CASHEL BLUE is a soft, mild, blue cheese made by hand from the milk of Louis and Jane Grubb's Friesian herd at Fethard in County Tipperary. When young it's mild and crumbly but will achieve a more mature flavour and creamier texture if allowed to ripen for an extra month or so.

ST. KILLIAN and **ST. BRENDAN BRIE** are handmade by Patrick Berridge at Carrigbyrne Farmhouse in County Wexford. Both are soft, natural, French-style cheeses made from pasteurised, full-fat cow's milk. St. Killian is a deep, hexagonal cheese, closely resembling a camembert in taste and texture. The larger St. Brendan Brie offers a fresh flavour and creamy consistency.

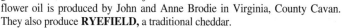

The CAHILL family blend a variety of tasty recipes with the finest vintage cheddar cheese to produce their range of colourful waxed truckles. Featured in the range are **BALLINTUBBER** (Chives), **ARDAGH** (Elderberry Wine), **IRISH WHISKEY** Cheddar and **IRISH PORTER** Cheddar.

The goats farm of Ann Van Campen is situated in south Wexford. Ann produces **CROGHAN,** a semi-hard mild cheese when young which increases in flavour as matured.

BOILIE, a soft cheese flavoured with fresh garden herbs, which comes in a jar of sunflower oil is produced by John and Anne Brodie in Virginia, County Cavan. They also produce **RYEFIELD,** a traditional cheddar.

COOLEA is a gouda cheese made by Dick and Helene Willems who came to live in the hills of Coolea from Holland. Most of their cheese is sold at about six to eight weeks old.

ST. TOLA it is a soft goats cheese made by Derrick and Meg Gordon on their farm near the village of Inagh in the heart of County Clare.

Olivia Goodwillie makes **LAVISTOWN** at her farm outside the famous city of Kilkenny. It is a white, crumbly cheese with a distinctive yellow rind.

DESMOND and **GABRIEL,** manufactured by Bill Hogan outside Schull in West Cork, are unique highly flavoured hard-pressed cheeses. These are matured for long periods to allow for full development of their texture, flavour and character.

Fivemiletown Creamery in Co. Tyrone has developed a number of unique soft ripened cheeses. The exquisite **COONEEN** pure goats milk brie is complimented by **BALLYOAK** (Smoked Brie), **BALLYBLUE** (Blue Brie), and **OAKWOOD** (Naturally Smoked Cheddar).

REGATO, produced by Dairygold Co-operative in East Cork is a parmesan-style cheese suitable for many recipes and most enjoyable as part of a cheese-board.

TRADITIONAL CHEESE
COMPANY
supply a comprehensive range of fine Irish
cheeses to Hotels, restaurants and catering
establishments through its
PINNACLE FOODSERVICE division.
Robinhood Industrial Estate
Clondalkin Dublin 22
Telephone: (01) 450 94 94 Fax: (01) 450 62 61

Ireland 1994
Coffee Award of Excellence

The Mustard Seed
Adare, Co Limerick

Wonderful aromatic coffee and home-made petits fours round off a splendid meal served in the picturesque surroundings of an old-world thatched cottage. Michael Weir is a confident, creative cook whose four-course dinner menus are based on the best of local and seasonal produce.

Sponsored by

Sharwood's
– A Taste of the Orient

As what were once the furthest horizons of the world draw daily closer great changes are also taking place in our daily diet. In the last 30 years we have seen a particular increase in Eastern cooking, popularised by the many families who left India, China and South East Asia to seek their fortunes overseas. Many opened restaurants which have become the culinary gateways through which so many of us now pass. Increasingly we look to exotic cultures to add flavour and finesse to our traditional cuisine. Mainstays of the Irish diet like pork, chicken and of course fish are now sautéed, stir fried, broiled and simmered in a medley of exotic flavours and colours. Sharwood's who have been the purveyors of fine foods for over a century make Eastern cooking easy with a guarantee of the highest standards of authenticity in their range of fine spices, chutneys and sauces.

Curries have come of age in Ireland. They are now a mainstay on restaurant and home menus alike. The old-fashioned curried chicken with apples and sultanas has given way to the Kormas and Koftas, which are just as easy to prepare and fulfil today's requirements for authentic dishes. Chinese food was introduced by the seafaring Cantonese. We marvelled at how a seemingly endless stream of dishes could appear on the restaurant table or take away counter within minutes of ordering. Then, we too learned to stir-fry and this 'instant' form of cooking became a familiar Western technique. Rice and noodles have virtually replaced potatoes in many homes, whilst soy sauce, ginger root and garlic have become

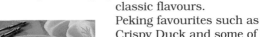

classic flavours.

Peking favourites such as Crispy Duck and some of the snacks such as Dim Sum have now begun to appear on menus all over Ireland.

In keeping with these expanding horizons, Sharwood's will, over the next few years, be introducing more and more of these flavours in an easy-to-use form for home cooking. This echoes the sentiments of our founder, James Allen Sharwood, who said a century ago...

"For the traveller in search of fine foods, every journey brings its rewards".

Ireland 1994
Oriental Restaurant
of the Year

Zen
89 Upper Rathmines Road, Dublin 6

An elegant, quite formal setting (originally a church hall) for one of Dublin's finest Chinese restaurants. Although specialising in the cooking of the Szechuan region, which is renowned for its generally hot and spicy food (an asterisk on the menu gives due warning!), the menu also deals in milder Cantonese dishes and both styles are prepared with exactly the same degree of attention to detail. Similarly solicitous service adds to the enjoyment.

Sponsored by

BY APPOINTMENT TO H.M. THE QUEEN
MANUFACTURERS OF CHUTNEY & PURVEYORS OF INDIAN
CURRY POWDER J.A. SHARWOOD & CO. LIMITED EGHAM

Sharwoods

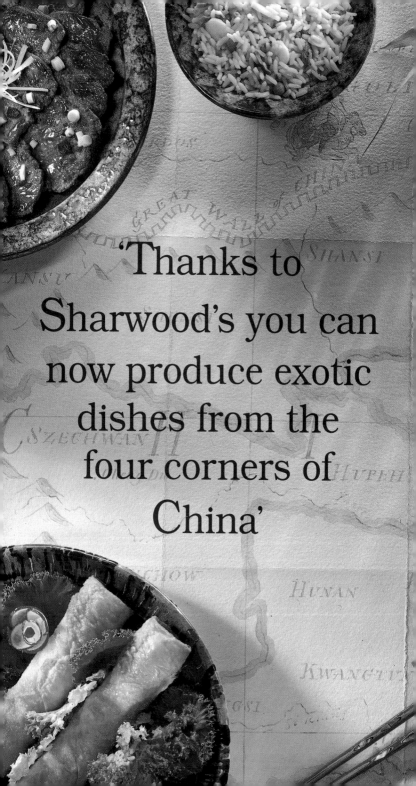

'Thanks to Sharwood's you can now produce exotic dishes from the four corners of China'

SHENKING
Peking
SHANTUNG
BY APPOINTMENT TO H.M. THE QUEEN
MANUFACTURERS OF CHUTNEY & PURVEYORS OF INDIAN
CURRY POWDER J.A. SHARWOOD & CO. LIMITED EGHAM
Sharwood's
ANHWEI
Shanghai
CHEKIANG

FROM RUSSIA WITH LOVE

FRAGILE

WITH GREAT CARE, FROM THE GREAT BEAR.

WORLDWIDE EXPRESS ®

Ireland 1994
Business Hotel of the Year

Hotel Conrad
Earlsfort Terrace, Dublin 2

Conrad is the international subsidary of Hilton USA, and Dublin's Conrad is a state-of-the-art hotel offering the full range of services for both leisure and business visitors. The latter can have a fax machine, computer and cellular phone installed in their room, and there's a 24-hour photocopying, telex and fax availability, plus a fully-equipped business centre whose offerings include a translation service.

Sponsored by

DHL – BRINGING EXCELLENCE TO IRISH BUSINESS

"Since 1979, DHL Ireland has enjoyed considerable growth to the point where we now employ over 170 people, each one of whom is dedicated to giving you the best possible service. By sponsoring the DHL Business Hotel of the Year Category in the Egon Ronay Guide, we know we will find the same standards of excellence that we offer our customers."

John McCarthy, Managing Director DHL Ireland

THE DHL SERVICE

DHL have shown commitment to the growth of Irish industry by investing heavily in Cork, Dublin and Shannon Airports. Single minded commitment to anticipating and to meeting our customers changing needs has led to the development of an unrivalled range of services. Each service is designed to get packages or documents to where they're going, with minimum fuss, the lowest cost, securely and on time.

IF YOU'RE IN BUSINESS, THEN DHL IS IN PARTNERSHIP WITH YOU

To be the best we must give our customers that competitive edge. We must be able to meet customers needs and to take an active part in helping to build their business. If you're in manufacturing, our professionals will work side-by-side with you to develop comprehensive air express programmes and take a little of your work load off you.

If you are in a service industry, DHL has to help you keep your promises and get your deliveries where they need to go on time and within your budget. Our global network is at your disposal. From pick-up to final delivery, DHL provide the most comprehensive door-to-door service for documents, packages and air freight available today.

DHL can expediate shipments overnight, clearing customs with the electronic transfer of shipping documents. Our staff in 200 countries are all working to make sure your shipment arrives securely and full automation means we can trace, book pick-ups and order supplies faster than ever before.

OUR NETWORK WORKING FOR YOU

There are over 32,000 DHL air express professionals working for you. DHL has offices in over 200 countries around the world, giving a unique local on-the-ground expertise and back-up. There's a fleet of aircraft and literally thousands of trucks and vans, at your disposal.

You have unrivalled access to anywhere in the world.

Every year, over 1 million customers choose DHL. For you too, all of these resources are just a 'phone call away.

DHL ARE COMMITTED TO IRELAND.
TO THE PEOPLE, TO YOUR BUSINESS.

Since setting up in Ireland, DHL has invested millions of pounds in warehousing, offices and training, employing nearly 200 people and now have offices at Dublin, Cork and Shannon Airports.

DHL understands that exports are the basis of economic growth. New markets mean new opportunities and new jobs. DHL can help our customers to gain access to these new markets. DHL will help you to create those new jobs, because you know that goods assembled here today can be shipped tonight directly to your customers wherever they are. And because you can meet the tightest deadlines, delivering your products as quickly as any other supplier, you know you can compete in the toughest market.

Ireland 1994
Pub of the Year

Smugglers Creek Inn
Rossnowlagh, Co Donegal

From the comfort of a bar warmed by open fires, visitors can watch the surge of Atlantic waves while tucking into some really first-rate snacks: fish soup, garlic mussels, oysters from the bay . . . or just tea with scones and home-made preserves. Conor Britton is the landlord, Maire Morrow the chef.

Sponsored by

Heineken®

There are dozens of lagers, but there is only one Heineken as far as millions of consumers at home and abroad are concerned. Walk into a bar in virtually any country and you will see the familiar green bottle. The best known beer brand world-wide, it is available in more than 150 countries with a staggering 25 million pints enjoyed every day.

Heineken is the number one exported beer brand in the world and the leading lager across Europe.

In Ireland, which has such a unique pub culture, Heineken is also one of the favourite beers of Irish drinkers, who savour the special flavour in draft or bottled form. From the cosmopolitan city pubs of Dublin to the traditional pubs in remote Western villages, Irish people are raising their glasses of Heineken and drinking "slainte" which is Irish for good health.

The secret of Heineken's success is its refreshing character, an essential part of the recipe created by Gerard Heineken 129 years ago. Today, this traditional recipe continues to be the favourite of beer drinkers all over the world.

Heineken also benefits from a multi-million pound programme of music and sports sponsorship. This includes high profile involvement with the Heineken Gold Cup at the Punchestown National Hunt Festival and the Whitbread Round the World Yacht Race for the Heineken Trophy. Sponsorship of these prestigious international events underlines Heineken's world class appeal both here in Ireland and abroad.

"85° in the shade... cold water trickling down my neck, enjoying a cool crisp Heineken 33cl... could this be heaven?..."

Heineken *33cl*
A great new number.

Seek Protection Under Our Wing

Ireland 1994
Newcomers of the Year

Le Mistral
16 Harcourt Street, Dublin 2

Le Mistral, as its name would suggest, specialises in the Mediterranean cooking of Provence and south-west France. Enthusiastic owners Ann and Philippe Misischi scour the markets daily for the best produce and with it their head chef Serge Mangin, a Toulousain, creates some truly mouthwatering dishes which evoke memories of blue-skied, sunny climes.

Sullivans
Holywood, Co Down

Young chef/patron Simon Shaw is putting his experience at *Roscoff* in Belfast to good use. Sullivans operates more as an informal coffee shop during the day (although 7 or 8 dishes are offered at lunchtime) but steps up several gears for dinner. Both à la carte and good-value table d'hote offer on-the-ball dishes, with good desserts from Jacqui Quinn worthy of a special mention.

Sponsored by

EAGLE STAR

1989

EAGLE STAR

PERSONAL PENSION PLAN

GRAND CRU CLASSÉ

EAGLE STAR

APPELLATION EAGLE STAR CONTROLÉE

13% VOL   75CL

AN EAGLE STAR PENSION WILL SHOW MORE THAN JUST GOOD TASTE...

an eye for detail...
A fine ageing wine made with a delicate blend of three top performing fund varieties, Adventurous, Performance and Balanced.

a nose for investment management...
An excellent start to Eagle Star

Pension Funds in 1989. All varieties yielded well in this vintage. Careful fund management has provided the best results over frosty conditions in the equity market. A hint of pronounced fruit in the future.

a taste for quality...
Well rounded & full bodied performance. Underlying fruit is very evident and should improve with age, giving an excellent finish.

Conclusions ...
Excellent quality, showing good promise for the future. Now talk to your financial consultant about an Eagle Star Personal Pension and don't forget to ask all about our Investment Awards.

EAGLE STAR

EAGLE STAR HOUSE FRASCATI ROAD BLACKROCK CO DUBLIN FAX 01 283 1578 TELEPHONE 01 283 1301

Fly Aer Lingus to Ireland

The Cliffs of Moher, County Clare, West Coast of Ireland.

and send a postcard from the edge.

Perched on the westernmost edge of Europe,
Ireland is undoubtedly one of the most beautiful
countries in the world.
It is also one of the friendliest.
So much so that your welcome to Ireland begins
before you've even left home. Because when
you step on board your Aer Lingus flight you step
into a little piece of Ireland. And there you'll enjoy
all the warmth and hospitality for which the Irish
and Aer Lingus are renowned.

Ireland 1994 International Hospitality Award

Ballymaloe House
Shanagarry, Co Cork

'Dine in a Country House' was how they first advertised thirty years ago, and since that time Ivan and Myrtle Allen's wonderful, individual hotel has gained a worldwide reputation for good, wholesome cooking and great hospitality. Ballymaloe is the centre of a group of family enterprises that includes a craft shop and cookery school as well as the Crawford Art Gallery Café in Cork.

Sponsored by

The Attraction of the Emerald Isle

by Georgina Campbell

Like Egon Ronay's Guides' managing editor, Andrew Eliel, and many others before me, I remember to the minute when the charm of Ireland first started to work its irresistible magic on me: it was at the very moment of my arrival on Irish soil as a student, touching down at Aldegrove (now Belfast International) – an ordinary enough airport, except that the rough grassy areas between the runways were teeming with hares nonchalantly going about their business, quite unaffected by the noise of aircraft. That first impression, of country life thriving alongside the inevitable changes that come with progress, has deepened with time and lies at the root of a joyous love affair with such a beautiful and hospitable country. Few would disagree that it's an emotive place, the many-faceted gem they call the Emerald Isle – and well named, for green it certainly is, in every shade: in its endearing patchwork of little fields seen, perhaps for the first time, from the air as it was for me – the brilliance of those pretty pastures symbolising the natural vitality of the produce for which this lush, song-inspiring island is rightly renowned.

Scenic beauty, uncrowded rural roads, hospitable people, comfortable accommodation at every level from grand castle hotels to private houses offering a few rooms and a share in family life, wholesome food, great pubs, fascinating history, a wide variety of cultural and country pursuits including some of the best golf courses in the world – this small country (a mere four hours' drive across and seven from top to bottom) has it all – and, even in these days of EU membership and strange new bank notes, the pace of life is still agreeably slow, leaving plenty of time for reflection. All year, in fact – while there is always plenty to do and see, Ireland provides the leisurely pace which allows for real relaxation regardless of season and weather.

Perched on the western edge of Europe, Ireland's rugged Atlantic seaboard is high on drama – soaring mountains, dizzying cliffs, miles of unpeopled strands – but it is also washed by the Gulf Stream, giving a temperate climate and pockets of lush, semi-tropical growth. Perhaps its sheer variety is the most surprising aspect of such a small island – the grandeur of Kerry is echoed at intervals through wave upon wave of stunning cliffs and mountains along the western seaboard, finally reaching the northern coast and the Giant's Causeway, dubbed the 'eighth wonder of the world'. Contrast mile after empty mile of moor and bogland, a thousand lakes and rivers – crowned by the mighty Shannon – and great green sweeps of fertile midland plains leading, through straggling villages and bustling market towns to the east coast and Dublin, home to a third of Ireland's population and to the hearts of countless Irish descendants throughout the world.

Although weather is the subject of much debate, the seasons can best be seen in terms of mood – the landscape deepens in tone with the fall of leaves in autumn, taking on a masculine strength, an austerity which vanishes with the first flush of spring but acts to highlight the value of a special sense of discovery experienced by the more adventurous traveller. And there is much to discover at any time of year. A good summer has its own charm – the rural idyll of wild strawberries growing carelessly on sun-warmed banks, the gentle tinkle of halyards on masts rocking gently in a sheltered anchorage, dog rose blossom seen against summer blue skies or the heady scent of honeysuckle in country lanes at dusk – but it is an unwise traveller who relies on heat and sunshine for relaxation in a country world-famous for its forty shades of green, the most obvious result of a 'soft' climate (euphemism is an Irish speciality). Fortunately, good rainwear is another speciality – and, in any case, there is plenty to do regardless of the weather, not least the gentle art of doing as little as possible, preferably with a glass in your hand. And many of the most beautiful and popular holiday areas – around the National Parks in Connemara, Killarney, Glenveagh (Donegal), the Wicklow Mountains and even the lunar landscape of The Burren in Co Clare – are particularly beguiling when there are very few people around, giving a real reward to the intrepid off-season visitor.

Driving in Ireland can be a memorable experience, for a variety of reasons including light traffic and 'characterful' roads (another euphemism, but it'll be a sad day when all the potholes have gone), and many a drive turns out to be a stunning moving picture show of light and shade as sun-chased clouds define the focus of each new view. Off-season driving can be especially rewarding, as colours in the winter landscape deepen, replacing lush summer greenery with russet bracken, red dogwood and dark reeds brightened by splashes of yellow gorse and the gleaming bark of leafless birches, shimmering stretches of water – now reflecting a deep blue sky, now palely silver against a watery sun – and snow-capped mountains high above moorland or patchworks of little stone-walled fields.

Although the occasional storm can add drama to any visit, only very rarely will extreme weather conditions make roads impassable, so the off-season traveller has all the advantages of getting to know this most hospitable of countries when the crowds have gone and the pubs are especially welcoming, banishing gloom over short, dark days or threatening storm clouds with their fragrant turf fires, hot whiskeys or the dark mysteries of a good pint of stout – and a gathering of locals, often including musicians who will start up a traditional session at the drop of a hat. On the practical side, although some seasonal closures may be disappointing, this is usually more than offset by the pleasure of visiting popular all-season attractions like Blarney Castle near Cork, or the unforgettable Cliffs of Moher in Co Clare without the crowds – and there are some really good bargains to be had, including special offers at many luxury hotels such as Ashford or Dromoland Castles.

For most people coming to Ireland for the first time, visiting Dublin is a priority. This characterful little capital is full of life and, although recent decades have seen a regrettable phase of plundering by property developers, growing public awareness should safeguard remaining treasures: elegant Georgian squares, with beautifully proportioned houses and striking doorways; impressive and historically interesting public buildings such as the Royal Hospital, Kilmainham, which now houses the Irish Museum of Modern Art and, like many of the city's outstanding buildings – including James Gandon's classic 18th-century Custom House on the north quays and the Bank of Ireland (once the Irish Parliament) – recently refurbished and looking splendid, with gleaming fresh stonework. Leinster House, familiar to Americans as the model for the White House in Washington DC is especially worth a visit, also Dublin Castle, Christchurch and St Patrick's Cathedrals, all of which are very central. Trinity College, founded by Elizabeth I in 1591, houses Ireland's greatest treasure, the Book of Kells, and Dublin's long association with literary figures such as George Bernard Shaw, Oscar Wilde, James Joyce, Samuel Beckett and Sean O'Casey is celebrated in the Dublin

Writers Museum on Parnell Square. Next door, the Hugh Lane Municipal Gallery of Modern Art, one of many interesting galleries of all sizes around the city, houses an excellent permanent collection of works by Irish and continental artists, including a number of famous French Impressionist paintings, while the star attraction across at the National Gallery is the recently restored Caravaggio, 'The Betrayal of Christ'. Dublin theatre is of a predictably high standard in widely varying styles, ranging from the famous Abbey Theatre to youthful experimental venues around Temple Bar (Dublin's 'Left Bank'); the same is true of the very active music scene, which ranges from classical at the National Concert Hall, through major events at the huge Point Depot, to a myriad of gigs and sessions at pubs and smaller venues all over the city. Pubs – for meeting, chatting, listening or just observing – are the hub of social life during opening hours, followed by a host of late-nightclubs including the after-midnight conversion of theatres such as the Olympia and the Tivoli into fully-licensed music halls. Shopping is another great attraction, with high-quality, hand-made Irish crafts such as tweeds, hand-knitted Arran sweaters, pottery, wood carvings, hand-blown glass and crystal, silver jewellery and hand-made lace – all typically Irish and often surprisingly reasonably priced.

The Dublin environs also have much of interest to offer: travelling north from Dublin, prosperous farming country is dotted with some of the country's most important historic sites, including the 5,000-year-old Newgrange neolithic burial chamber; travelling west soon brings you to the

p90: Connemara Landscape
p91: Fishing in Kinsale, Co Cork (L), Golf at Mount Juliet, Thomastown, Co Kilkenny (R)
p92 Top: Jameson Whiskey Heritage Centre, Midleton, Co Cork (L), Patrick Kavanagh Statue, Dublin (R)
Bottom: Howth '17s' & The Custom House, Dublin
p94: Glandalough, Co Wicklow
This page: Dublin Writers' Museum

rich green horse country of County Kildare, a major centre for breeding, training and racing – the Flat Racing season begins in May and five Irish Classics at the world-famous Curragh racecourse at Newbridge mark the highlight of the calendar, the Goff's Irish 1,000 Guineas in May and the Budweiser Irish Derby in July. Motor sport features nearby too, at Mondello Park race track. By contrast, twenty minutes' drive south of Dublin brings you to the majestic Wicklow Mountains, popular for climbing and hill walking but also famous for monastic remains at the atmospheric beauty spot of Glendalough, historic houses including Russborough (Beit art collection) and Avondale (home of Parnell) and the magnificent Powerscourt waterfall and gardens – indeed gardens are a very special feature of Wicklow, known as 'the Garden of Ireland' for its climate and now also for an annual Gardens Festival in late May/June, when private gardens around the county are open to the public.

Beyond Dublin, many equally beguiling areas beckon – and all within 5½ hours' drive. Where to choose? Not an easy decision, I can vouch for that – over the last few years, a happy combination of work and pleasure has taken me to virtually every corner of the country and, paradoxically, the one shared factor is individuality, so wherever you happen to find yourself usually seems the best of all possible places to be ... It is clearly pointless to pit Kerry's striking mountain peninsulas against the colour and charm of Cork City, or the rugged landscapes of Connemara with its Gaeltacht culture against the medieval city of Kilkenny, the peaceful wooded valleys and sandy coast of the 'sunny south-east' – any more than it makes sense to compare the wild dignity of the undiscovered north-west with the lush angler's paradise of the equally unspoilt lakelands, or the peace and tranquillity of cruising on the Shannon, the longest river in Britain or Ireland. Hard choices may have to be made – but take consolation in knowing that the wise traveller always keeps back some treats for the next visits.

Dunluce Castle.

Take it all in.

Make sure Northern Ireland is part of your holiday plans this year. And experience all the wonders for yourself.

A cruise on the Fermanagh lakes. A hill walk in the Sperrins. Breathe in the beauty of the Giant's Causeway. The mountains of Mourne. The green Glens of Antrim.

Touch the history of Derry. Of Armagh's Cathedral city. And the warmth of the people.

Golf. Fishing. Sailing. Horse-riding. Activities awaiting discovery in idyllic surroundings. Superb restaurants. Pubs and live entertainment. You're really spoilt for choice.

And don't forget to visit Belfast. A city steeped in history with a fine tradition of culture, crafts, sports and business.

Northern Ireland Tourist Board

Useful Information

Climate: Ireland's climate is generally mild and temperate, with summer temperatures generally ranging from 60–75 degrees F. Spring and autumn temperatures are generally in the 50s and in winter in the 30s and 40s. Rainfall is quite high and it can be showery at any time of the year.

Public Holidays 1994:

New Year's Day Holiday	3rd January
St Patrick's Day	17th March
Good Friday*	1st April
Easter Monday	4th April
May Day	2nd May
June Holiday	6th June
August Holiday	1st August
October Holiday	31st October
Christmas Day Holiday	26th December
Christmas Holiday	27th December

* Although not a statutory Public Holiday, Good Friday is observed as a Public Holiday in most parts of the country.

Licensing Hours: Unless there are special circumstances – service of food affects the rules, or there may be a special licence – official opening times for pubs in Ireland are: Mon–Sat 10.30am–11.30pm in summer, 10.30am–11pm in winter (ie from the first Monday in October), Sun 12.30–2 and 4–11 (all year). Half an hour's 'drinking up time' is allowed. Pubs are closed on Good Friday and Christmas Day. Irish pubs are generally family-friendly (45% of Ireland's population is under 25), particularly those where food is served; however, parents are expected to observe reasonable hours when accompanied by their children – many pubs ask parents not to bring children into the bar in the evenings, usually after about 7pm.

Telephones: When calling from outside the Republic omit the initial zero and prefix the number with international access code (010 from Britain, 011 from USA) + 353. Card phones are cheaper than pay phones and are widely available. Callcards are sold in denominations of £16, £8, £3.50 and £2.

Pets: Pets coming directly from Britain, the Channel Islands or the Isle of Man and resident there for at least six months are permitted. Animals coming from continental Europe must remain in quarantine for six months.

Travel Tips: Cut transport costs by using an *Irish Explorer Pass*, giving unlimited bus/rail travel. The *Emerald Card* covers both the Republic of Ireland and Northern Ireland, all for one price. In Dublin City, transport passes can be bought for four days or one day. *Heritage Cards*, available from Ireland's Office of Public Works, offer unlimited admission to more than 30 attractions all over Ireland – national monuments, castles, historic sites, gardens. Ask about other similar schemes.

Development of Irish Food and Hospitality

by Georgina Campbell,
author of *Good Food from Ireland* and *Meals for all Seasons*

Ireland as a gourmet destination? Few would have thought of it until recently, although some very distinguished guests indeed showed early recognition of the quality of Irish produce – it is now widely acknowledged that President and Madame de Gaulle's Irish holiday at Killarney, Co Kerry and *Cashel House*, Cashel, Co Galway in 1968 encouraged growing numbers of the discerning French to visit Ireland during the 1970s; appreciative of the country's wonderful natural resources but (unlike the Irish themselves who hate to complain or even visitors from Britain too polite to do so) also quick to criticise standards of cooking and presentation if necessary, this development had the immediate effect of raising standards everywhere they went. Not that confidence in fine produce and the value of simplicity were always lacking – even before the famous presidential visit, Paul Bocuse came on regular fishing holidays with his friend Jean Troisgros, staying at Ernie Evans's famous Kerry hotel *The Towers* in Glenbeigh. Visiting Ireland more recently, M. Bocuse said he still remembers vividly 'a fantastic gastronomic experience' which, he claimed (albeit with a wicked twinkle in his eye) was the birth of Nouvelle Cuisine: 'Monsieur Evans presented us with a dish of wild salmon which was undercooked. It was still firm and succulent, only just cooked to the bone – we had discovered the true way of cooking salmon and went back to France to tell the French how to do it. The Irish, of course, had

been doing it right all the time, so here it was called traditional cooking – but it was new to us and from that experience we went on to develop Nouvelle Cuisine.' Asked if standards today matched up to that memorable salmon of thirty years ago, the great man was adamant that they do, quoting the example of some 'superb native Irish oysters' he had eaten the day before, but also paying tribute to people like Myrtle Allen of *Ballymaloe House*, Shanagarry, Co Cork, who are 'defending the quality and natural production methods of Irish food so

fiercely that the standard of, for example, Irish fish and meat is outstanding'. It is especially fitting that Myrtle Allen herself should be elected to take over from Paul Bocuse this year as president of Euro-Toques, an international chefs' organisation that is committed to safeguarding the identity of national and regional cooking and a major driving force behind the current upsurge of culinary talent.

Confidence is perhaps the key word in Ireland today and nowhere is this more obvious than in the kitchen, largely because the country's environmental good fortune which is so crucial to the purity of produce has attracted widespread praise (and, indeed envy from an overcrowded European mainland who now see an element of backwardness in a country as a positive advantage) and also because so many of today's young chefs are returning to Ireland after experience abroad, with the knowledge that they are up there with the best. Throughout the period of rapid development since the late '60s, growing interest in regional food has been a spur to the minority who have worked so hard against the current to raise standards and it has been rewarding to see the tide of fashion turning in their favour. Established chefs like Michael Clifford (*Cliffords*, Cork) and Colin O'Daly (*Roly's Bistro*, Dublin) have provided strong leadership in creating a new Irish style of cuisine, influenced by international trends towards lightness and attractive presentation, yet balanced by a wholesomeness – the home-made brown bread, the potatoes steamed in their jackets – that is typically Irish. Also, top kitchens have not been afraid to revive and, in some cases, adapt traditional dishes so old Irish favourites like crubeens (pigs' trotters), bacon and cabbage and Irish stew can now appear with pride on some of the most sophisticated menus in the land, albeit not as often as visitors might like.

p97: Lovetts, Cork
Irish farmhouse cheeses

Interestingly, however, although there is now widespread healthy respect for the goodness of simple traditional country cooking, current trends at the cutting edge of food fashion show a swing away from traditional roots and, far from developing a distinctive modern Irish cuisine, today's most exciting young chefs are in buzzy, trendy restaurants – places like *Roly's Bistro, Cooke's Café* and *La Stampa* in Dublin; *Isaacs, Niblick's* and *Cliffords* in Cork; *Roscoff* in Belfast; *Ramore* in Portrush – and little gems, like *Packie's* of Kenmare, *Destry Rides Again* of Clifden and *Truffles* of Sligo, in interesting clusters of restaurants which seem to be developing all over the country in much the same way as they did originally in Kinsale, a town which is also showing signs of renewed energy since the arrival of *Chez Jean-Marc* and a general feeling of new confidence and creativity in long-established places like the *Blue Haven Hotel* and *Max's Wine Bar*. Lively influences from around the world predominate, especially Cal-Ital and Pacific Rim cuisines, but the main thing these restaurants share is a relaxed, informal atmosphere with the emphasis on enjoyment – certainly not a new development in Ireland, where (except, perhaps, for business entertaining) a warm ambience and a tolerant attitude to people enjoying themselves is regarded as a prime requirement for a good meal out, but a move away from formal dining which the public is embracing with enthusiasm, not least because the simpler surroundings of these new-wave establishments usually mean more affordable prices, making eating out an accessible pastime for more and, especially, younger people.

Another very different but equally important strand in the development of a national reputation for good food – and one which continues to grow and strengthen – is the country house movement, and particularly the leading group known as "The Blue Book". Ever since President de Gaulle's

1968 visit to a founding member, *Cashel House*, this small group of about thirty establishments has worked tirelessly to earn an international reputation for excellence and is highly regarded as a benchmark when it comes to a combination of high standards of accommodation, good food and, as all are owner-run, that elusive but all-important ingredient, Irish hospitality. The houses vary considerably from the very grand, such as Ray and Mary Bowe's *Marlfield House*, Gorey, Co Wexford, or Francis Brennan's *Park Hotel Kenmare*, through lovely old family homes like the O'Hara's *Coopershill*, Co Sligo and Harry & June Hodgson's *Currarevagh*, Co Galway, to Constance Aldridge's wonderfully wacky *Mount Falcon Castle*, Co Sligo, and the equally characterful Maureen Gelletlie's *Hunter's Hotel*, Co Wicklow – all have played a vital role in today's image of Ireland as a different kind of destination, offering a sense of discovery with all the comfort and cosseting the rest of the world seems to have left behind. Good food based on the very best of local ingredients is a common factor – many of the houses have magnificent walled

Fine, fresh produce at
Rathsallagh House,
Dunlavin, Co Wicklow

kitchen gardens supplying ultra-fresh seasonal produce and special arrangements with local farmers and fishermen – and some kitchens are showing particular promise under a new generation of chefs – at *Longueville House*, Mallow, for example (perhaps best known for Michael O'Callaghan's unique little vineyard, producing a house wine which is just that) young William O'Callaghan is doing wonderfully creative things in the kitchen with produce including their own lamb, salmon from the river Blackwater only yards away and organically grown fruit and vegetables from the garden, all magnificently presented in their famous 'Presidents' Restaurant', an elegant dining room graced with portraits of Ireland's presidents. Almost next door, at *Assolas House*, Kanturk, the Bourke family weaves a special kind of magic over everything, not least through Hazel Bourke's talent in the kitchen; their lovely, meticulously maintained walled garden supplies a wide range of fruit, vegetables and herbs which, augmented by the best of local meat and seafood, forms the basis of her particular blend of sophistication and stunning simplicity, a confident sense of style content to present nature's gifts with a restraint which ultimately gives the sheer goodness of the produce, with its vivid natural colours and deep flavours, greater impact.

For the more adventurous traveller who prefers a more pronounced sense of discovery, perhaps with a good dash of eccentricity plus a ghost or two thrown in, the younger Hidden Ireland group of country houses offers a wackier choice, ranging from some titled hosts with very smart addresses indeed (but including at least one who claims to keep a begging bowl in the hall, for the roof restoration fund) and one or two, such as Bantry House, grand enough to be open to the public, to the majority of big old houses with high maintenance costs, a few rooms to spare, extremely hospitable owners and good food, usually taken at communal tables; less a professional operation, more a matter of allowing guests to share in family life – and, many would say, all the more fun for that. Hidden Ireland houses – and many others around the country which are loosely grouped under the Friendly Homes banner or operate independently of any association – often sum up the special attractions of unspoilt rural life in Ireland and many are closely involved with a wide range of country pursuits – hunting, horse-riding, shooting, fishing, falconry, climbing, walking, bird-watching or whatever – making an ideal base for an activity holiday.

But what of more conventional hospitality in hotels and, perhaps, pubs? Hotels generally have improved dramatically over the last few years, both in terms of the facilities offered and room standards, which are being raised all the time and, although restaurants generally still have a much more exciting

Afternoon tea at
Hunter's Hotel,
Rathnew, Co Wicklow

image than hotel dining rooms, hotels are fighting back and there are definite signs of a new trend emerging. Grand hotels like *Adare Manor*, *Dromoland Castle*, *Sheen Falls Lodge* and *Park Hotel Kenmare*, for example, are all renowned as much for their cuisine as for luxury, while less prominent hotels are increasingly making their mark through excellence in the dining room – *Beech Hill House Hotel*, Derry, has quickly established an enviable reputation for its restaurant, Fredrick's Restaurant at *Aghadoe Heights Hotel*, Killarney, has much more than a stunning view to offer, The Maigue Room, *The Dunraven Arms*, Adare, complements perfectly the sophistication of *Adare Manor* and *The Mustard Seed* restaurant across the road, Kinsale's *Blue Haven* is another example and a glance at the friendly competition between the kitchens of hotels like *Erriseask House*, *Ardagh Hotel* and *Rock Glen Manor* in the Clifden area confirms that a serious restaurant can once again be part of the appeal at any hotel.

In the growing number of pubs doing good food we are currently witnessing the beginnings of a parallel success story – although the traditional Irish pub culture is unique, revolving around drinking, socialising and, perhaps, music, with food very much an afterthought, times are changing. Reliable demand ensured that dozens of city pubs have served reliable, if predictable, bar food for a long time but it is encouraging to see so many rising above the average – in Dublin alone, *Ashton's*, *McCormack's*, *The Stag's Head*, *The Old Stand*, *Davy Byrnes* and *The Queen's*, Dalkey are just a few examples of pubs making an effort to meet the demands of increasingly discerning customers but, as is often the case with hotels and restaurants as well, many of the best are dotted around the country in less populated areas. Several pubs – *Mary Ann's*, Castletownshend, *Smugglers Creek Inn*, Rossnowlagh, *The Roundwood Inn*, Co Wicklow, *Moone High Cross Inn*, Moone, Co Kildare, *The Lord Bagenal*, Leighlinbridge, *The Lobster Pot*, Carne, *Reidy's Wine Vaults*, Cork, *Goosers*, Killaloe are outstanding examples, but

The Lobster Pot,
Carne, Co Wexford

there are many more like *The Ship*, Dunmore East; *Dan Lowrey's* and the *Country Squire*, Cork; *Cronin's*, Crosshaven; *Marlogue Inn*, East Ferry; *The Spaniard* and the *Blue Haven*, Kinsale; *The Purple Heather* and *The Horseshoe*, Kenmare; *The Islandman* and *The Lord Baker's*, Dingle; *The Smugglers Inn* and *The Huntsman*, Waterville; *The Point Bar*, Cahirciveen; *The Dunraven Arms*, Adare; *Monks*, Ballyvaughan; *The Brake Tavern*, Blackrock to name but a smattering . . . Changed times indeed, although it must be said that the unspoilt old-style pub, innocent of anything other than liquid sustenance, is still highly revered and the atmosphere of these establishments is unrivalled –

many connoisseurs would aver that the pub is no place for food and who, having visited such places as *Morrissey's* of Abbeyleix, *Dick Mack's* or *James Flahive* in Dingle or *Paddy Bourke's* on Cape Clear Island, who could argue with them?

While pubs are doing much to satisfy the demand for inexpensive food in informal surroundings – often with the simple, wholesome traditional Irish dishes such as Irish stew, corned beef and cabbage, champ or Dublin coddle – there has also been a huge upsurge in fast food outlets of widely varying standards. Some, especially in the trendy *Temple Bar* ('Dublin's Left Bank') area near Trinity College, have a particular appeal to students – and some, such as *Pizzeria Italia*, *Pasta Fresca*, *Little Caesar's* and *Chicago Pizza Pie Factory* (all very central), offer honest, simple food and genuinely good value. But it is a scene of rapid change and one where 'trendiness' is often seen as an

Irish meat at
its best: Steak,
herbs and Guinness

acceptable replacement for consistent standards. Perhaps this is an area where Oriental restaurants might be able to make a special mark – restaurants like the *Ayumi-Ya Steakhouse* (Japanese), *Zen* (Chinese), *Langkawi* (Malaysian) and *The Chili Club* (Thai) are beginning to break new ground in what has been a very predictable ethnic market so it will be interesting to see how this potential for authentic ethnic food at reasonable prices is developed. Meanwhile, welcome to Ireland – and *bon appétit* – or *Bain taitneamh as do bhéile!*

Republic of Ireland

Abbeyfeale   The Cellar

Tel 068 31085   **P**

Abbeyfeale Co Limerick   Map 2 B5

Easily spotted as you drive through Abbeyfeale by the rows
of bottles of every shape and size displayed in the end window,
this very pleasant old-fashioned pub will not disappoint – the
locals are friendly and the open fire and piano are not just for
show, so sessions can get going at the drop of a hat. Nice walled
garden at the back for sheltered summer drinking. *No credit cards.*

Abbeyleix   Morrissey's

Tel 0502 31233   Fax 0502 31357   **P**

Main Street Abbeyleix Co Laois   Map 2 C4

A discreet black and gold sign singles out Morrissey's from its
neighbours in this handsome village; inside the lofty shelf-lined
grocery-bar, old-fashioned shades of black and brown
predominate, relieved here and there by a little cream. Mundane
groceries change hands along with their special blend of tea
(packed on the premises) and an unusually wide selection of loose
sweets like aniseed balls, pineapple chunks and bull's eyes, kept
in rows of big glass jars and sold by the 1/4lb in paper pokes.
On cold days customers reflect on their pints around an ancient
pot-bellied stove while reading the paper or exchanging the news
of the day – but card-playing and singing are not allowed. A good
place to take a break on the Dublin-Cork road but, although a cup
of tea or coffee will be served with charm, don't expect any food,
other than a sandwich. *No credit cards.*

Adare   Adare Manor   81%   £220

Tel 061 396566   Fax 061 396124   **HR**

Adare Co Limerick   Map 2 B5

Home, for two centuries, of the Dunraven family, this magnificent
neo-Gothic mansion is set in 900 acres on the banks of the river
Maigue. Its splendid chandeliered drawing room and the glazed
cloister of the dining room look over formal box-hedged gardens
towards the Robert Trent Jones golf course (currently still being
developed and not available for play, although arrangements are
made with a club nearby). Other grand public areas include the
gallery, modelled after the Palace of Versailles, with its Flemish
choir stalls, fine stained-glass windows and hand-carved
bookshelves. Gracious bedrooms have individual hand-crafted
fireplaces, fine locally-made mahogany furniture, cut-glass table
lamps and impressive marble bathrooms with strong showers over
huge bathtubs. Children under 12 are accommodated free in their
parents' room. No dogs. **Rooms** *64. Garden, indoor swimming pool,
gymnasium, sauna, games room, snooker, golf driving range, riding,
fishing, clay-pigeon shooting.* AMERICAN EXPRESS *Access, Diners, Visa.*

Restaurant   ↑   £85

Dining in style comes easy at Adare: after taking an aperitif
in the drawing room overlooking the parterre gardens and
developing golf course beyond, move through to the elegant
panelled dining room with views of the river Maigue and
consider chef de cuisine Gerard Costelloe's imaginative fare
on a choice of table d'hote or à la carte menus. Local produce,

including vegetables from the estate's own gardens, features
in dishes like garden leaf salad, a colourful, piquant combination
of mixed leaves tossed in a creamy blue cheese dressing and
scattered with crisp deep-fried beetroot 'chips', or a main course
'stew' of Irish seafood – salmon, sole, monkfish, scallops – in
a tangy lemon sauce. Desserts range from homely (individual
blackberry and apple crumble, crème anglaise) to the richly exotic
(chocolate marquise on a marmalade sauce). Tempting selection
of home-made breads; excellent service. *Seats 65. Private Room 25.
L 12.30-2.30 (Sun to 3) D 7.30-9.30. Set L £21 Set D £29.50.*

If we recommend meals in a hotel a **separate**
entry is made for its restaurant.

Adare	Dunraven Arms Hotel	72%	£125
Tel 061 396633 Fax 061 396541			**HR**
Adare Co Limerick			Map 2 B5

Sporting activities, including golf, fishing and especially hunting
and all things equestrian, are a particular attraction here at 'the
fox-hunting centre of Ireland' but the Dunraven Arms also attracts
a wide range of guests, including business clients and many
travellers who are tempted by imaginative bar food to break
a journey here. Meticulously maintained public areas have
a timeless, traditional atmosphere with old furniture lifted
by softly bright classical colour combinations in the decor
in everything from the busy pubby bar to the serenity of the
residents' drawing room, known as 'the library'. Bedrooms are
individually furnished to a high standard with excellent
bathrooms, antiques and many thoughtful extras, like fresh
flowers, fruit and mineral water. The turn-down service includes
fresh towels and chocolates on the pillow. No tea/coffee-making
facilities, but room service is prompt. Frequent functions create
a buzz around the hotel, but newer rooms away from public areas
are quiet. Children up to 14 may stay free in their parents' room.
Rooms 43. Garden, tennis, shop. AMERICAN EXPRESS *Access, Diners, Visa.*

The Maigue Room £55

Banqueting and dining are kept separate at the Dunraven Arms
and head chef Mark Phelan is building up an excellent reputation
for his elegant restaurant, named after the local river. Table d'hote
or à la carte menus might typically start with a variation on a
traditional local dish like black pudding, pan-fried and
imaginatively served with featherlight apple fritters and
a colourful red onion confit, or a stunningly pretty warm terrine
of trout and fresh prawn tails in a vermouth-scented beurre blanc
with dill. Main courses also highlight the quality of local produce,
including the finest roast beef (carved from a trolley in the
evening) – winner of our Irish Meat Restaurant of the Year award
– and game. Delicious desserts like good old lemon meringue pie,
lightly baked and served with an orange sauce. Lovely brown soda
bread, aromatic coffee. *Seats 60. Parties 20. Private Room 35.
L 12.30-2.30 D 7.30-9.30. Bar Food 12-6pm. Set L £11.50
Set D £21. Closed Good Friday.*

Adare   The Mustard Seed   ↑   £60

Tel 061 396451   **R**

Main Street Adare Co Limerick   **Map 2 B5**

Picturesque surroundings in this olde-worlde thatched cottage and
a warm welcome from the proprietor, Dan Mullane, provide the
perfect ambience for Michael Weir's confident, creative cooking.
Four-course dinner menus based firmly on the best of local and
seasonal produce present difficult choices but, once the decisions
are made, the cosy little reception/bar makes an enjoyable place
to anticipate the pleasures ahead: an oriental terrine of layered
pork, leeks and spinach is a sight to behold on a bed or puréed
apples sharpened with balsamic vinegar, while a salad of crisp
green beans, with quails' eggs, slivers of Parmesan and black olives
in a chive nut oil is, quite simply, moreish. Smoked haddock
chowder comes with a spicy rouille and irresistible home-baked
breads, while main courses feature game in season, local free-range
duck and elegant fish dishes such as trio of fish – baked escalope
of salmon with steamed sole and pan-fried scallops on a chive and
spring onion sauce. Good farmhouse cheeses and imaginative
variations on homely desserts, like delicious banoffi pie with
caramel sauce and banana coulis. The home-made petits fours and
fragrant coffee are fully deserving of the Coffee Award of
Excellence. *Seats 50. Parties 18. Private Room 30. D only 7-10.
Set D £23. Closed Sun & Mon, Bank Holidays, Feb.* AMERICAN EXPRESS
Access, Diners, Visa.

Adare   Woodlands House Hotel   60%   £50

Tel 061 396118   Fax 061 396073   **H**

Adare Co Limerick   **Map 2 B5**

From small beginnings in 1983 the Fitzgerald family have
developed their hotel to its present stage, with facilities for
weddings, banquets and conferences for up to 350. Roomy public
areas include two bars and a strikingly decorated lobby/lounge
with comfortable seating and a colourful mural, while both
banqueting suites and the restaurant overlook well-maintained
gardens and countryside. Bedrooms, including two suites and most
with a pleasant outlook, vary in age and amenities (the older ones
are due for refurbishment during '94) but are well maintained.
No dogs. *Rooms 32. Garden. Closed 24 & 25 Dec.* AMERICAN EXPRESS
Access, Diners, Visa.

Adare   Place of Interest

Castle Matrix   Rathkeale Tel 069 64284

Ahakista   Ahakista Bar

No Telephone   **P**

Ahakista nr Bantry Co Cork   **Map 2 A6**

Unchanged for as long as anyone can remember, this little bar
is just opposite the entrance to the *Shiro Japanese Dinner House* and
its corrugated iron roof conceals as pleasant an old-fashioned dart-
playing pub as is to be found. Beyond the unspoilt bar lies another
treasure – a delightfully ungroomed garden reaching right down
to the beach, with a big lawn where, as landlord Tom Whitty
puts it, 'kids can scream and run around'; not much room inside,

though, for children. *Open 3.30-11 (winter), 1-11.30 (summer)
Mon-Sat, 12.30-2 & 4-11 (Sun all year). Garden. No credit cards.*

Ahakista	Hillcrest House	£31
Tel 027 670415		A
Ahakista Durrus Co Cork		Map 2 A6

Comfortable accommodation and home-cooked food are the main
attractions at this neat farmhouse, situated on a working farm
overlooking Dunmanus Bay. Of the four rooms, three are upstairs
and en suite while one double (with bath) is on the ground floor
with direct access to parking facilities. Suitable for families.
Residents' dinner is £24 for two. **Rooms 4.** *Games room.
Closed Nov-Apr. No credit cards.*

Ahakista	Shiro ★	£80
Tel 027 67030		R
Ahakista nr Bantry Co Cork		Map 2 A6

A visit to the remote Shiro Japanese Dinner House, situated
in a fine, meticulously maintained Georgian house overlooking
Dunmanus Bay, is likely to be both unique and unforgettable. The
dining room may only accommodate small numbers, but both the
welcome and the food are big-hearted. Often referred to as
an experience which defies description, Kei Pilz's authentic
Japanese food is so exquisite in both preparation and presentation
that it remains in the mind as a finely detailed patchwork,
an impressionistic mirage of culinary delights. With great charm
Werner Pilz guides newcomers through the menu, which changes
daily and may consist of three short courses – perhaps *zensai*
(flower-decked appetisers), *moriawase* (delicate egg dishes and
sushi) and *suimono* (a seasonal soup), followed by a choice of eight
main courses including a selection of lightly-battered deep-fried
tempura dishes, *sashimi* (seasonal raw fish, served with soy sauce
and *wasabi* – hot green mustard) and *yakitori* (chicken breast, liver
and vegetables on bamboo skewers, with a traditional spicy sauce).
Several dishes are suitable for vegetarians. A selection of home-
made ices, including green tea, dramatically arranged with some
colourful fruit against a black plate and followed by a choice
of teas and coffees, rounds off the experience. There's a pleasant,
short wine list that lists French classics alongside the *sake.* 5%
supplement for paying by credit card. Bookings only. A charming
traditional cottage (sleeping two) in the grounds is available for
self-catering. **Seats** 12. *Private Room 8. D only 7-9. Set D £34.*
AMERICAN EXPRESS *Access, Diners, Visa.*

Annascaul	Dan Foley's	
Tel 066 57252		P
Annascaul Co Kerry		Map 2 A5

Dan Foley's pub owes its colourful, much-photographed exterior
to the theatrical personality of the man himself – farmer, expert
on local history and magician. Inside, it's a great, unspoilt bar
in the rural tradition, made special by Dan's particular interest
in people and chat – and an unexpected collection of about fifty
liqueurs. Food is not the thing here although 'emergency rations'
of sandwiches, sausage rolls and the like will be served (11am-   *See over*

8pm) to those who resist directions to the proper restaurant next door. Children during daylight hours only. One of Ireland's most famous pubs. *No credit cards.*

Ardee   The Gables   £60
Tel 041 53789   **RR**
Dundalk Road Ardee Co Louth   **Map 1 D3**

In what might still seem, relative to other areas which have developed so dramatically over the last few years, something of a culinary desert, this bourgeois restaurant is enormously popular. Owner-chef Michael Caine uses the best of local ingredients without allowing the forces of fashion to intrude on a French menu distinctly reminiscent of the 60s, with huge servings and rich sauces, typically in dishes like French snails with garlic butter, fresh Clogherhead prawns thermidor, honey roast duckling with port and orange sauce and breast of chicken stuffed with smoked salmon and crab, finished with butter, cream and Chablis – to the evident satisfaction of an appreciative local clientele who like things just the way they are. *Seats 34. D only 7-10. Set D £18.95. Closed Sun & Mon, 2 weeks Jun & 2 weeks Nov.* AMERICAN EXPRESS® *Access, Visa.*

Rooms   £34
Accommodation is offered in five rooms, all en suite. *Garden.*

Athleague   Fitzmaurice's Tavern
Tel 0903 63383   **P**
Athleague Co Roscommon   **Map 1 B3**

This award-winning, seriously olde-worlde pub could take prizes as an agricultural museum, but it's a very real place when it comes to efficient, cheerful service and a good local, judging by the gathering likely to be found around the open fire on a winter evening. As owner Roger Dobson says, "whether or not everybody likes the clutter, it's always a great conversation piece" – which is fair enough and, anyway, it is interesting rather than twee. The outside has recently been repainted brick red. Food here is basically generous sandwiches of home-cooked meats. *No credit cards.*

Athleague   Place of Interest
Clonalis House   Castlerea Tel 0907 20014

Athy   Tonlegee House   £55
Tel & Fax 0507 31473   **RR**
Athy Co Kildare   **Map 2 C4**

Just outside town, Mark and Marjorie Molloy's restored Georgian home offers good cooking, a warm welcome, excellent bedrooms and a favourable price/quality ratio. Dinner is a five-course affair (priced according to the choice of main dish), or six if opting for the selection of four Irish farmhouse cheeses (the small extra charge includes a glass of port). The likes of duck liver parfait with toasted brioche and onion confit, venison pithiviers, ravioli of crab with grain mustard and shellfish sauce are among the starters, and guinea fowl with wild mushroom sauce or breast of Barbary duck with a confit of its leg and a port and caper sauce might

be included in the main-course options. All are prepared with
a skill and care that extends to a choice of home-baked breads and
desserts like pear and almond tart cooked to order. The day's fish
and seasonal game dishes are recited when the menu is offered.
Diners and overnight guests share a comfortable period sitting
room. *Seats 40. L by arrangement D 7-9.30 (to 10.30 Fri & Sat).
Set D from £20. Closed D Sun (residents only), 24-26 Dec and Good
Friday. Access, Visa.*

Rooms   £58

Five spacious, antique-furnished bedrooms have been individually
decorated with attractive fabrics and offer various homely
comforts in addition to remote-control TV, direct-dial telephones
and good, large en-suite bathrooms. Breakfast, using free-range
eggs, makes an excellent start to the day.

Aughrim	Aughrim Schoolhouse Restaurant	£45
Tel 0905 73936		**R**
Aughrim nr Ballinasloe Co Galway		Map 2 B4

The work of conversion from schoolhouse to a charming country
restaurant can be followed in a scrapbook kept by the fire in the
reception area. Geraldine Dolan and Mícheál Harrison produce
intelligent menus of interesting modern dishes which have quickly
won a fair following. Cheese and spinach tartlet, confit of duck
salad, hot crab claws with lemon pasta and Hungarian goulash
soup are typical starters, followed perhaps by poached salmon with
a basil white wine sauce, roasted breast and braised leg of pheasant
or sirloin steak with green peppercorn or béarnaise sauce. Good
vegetables; 'bonnofie' pie a speciality dessert. *Seats 50. L 12.30-3
(Sun only) D 6.30-11. Closed D Sun Oct-May, all Mon, 24-26 Dec.
Set Sun L £9 Set D £16.* AMERICAN EXPRESS *Access, Visa.*

Aughrim	Place of Interest
Battle of Aughrim Centre Tel 0905 73939	

> We endeavour to be as up-to-date as possible,
> but inevitably some changes to key personnel
> may occur at restaurants and hotels after the
> Guide goes to press.

Ballina	Downhill Hotel	65%	£86
Tel 096 21033 Fax 096 21338			**H**
Ballina Co Mayo			Map 1 B3

Set in landscaped gardens overlooking the river Brosna, with
extensive leisure and conference facilities and good fishing nearby
as major attractions. The purpose-built conference centre and
hospitality rooms accommodate groups from 10 to 400 and the
leisure centre has a 50ft oval swimming pool; nightly
entertainment in Frog's Pavilion piano bar. Good facilities for
families include cots, high-chairs, baby-listening, baby-sitting (by
arrangement), playroom and a supervised crèche. Easy parking for
300. *Rooms 50. Garden, indoor swimming pool, keep-fit equipment,
squash, sauna, spa bath, solarium, tennis, games room, snooker.
Closed 3 days Christmas.* AMERICAN EXPRESS *Access, Diners, Visa.*

Ballina   Mount Falcon Castle   60%   £72

Tel & Fax 096 21172   **AR**

Ballina Co Mayo   **Map 1 B3**

The castle was built in neo-Gothic style in 1876, and the 100
acres of grounds extend to the banks of the River Moy (fishing
is available either here or on Lough Conn). Woodland walks
unfold the beauty of the surroundings, while back inside huge log
fires and convivial company make for instant relaxation. Simple
bedrooms are furnished with antiques. Constance Aldridge, who
has owned the castle and greeted visitors for over 50 years,
is an indispensible part of the charm of the place. ***Rooms** 10.
Garden, tennis, game fishing, games room. Closed Christmas week,
Feb & Mar.* AMERICAN EXPRESS *Access, Diners, Visa.*

Restaurant   £50

Local produce, much of it from the estate farm and walled
gardens, is the basis of confident, uncomplicated country house
cooking. Soup, salmon, leg of lamb, spicy chicken, crème caramel
and bread-and-butter pudding typify the menu. No smoking
in the dining room, where guests gather round one table. Lunch
available by arrangement. ***Seats** 22. D only at 8. Set D £18.*

Ballisodare   The Thatch

Tel 071 67288   **P**

Ballisodare Co Sligo   **Map 1 B2**

This attractive, low-ceilinged thatched pub just south of Sligo
town is very much a local and its open fire is as welcoming on a
winter evening as the tables outdoors on a fine summer day.
Whatever the weather the welcome from Brian and Denise
Fitzpatrick (long-standing owners in a family business) is warm
and the pint is good. Traditional music is played 3 or 4 nights
a week. *No credit cards.*

Ballyconneely   Erriseask House   64%   £72

Tel 095 23553   Fax 095 23639   **HR**

Ballyconneely Clifden Co Galway   **Map 2 A4**

In a stunning shoreside location seven miles south of Clifden, with
immediate access to miles of empty beaches, brothers Christian
and Stefan Matz have been running this discreet hotel since 1988
and their success is doing much, not only for their own
reputation, but for the growing recognition of culinary clustering
in the Clifden area. Except for the raw beauty of its setting and
a tendency to mount unusual art exhibitions, the hotel
is understated, cool, continental in style throughout the public
areas. Bedrooms, which are neatly decorated in somewhat neutral
tones, follow suit – the atmosphere suggests a reversal of the usual
priorities, more restaurant with rooms than hotel with interesting
food. ***Rooms** 13. Garden. Closed Nov-Easter.* AMERICAN EXPRESS *Access,
Diners, Visa.*

Restaurant   £60

The restaurant is formally well appointed but has more warmth
than elsewhere – a hint, perhaps, of the passion and perfectionism
which Stefan Matz brings to his cooking. In concept and balance,
choice of prime ingredients and the skill with which he blends

originality with classical and modern French cuisine to create
memorable meals, Stefan is making a serious contribution to the
developing Irish food scene. His attention to detail in wonderful
little amuse-bouche, petits fours and fragrant home-baked breads,
for example, is outstanding but the bold strokes are equally well
conceived in dishes that are as flavoursome as they are beautifully
presented – terrine of duck foie gras with glazed apples, pigeon
breast in a sherry vinegar sauce, veal medallions with wild
mushrooms and home-made pasta. Good French and Irish
farmhouse cheeseboard and lovely classic desserts. Light lunches
only. No smoking. **Seats** 35. Parties 20. Private Room 20.
D 6.30-9.30. Set D £17.50/£21.50 & £29.

We welcome bona fide complaints and recommendations on
the tear-out pages at the back of the Guide for readers'
comments. They are followed up by our professional team.

Ballyconnell	**Slieve Russell Hotel**	**78%**	**£120**
Tel 049 26444 Fax 049 26474			**H**
Ballyconnell Co Cavan			**Map 1 C3**

Hotel, golf and country club and major conference venue, Slieve
Russell stands in a lovely fishing area and takes its name from
a nearby mountain. A marbled colonnade and grand central
staircase set a tone of subdued luxury in the day rooms, where
guests have a good choice of eating and drinking outlets. Spacious
bedrooms have extra-large beds, with good amenities including
trouser press as standard and large marble bathrooms, all with
jacuzzi air baths. The championship golf course is in full swing
and excellent leisure facilities adjoining the hotel include
a 20 metre pool. **Rooms** 120. Indoor swimming pool, children's pool,
gymnasium, squash, sauna, spa bath, steam room, tennis, golf (18).
AMERICAN EXPRESS Access, Diners, Visa.

Ballydehob	**Annie's Restaurant**	**£55**
Tel 028 37292		**R**
Main Street Ballydehob Co Cork		**Map 2 A6**

Faces light up when Annie Barry's tiny restaurant is mentioned.
It's all so laid back: the way Levis' old grocery/bar across the road
serves aperitifs while you wait for your table and, quite likely,
digestifs afterwards, to relieve pressure on space. Daytime snacks
and lunches offer simple, honest fare, memorable for its freshness
and the flavours of good home cooking. Try their seafood salad
with home-made mayonnaise and crusty home-baked bread, or a
hot lunch dish of old-fashioned steak and kidney pie. Set 4-course
dinners change daily and, although understandably leaning
towards local seafood, give a wide range of choices at each course,
including a vegetarian dish of the day. Lamb kidneys in filo, baked
fresh wild salmon with lemon and fresh herb sauce, followed
by roasted almonds and Baileys ice cream or local Gubbeen
cheese typify the style. **Seats** 24. L 12.30-2.30 D 6.30-9.30.
Set L £6.50/£7.50 Set D £18/£20. Closed Sun, Mon, first three
weeks Oct + ring in winter to check opening times. Access, Visa.

Ballydehob   Levis Bar

Tel 028 37118	P
Corner House Main Street Ballydehob Co Cork	Map 2 A6

A friendly welcome awaits visitors to this 150-year-old grocery store and bar, which sisters Julia and Nell Levis have run for quite a few of those years. The bar is not only host to 'resident' drinkers but also serves as a reception and aperitif area for the tiny *Annie's* restaurant over the road. *Open 10.30am-11.30pm (Sun 12.30-2 & 4-11). No credit cards.*

Ballyferriter   Long's Pub

Tel 066 56344	P
Ballyferriter Village Ballyferriter Co Kerry	Map 2 A5

Right next door to the Well House in Ballyferriter village, this colourful little Irish-speaking pub has probably changed little since it first opened in 1854. A good spot for a quiet pint during the day, or traditional music sessions, held nightly in summer. En-suite accommodation also available. *No credit cards.*

Ballyferriter   Tigh an Tobair (The Well House)

Tel 066 56404	R
Ballyferriter Co Kerry	Map 2 A5

In an area otherwise surprisingly badly served, this pleasant, informal restaurant is an oasis for parched travellers and, although initially run as a daytime place in 1993, evening meals will also be available this season. Walk through the grocery shop at the front and you will find a stylish little restaurant arranged, quite literally, around a deep well (glass-topped for safety but still clearly visible) and furnished with the unmistakable tiled tables and chunky wares of Louis Mulcahy's nearby pottery – and, along with his own lovely products, those of his wife Lisbeth Mulcahy, the weaver, bring colour and interest to a joint display area at the back. The emphasis of daytime food is very much on simple home cooking in traditional dishes like Irish stew and Dublin coddle, good thick soups and big, wholesome salads and sandwiches made with home-made bread. Evening menus were still to be decided at the time of going to press. *Seats 30. Parties 8. Food 12-9. L 12.30-2.30 D 6.30-9. Set L £7.50. Closed Jan & Feb. Access, Visa.*

Ballyhack   Neptune Restaurant   £50

Tel 051 89284	R
Ballyhack New Ross Co Wexford	Map 2 C5

Instead of sweeping away on the Wexford road to the right when leaving the Passage East Car Ferry, turn left and look up towards the restored Ballyhack Castle and, just below it, one of the South-East's most attractive little informal bistro/restaurants will beckon. There are three distinct rooms and a patio that overlooks the harbour. The emphasis is, not surprisingly, on seafood; whether it is Neptune creamy fish soup, shrimp and ginger hotpot or scallops in orange and gin sauce with rice for a light lunch, a 'tourist' restricted-choice menu dinner at £11.90, the works from the à la carte – light game terrine, perhaps, hot crab brehat – or a delicious Sunday lunch at under £10, Pierce and Valerie McAuliffe's light and airy restaurant with its Mediterranean

colours, water views and unexpectedly reasonable prices will draw
you back. Interesting short wine list – and one of very few Irish
restaurants to encourage BYO. Lunch Sunday, other days
by arrangement. *Seats 45. Private Room 30. L (Sun only) 12.30-3
D 6.30-10 (Sat to 10.30). Closed Mon (except Jul & Aug),
Christmas-mid Mar. Set Sun L £9.90 Set D £11.90.* AMERICAN EXPRESS
Access, Diners, Visa.

Ballylickey	Ballylickey Manor House	67%	£110
Tel 027 50071 Fax 027 50124			**A**
Ballylickey Bantry Co Cork			**Map 2 B6**

Ballylickey has been the Graves' family home for four generations
and run as a hotel for over four decades. The main house, which
is impressively furnished with antiques, has views over Bantry
Bay and five spacious suites with well-appointed bathrooms. Ten
acres of award-winning gardens afford a splendid setting for an
outdoor swimming pool and garden restaurant, in addition to
simpler accommodation in eight chalets, all with en-suite rooms.
*Rooms 5 in main house. Garden, outdoor swimming pool, fishing,
croquet. Closed early Nov-end Mar.* AMERICAN EXPRESS *Access, Visa.*

Ballylickey	Larchwood House		£60
Tel 027 66181			**R**
Pearsons Bridge Ballylickey Bantry Co Cork			**Map 2 B6**

Owner-chef Sheila Vaughan and her husband Aidan have been
steadily building up a reputation for good food and
accommodation at Larchwood since they opened in 1990.
Although located in a private home, the restaurant is cleverly
designed to take full advantage of views over garden and river
to the mountains beyond and also to allow maximum privacy in a
limited space. Five-course, fixed-price-only menus offer a wide
selection, priced according to the choice of main course and
highlighting the best of local produce, particularly a good range
of fish: seafood and apple soup, rhubarb sorbet, paupiettes of sole
with mustard sauce and pigeon breasts with blackcurrant sauce are
typical, followed by warm chocolate cake with caramel sauce,
perhaps, or local farmhouse cheeses. Excellent breakfasts also offer
an unusual range of options, including several fish choices and
a cheese plate. Accommodation is offered in five comfortable en-
suite rooms, including two family rooms. Rooms at the back have
lovely views. No dogs. *Seats 20. Parties 13. D only 6.30-10.
Set D from £18. Closed Sun, 1 week Christmas.* AMERICAN EXPRESS
Access, Diners, Visa.

Ballylickey	Seaview House Hotel	70%	£100
Tel 027 50462 Fax 027 51555			**HR**
Ballylickey Bantry Co Cork			**Map 2 B6**

Since converting her family home to a hotel in the mid-70s,
Miss Kathleen O'Sullivan has built up an impressive reputation –
not only for consistently high standards of essentials like comfort
and housekeeping, but also for her personal supervision and
warmth of welcome. Spacious, well-proportioned public rooms
include a graciously decorated drawing room, a library and
comfortable television room, while generously-sized bedrooms are
all individually decorated and some have sea views. Family

See over

furniture and antiques enhance the hotel throughout and
a ground-floor room has been thoughtfully equipped for disabled
guests. No dogs. **Rooms** *17. Garden. Closed mid Nov-mid Mar.*
AMERICAN EXPRESS *Access, Visa.*

Restaurant   £55

Overlooking the garden, with views over Bantry Bay, several
well-appointed rooms linked by arches and furnished with
antiques and fresh flowers combine to make an elegant restaurant
with plenty of privacy. Set five-course dinner menus change daily
and offer a wide choice on all courses, with the emphasis firmly
on local produce, especially seafood, in dishes ranging from
a simple fresh crab salad or a scallop mousse with vermouth sauce
to John Dory with a mussel and spinach sauce. No children under
5 in dining room; separate arrangements are made for them.
Seats *45. Parties 20. L (Sun only) 11.45-2 D 7-9.30. Set Sun L £11
Set D £22.*

Ballymote   Temple House   £70

Tel 071 83329 Fax 071 83808	A
Ballymote Co Sligo	**Map 1 B3**

Temple House is a magnificent Georgian mansion set in 1000
acres of parkland with terraced gardens, a working farm and
a lake well known for the size of its pike. Imposing, even austere
externally, the house is warm and welcoming behind its front
door, in spite of the grand scale of the outer hall (note the trophies
of outdoor pursuits) and the elegant inner hall. There are four
centrally heated double bedrooms – two of them very large, all
very comfortable – and a single with shower. Deb Perceval does
the cooking, using home-grown or home-reared produce to good
effect in her no-choice dinners (residents only). Guests gather for
drinks in a cosy sitting room with an open fire, and coffee
is served in the drawing room afterwards. The day starts with the
double delight of marvellous views and a super breakfast. High tea
for kiddies is served at 6.30 – children's room rates are negotiable.
Perfumes are unwelcome as Deb's husband has an allergy.
Rooms *5. Garden, coarse fishing, snooker, lake boats (3).
Closed Dec-Mar (except shooting parties Dec & Jan). Access, Visa.*

Ballynahinch   Ballynahinch Castle   71%   £104

Tel 095 31006 Fax 095 31085	H
Recess Ballynahinch Co Galway	**Map 1 A3**

Standing in 350 acres of private grounds and overlooking the
famous Owenmore River, this crenellated mansion dates back
to 1784. The renowned Ballynahinch Fishery is the main
attraction, although anyone drawn to the country will enjoy the
log fires and atmosphere in the Fishermans pub, where the catches
are measured, weighed and entered in the fishing log. Open fires
and antiques in public rooms set the tone and bedrooms, furnished
with traditional mahogany, have views of the river and the
Twelve Bens mountains. Facilities for small (25) conferences.
Rooms *28. Garden, tennis, fishing, shooting, bicycles.
Closed 3 weeks Feb.* AMERICAN EXPRESS *Access, Diners, Visa.*

Ballyvaughan   Gregans Castle   71%   £88

Tel 065 77005   Fax 065 77111   **HR**

Ballyvaughan Co Clare   Map 2 B4

The Haden family (Peter, Moira, and son Simon-Peter) run this
friendly, welcoming hotel, which stands three miles from the
village in the Burren's limestone landscape overlooking Galway
Bay. The building has an austere, grey appearance, but there's
a deal of comfort and style within. Public rooms include
an elegant, traditional drawing room, the Corkscrew Bar and the
library, which is home not only to books but also to an important
collection of murals of Burren flora. Rooms, which vary in size
and shape but are all decorated to a high standard, some with
four-posters, have a refreshing emphasis on peace and quiet,
without radios or televisions. No dogs. *Rooms 22. Garden.
Closed Nov-Mar. Access, Visa.*

Restaurant   £75

Before settling into the elegant dining room, relax in the bar and
order from Margaret Cronin's carefully constructed five-course
menus which change daily but are always based on the best
of local ingredients, notably lamb and seafood, in dishes like whole
black sole with a chive sauce, fillets of John Dory with herb
butter, and roast rack of Burren lamb with a rosemary jus. Good
locally-made Irish farmhouse cheeses. Light meals are served all
day in the bar. *Seats 60. Private Room 40. L 12-3 (in bar) D 7-8.30.*
Set D £26.

Ballyvaughan   Monks Pub

Tel 065 77059   **P**

The Quay Ballyvaughan Co Clare   Map 2 B4

In 1983 Bernadette and Michael Monks took over this away-
from-it-all quayside pub, modernised it sensitively so that it has
retained its cottagey character, then set about acquiring
a reputation for good, simple bar food, especially local seafood.
There are several smallish, low-ceilinged, white-walled
interconnecting rooms with wooden country-kitchen furniture.
Open fires give a cosy atmosphere. Interest in food is emphasised
by a cluster of sturdy family-sized tables at the far end of the main   *See over*

bar and in summer the pier provides a sunny overspill. Everything is home-made by Bernadette, or under her supervision – and she has the wisdom to keep it simple. Regulars include a big bowl of seafood chowder, served with home-made brown bread (£2), or a seafood platter which varies with the catch but might typically include salmon, crab, Dublin Bay prawns, mussels and oysters; home-made apple pie is always popular and there may be daily specials added to the short bar menu. **Bar Food** *12-9.30 (Oct-May to 6.30). Children's portions. No credit cards.*

Ballyvaughan   Places of Interest

Tourist Information   Tel 065 81171
Aillwee Cave   Tel 065 77036
Cliffs of Moher
The Burren

Baltimore   Bushe's Bar

Tel 028 20125	**P**
Baltimore Co Cork	Map 2 B6

Richard and Eileen Bushe have run their famous old bar overlooking the harbour for over 20 years; it has a remarkable collection of maritime artefacts in the public bar, including admiralty charts, tide tables, ships' clocks, compasses, lanterns, pennants – all of real interest and guaranteed to make those arriving in Baltimore under sail feel at home. Eileen's homely bar food includes a choice of soups – always a fish one and something vegetable-based, changed daily, in summer – and open or closed sandwiches with fresh or smoked salmon, smoked mackerel and a choice of meats such as turkey, ham, roast beef and corned beef, all home-cooked. Three large en-suite rooms have television, comfortable armchairs and kitchenette facilities (with food provided) for making Continental breakfast. Children welcome "if controlled"; each room has both a double and single bed. No dogs. *Open 9.30am-11pm (11.30 in summer) & 12.30-2, 4-11 Sun. Garden.* **Accommodation** *3 bedrooms, all en suite, £25 (single £20). Outdoor eating. No credit cards.*

Baltimore   Chez Youen   £75

Tel 028 21036	**R**
The Pier Baltimore Co Cork	Map 2 B6

Youen Jacob has been delighting visitors to Baltimore with his distinctly Breton style of seafood cooking since 1978 and it's a case of *plus ça change*: concessions will be made to non fish-eaters in the shape of an occasional vegetable soup or melon with port and perhaps a steak with green peppercorn sauce, but it is the dramatic presentation of seafood in the shell which draws admiring sighs. Lobster is very much a speciality and available all year round and the shellfish platter on the £28 dinner menu includes Dublin Bay prawns, oysters or Baltimore shrimps, crab and velvet crab as well as lobster – all served in shell, this dish is indeed a sight to behold. A most appropriate recipient of the Seafood Restaurant of the Year Award. **Seats** *45. Parties 12. Private Room 50. Meals 12.30-midnight in summer L 12.30-3 (summer only) D 6.30-11. Closed L (low season), mid Nov-mid Feb, booking essential in winter. Set L from £12.50 Set D from £19.50.* *Access, Diners, Visa.*

Baltimore   McCarthy's Bar

Tel 028 20159   **P**

The Square Baltimore Co Cork   Map 2 B6

A lively bar overlooking the harbour. Decor takes two main themes, one nautical (including a map of sea disasters in the area), the other musical, with a wall of photographs relating to the music business back in the 60s. The bar menu covers a good range of dishes, from garlic mussels and crab claws via spaghetti bolognese and lasagne (beef or vegetarian) to Irish stew and casseroled beef with Guinness. These dishes are available only in the summer – at other times the choice is limited to soup and sandwiches. *Open 10.30am-11pm (from midday in winter, to 11.30pm summer) (Sun 12.30-2 & 4-11).* **Bar Food** *(Summer) 12-9 (Sun 12.30-2 & 4-9) Garden.* AMERICAN EXPRESS *Access, Diners, Visa.*

When telephoning establishments in the Republic from *outside* the Republic, dial 010-353 then the number we print without initial zero: e.g. Cliffords in Cork is 010-353 21 275333.

Bantry   Anchor Tavern

Tel 027 50012   **P**

New Street Bantry Co Cork   Map 2 A6

A town-centre pub with a history going back 140 years, currently run by William E O'Donnell, the third generation of his family to hold the reins. Pubs are for conversation and the exchange of ideas, says William, who sees the family's vast collection of mainly nautical memorabilia displayed around the two bars as a talking point most of all – although he does admit to a special fondness for one item, an original 'croppy pike' from the rising of 1798 which will go with him if he ever leaves. There's also a morning crossword club for regulars and soup and sandwiches are offered as sustenance throughout opening hours. Well-behaved children are welcome at reasonable hours (not after 9pm). *Open 10.30am-11/11.30pm in season, 12.30-2, 4-11 Sun (rest of year). No credit cards.*

Bantry   Place of Interest

Bantry House   Tel 027 50047

Barna   Donnelly's of Barna

Tel 091 92487   Fax 091 64379   **P**

Barna Co Galway   Map 2 B4

Seafood is the thing at Donnelly's, built as a thatched cottage, extended at the turn of the century and run by the same family ever since. In the cosy, cottagey bar rooms the menu choices run from smoked fish and potato cakes, seafood pancakes and crab claws for starters ('bait') to grilled trout, salmon and mushrooms with white wine sauce and a festival of seafood and pasta as main courses ('the catch'). Also a few meat dishes and an evening menu in the restaurant at the back. **Bar Food** *12-10.* **Restaurant Meals** *7-10. Set D £16.95. Patio, outdoor eating.* *Access, Diners, Visa.*

Beaufort   Dunloe Castle   71%   £96

Tel 064 44111   Fax 064 44583   **H**

Beaufort nr Killarney Co Kerry   Map 2 A5

In a glorious, verdant setting of parkland, only the empty shell
of the keep from the original 13th-century castle remains at this
modern hotel. Nevertheless, the building gives a good first
impression and all public areas, including the cocktail bar and
restaurant, have been refurbished. The main public room is a
spacious, comfortably furnished first-floor drawing room with
some well-chosen antiques and lovely views of the Gap of Dunloe.
All bedrooms have good bathrooms; twenty new junior suites
were created last winter. 24hr room service. Sister hotel to *Hotel
Europe* (Killarney, 2½ miles away) and *Ard-na-Sidhe* (Caragh Lake).
Banqueting/conference facilities for 200/300. *Rooms 120. Garden,
indoor swimming pool, sauna, tennis, riding, putting, game fishing,
cycling. Closed Oct-Apr.* AMERICAN EXPRESS *Access, Diners, Visa.*

Birdhill   Matt the Thresher

Tel 061 379227   **P**

Birdhill Co Tipperary   Map 2 B4

On the main Dublin road a few miles outside Limerick, this pub
has succeeded in becoming one of Ireland's best-known inns since
Ted and Kay Moynihan took over in 1987. It's as reliable for its
food as for its foolproof location and makes a perfect meeting
place. Characterful in the modern mode – red-tiled floors,
country-kitchen furniture (including some settles, thankfully
cushioned) and bar stools made from old tractor seats – chintzy
curtains and gas coal-effect fires introduce a slightly suburban note.
But the agricultural theme is developed to its logical conclusion
in an unexpected way – home-grown, stone-ground flour is used
in all the bread, which is baked on the premises and served with
a wide variety of home-made soups and bar snacks on the 'Snug
Menu'. Seafood is a speciality, with West Cork mussels and crab
claws, or salmon from local rivers served hot, or cold in salads and
open sandwiches, while carnivores may prefer home-baked ham
or a good steak. 10% service charge is added to 'After Six' dishes
(served 6-10pm, to 9pm Sun) such as avocado with crab and
grilled fresh salmon. Ample parking in the yard, which backs on
to a quality craft shop. *Bar Food 11am-10pm (Fri & Sat to 10.30,
Sun noon-9).* AMERICAN EXPRESS *Access, Visa.*

Birr   Dooly's Hotel   60%   £50

Tel 0509 20032   Fax 0509 21332   **H**

Birr Co Offaly   Map 2 C4

Right on Emmet Square, in the centre of Georgian Birr, this
attractively old-fashioned hotel is one of Ireland's oldest coaching
inns, dating back to 1747. It's a good holiday centre with plenty
to do locally – Birr Castle gardens are very near, also golfing,
fishing, riding and river excursions. Public rooms include two
characterful bars and are traditionally furnished and well
maintained. Pleasant, modest bedrooms are all en suite; some may
be noisy when there's a function in the night-club. Children
up to 7 share parents' room at no charge. *Rooms 18. Garden,
coffee shop (10am-10pm), night club, coarse fishing. Closed 25 Dec.*
AMERICAN EXPRESS *Access, Diners, Visa.*

Birr   Tullanisk   £76

Tel & Fax 0509 20572   **A**

Birr Co Offaly   **Map 2 C4**

George and Susie Gossip have run their carefully restored 18th-
century Dower House in the demesne of the Earls of Rosse (still
resident at Birr Castle) as a delightful country house hotel since
1989. The house is beautiful, interesting and comfortable, the
surrounding gardens and parkland lovely and full of wildlife,
of which a fair cross-section may make an appearance while you
watch from the big mahogany dining table at dinner. George is an
excellent chef and enjoys producing memorable no-choice dinners
(£20 per head) and breakfasts live up to the promise of the night
before and more. *Rooms 7. Garden, croquet, table tennis. D only
8.30. Closed 4 days at Christmas. Access, Visa.*

Birr   Places of Interest

Birr Castle   Tel 0509 20056
Charleville Forest Castle   Tullamore Tel 0506 21279 *20 miles*

Blacklion   MacNean Bistro   £40

Tel 072 53022   **R**

Blacklion Co Cavan   **Map 1 C2**

A modest little room on Blacklion's main street is the setting for
some excellent and imaginative cooking by Vera Maguire and her
son Nevan. Courgette flowers filled with sole and dill mousse is a
typical starter, which could precede braised leg and fried saddle
of rabbit, steamed monkfish with shallots and burgundy sauce,
or even fried fillet of ostrich served on rösti accompanied by
organic vegetables. Splendid desserts (typically roast pear with
caramel sauce, passion fruit ice cream and a compote of berries),
befitting Dessert of the Year, to finish the meal in fine style.
*Seats 35. L 12.30-3 light meals 3-6 D 6-9.30. Closed in winter except
Fri & Sat eve and all Sun. Set L (Sun) £9.50 Set D from £12.
Access, Visa.*

Blackrock   Ayumi-Ya   £40

Tel 01 283 1767   Fax 01 662 0221   **R**

Newpark Centre Newtownpark Avenue Blackrock Co Dublin   **Map 4 C1**

Situated in a small shopping centre, Ayumi-Ya opened in 1983
and offers a wide range of authentic Japanese dishes. Diners are
given the choice of western or Japanese-style seating when
booking – also the time to opt for a teppanyaki table if you want
food cooked in front of you. In addition to teppanyaki and an
à la carte menu for old hands, set menus ranging from vegetarian,
through the Ayumi-Ya dinner course to a special seasonal dinner
make the choices easier. Staff are very ready with advice, and
owner Akiko Hoashi uses the menu to impart a few tips on how
to order and even how to eat ('Japanese customers tend to make
noise when sipping soup'). No children after 8.15. The Dublin
Ayumi-Ya (qv) is slightly more geared to western tastes. *Seats 60.
Private Room 25. D only 7-11 (Sun 6-10). Closed 24-26 Dec, Good
Friday. Set D £13.50 (Sun £10.25).* AMERICAN EXPRESS *Access,
Diners, Visa.*

Blackrock   Clarets   ↑   £70

Tel 01 288 2008   Fax 01 283 3273   **R**

63 Main Street Blackrock Co Dublin   Map 4 C1

An unpretentious, comfortable and welcoming restaurant where
Alan O'Reilly offers creative, interesting cooking. There may be a
special tasting menu one week, or a theme menu based on a
specific cuisine another, but there will always be imaginative,
carefully cooked food at fair prices. Mousseline of seafood
in a ginger sauce, salad of Stilton and avocado, brill with scallop
mousse and angel hair pasta and fillet of veal on a bed of rösti
with a wild mushroom sauce show the style. Game is a speciality
in season; breads are good, also their tangy lemon tart. *Seats 50.
L 12.30-2.30 D 7-10. Closed L Sat, all Sun & Mon, Bank Holidays.
Set L £10.95 Set D £18.95.* AMERICAN EXPRESS *Access, Diners, Visa.*

Blackrock   The Brake Tavern

Tel 042 21393   **P**

Main Street Blackrock nr Dundalk Co Louth   Map 1 D3

A warm, bustling seafront pub with a characterful wooden
interior and mountains of fascinating local memorabilia. The bar
is broken up into several room-sized areas, with unpretentious but
comfortable arrangements of country furniture in welcoming
groups and – increasingly unusual these days – a real open fire
to settle round. The Brake is especially well known for the quality
and variety of food, served only in the evenings. Seafood is a
speciality – Dublin Bay prawns, fish platters, salmon mayonnaise,
crab claws in garlic butter – but there's also a good choice for
carnivores, including a range of steaks, casseroles and the like.
Everything is home-made and very wholesome. The bar itself
opens at 2 on weekdays. On Sunday it's open 12.30-2 and 6-11.
Bar Food 6.30-10.30 (Sun to 9.30). Access, Visa

Blessington   Downshire House   59%   £63

Tel 045 65199   Fax 045 65335   **H**

Downshire House Blessington Co Wicklow   Map 2 D4

It's difficult not to be charmed by the friendly atmosphere and
unpretentious comfort of this substantial village hotel built
in 1800 and run by Rhoda Byrne since 1959. One enters into the
recently refurbished bar-lounge, where all the seats are small
armchairs, before finding the reception desk at the head of a broad
flight of stairs leading down to the function room – a modern
addition. Decoratively modest bedrooms – plain white walls,
candlewick bedspreads, functional fitted furniture – nevertheless
offer all the modern comforts including remote-control TV,
hairdryer, direct-dial phones and beverage kit plus crisp, pure
cotton bedding. Bathrooms are a little dated and boast only
unwrapped soap on the toiletries front but, like the whole hotel,
are immaculately kept. *Rooms 25. Garden, croquet, tennis.
Closed mid Dec-early Jan. Access, Visa.*

Blessington   Place of Interest

Russborough   Tel 045 65239

Boyle	Cromleach Lodge	78%	£118

Tel 071 65155   Fax 071 65455   **HR**

Ballindoon Castlebaldwin nr Boyle Co Sligo   **Map 1 B3**

In a setting of unsurpassed beauty in the hills above Lough Arrow,
Christy and Moira Tighe have furnished this purpose-built
modern country house to the highest international standards and
it is impeccably maintained. Comfort is a high priority
throughout: public rooms include a cosy sitting room and bar
with an open fire and a cane-furnished conservatory along the
front of the building. All rooms, including the spacious,
individually decorated bedrooms, enjoy breathtakingly beautiful
views over the lake and mountains. Exceptionally well-appointed
bedrooms (half of them designated non-smoking) have queen-size
and single beds, safe, mini-bar, hairdryer, comfortable armchairs,
writing and dressing areas, tea/coffee-making facilities with teapot
and fresh milk daily in the fridge. Fully-tiled bathrooms are also
large and well-planned, with full-size bath, strong overbath
shower, efficient extraction, generous towels and good toiletries.
Kennelling for dogs. *Rooms 10. Garden, game fishing, boating.*
Closed 18 Dec-30 Jan. AMERICAN EXPRESS *Access, Diners, Visa.*

Restaurant   ★   £75

The restaurant comprises three separate dining areas, each carefully
designed to take full advantage of the beautiful views over Lough
Arrow and table settings, including wonderful Villeroy & Boch
china, are exquisite. Menus are sophisticated and Moira Tighe,
a self-taught cook, combines flair, imagination and lightness
of touch, starting with the pick of local produce. Roulade of Irish
smoked salmon and trout, pastry basket of pan-fried monkfish and
asparagus, or sausage of chicken mousse and crab meat on a
Sauternes sauce could get dinner under way, followed by soup
(leek and herb cream) or a salad, a sorbet, then the main dish,
perhaps boned and stuffed quail with a grain mustard sauce, beef
fillet with Roquefort cheese sauce, or loin of lamb scented with
Irish Mist and rosemary. Desserts taste as beautiful as they look.
A six-course, set (by arrangement) gourmet menu is also offered
for residents only; typically, this could comprise courgette flower
filled with seafood mousse on a tomato sauce, ravioli with veal
and smoked bacon, trio of consommé, fillet of Dover sole with
fennel purée, radicchio and blue cheese salad and, finally, a tasting
plate of desserts. Apart from the excellent under-£15
recommendations, the wine list is predominantly French and
relatively expensive; at the prices charged, champagne drinkers are
unlikely to be encouraged! No smoking in the dining rooms, but
smokers can indulge over coffee in the lounge. *Seats 50. Parties 16.*
Private Room 20. L by arrangement D 7-9 (Sun 6.30-8).
Set L £16.95 Set D £26.50.

Bray   Tree of Idleness   £65

Tel 01 286 3498   **R**

Seafront Bray Co Wicklow   Map 2 D4

The original Tree of Idleness was situated in Bellapais, Cyprus, with views of the coastline and the hillside citrus groves. This one, on the seafront at Bray, continues the Greek-Cypriot tradition and in the capable hands of owner Susan Courtellas and chef Ismail Basaran is firmly established among Ireland's favourite restaurants. Dips and dolmades, moussaka and souvlaki, halloumi and calamares account for only part of the menu, and other choices include spinach ravioli filled with crab mousse served with a carrot sauce, chicken saffron, roast pheasant with grapes and chestnuts and fillet steak with a red wine sauce and truffles. Supplementing the à la carte menu is a table d'hote (not available Saturday), the latter's whose price depending on the main course. A truly exceptional wine list with a huge choice, especially among red bordeaux; most wine-producing regions are covered and the top growers are chosen; ports include some from the Russian Massandra collection. *Seats 50. Parties 18. D only 7.30-11 (Sun to 10). Closed Mon, Bank Holidays, 1 week Christmas, 2 weeks Sep. Set D from £15.50.* AMERICAN EXPRESS *Access, Diners, Visa.*

Bray   Place of Interest

Killruddery House and Gardens   Tel 01 286 3405

Bunratty   Fitzpatricks Shannon Shamrock   60%   £137

Tel 061 361177   Fax 061 471252   **H**

Bunratty Co Clare   Map 2 B4

A low-rise modern hotel alongside Bunratty Castle with a leisure centre and banqueting facilities for up to 200. Only four miles from Shannon airport, this would make a good base for touring Clare and the Burren; children under 12 stay free in parents' room. *Rooms 115. Indoor swimming pool, sauna, steam room. Closed 25 Dec.* AMERICAN EXPRESS *Access, Diners, Visa.*

JAMESON The Spirit of Ireland

Bunratty   MacCloskey's   £70

Tel 061 364082   **R**

Bunratty House Mews Bunratty Co Clare   Map 2 B4

Gerry and Marie MacCloskey have established a successful formula over a dozen years at their atmospheric restaurant in the cellars of 17th-century Bunratty House. A five-course fixed-price menu offers straightforward dishes such as asparagus beurre blanc, grilled kidneys on a bed of braised onions, cod with parsley and lemon butter, duck with orange sauce and steak with green peppercorns. Icky sticky pudding, passion fruit mousse or honey and lime cheesecake to finish. *Seats 60. Private Room 22. D only 7-10. Closed Sun & Mon, 20 Dec-25 Jan, Good Friday. Set D £25.* AMERICAN EXPRESS *Access, Diners, Visa.*

Bunratty   Place of Interest

Bunratty Castle and Folk Park   Tel 061 361511

Butlersbridge   Derragarra Inn

Tel 049 31003 Fax 043 83327	**P**
Butlersbridge Co Cavan	Map 1 C3

A few miles north of Cavan, on the N3, the Derragarra Inn
is well situated to break a journey and is easily recognised by its
thatched roof and the old agricultural implements and rural
artefacts at the door. The agricultural theme is developed inside
with items of local interest as well as curiosities from further afield
such as a wall covered with currencies from different countries.
The inn's riverside location means freshwater fish will be on the
menu, as well as ever-popular seafood like smoked salmon (£4.35)
and garlic mussels (£3.95), but carnivores are also well catered for
with the likes of burgers (£3.75), steaks and a mixed grill
(£5.95). The restaurant menu is also available in the bar,
extending to stuffed whiting, chicken curry and surf and turf.
Music is also an attraction, with traditional Irish music on Friday
nights in summer. ***Bar Food*** *10.30am-10pm (plus à la carte 12-3
and from 7pm). Riverside terrace, outdoor eating. Access, Visa.*

Caherdaniel   Derrynane Hotel   62%   £66

Tel 066 75136 Fax 066 75160	**HR**
Caherdaniel Co Kerry	Map 2 A6

In a spectacular location on the southern stretch of the Ring
of Kerry, this unprepossessing 1960s' hotel offers a warm welcome
and good facilities for family holidays. Accommodation is simple
but a high standard of housekeeping, good value for money and
lovely sea views ensure satisfaction. 12 family rooms have bunk
beds; supervised crèche in the evenings. ***Rooms*** *75. Garden, outdoor
swimming pool, games room, snooker, shop. Closed Oct-Apr.*
 Access, Diners, Visa.

Restaurant   £44

The bar and restaurant overlook the open-air swimming pool and
are well placed to take advantage of the magnificent sea views.
Good, fresh ingredients are used to produce enjoyable 'home-
cooked' food and attractive desserts at very reasonable prices.
Children's menu; high-chairs provided. ***Seats*** *100. L 12.30-2
D 7-9. Set L £6.50 Set D £17.*

Caherdaniel   Loaves & Fishes   £55

Tel 066 75273	**R**
Caherdaniel nr Derrynane Co Kerry	Map 2 A6

Helen Mullane and Armel Whyte set up this charming little
restaurant in 1990. The style is comfortably cottagey, with an old
range, low ceilings and random plate collection and an interesting
little bar/reception area at the back with light filtering through
a stained-glass skylight. Armel's imaginative, shortish à la carte
menu offers plenty of interest starting, perhaps, with a platter
of smoked wild fish with a cucumber pickle or country terrine
of pork with garlic and a tomato and mustard-seed relish – for

See over

serious garlic-lovers, also with an excellent relish. Well-balanced main courses include favourites like crab claws on a beurre blanc, sirloin steak and local Kerry lamb, with a rosemary scented potato stuffing and port jus, perhaps, and fish, typically darne of salmon with a creamed Noilly Prat sauce. Good desserts include a tangy lemon tart. **Seats** 30. *Parties 8. Private Room 12. D only 6-9.30. Closed Mon Jun-Aug, Mon & Tues Sep, all Oct-Easter. Access, Visa.*

Cahirciveen	Brennan's Restaurant	£55
Tel 066 72021		**R**
13 Main Street Cahirciveen Co Kerry		Map 2 A6

The Brennans moved from Castlequin into new premises in the main street in 1993 and, although not totally settled in on the evening of a recent inspection, the wagon is starting to roll. The place has a sense of style, menus are interesting and imaginative use of fresh local ingredients seems to be their hallmark. Opening hours have recently been extended, giving owner-chef Conor Brennan a chance to improve the image of daytime food on the Ring of Kerry. **Seats** 30. *Parties 20. L 12-2.30 D 7-10 snacks 10-5 (except Sundays). Set L £6/£8 Set D £19.50. Closed 24-26 Dec, Nov & Feb for dinner. Access, Visa.*

Changes in data sometimes occur in establishments after the Guide goes to press. Prices should be taken as indications rather than firm quotes.

Cahirciveen	The Point Bar	
Tel 066 72165		**P**
Renard Point Cahirciveen Co Kerry		Map 2 A6

In the same family for ten generations (at least 150 years), this magical little place, at what was until 1960 the final stop on the Great Southern & Western Railway line, overlooks Valentia Island and harbour and has been sympathetically modernised to retain its charm without gimmicks. During the summer Michael and Bridie O'Neill serve ultra-fresh fish and seafood in simple, wholesome dishes ranging from plain and toasted sandwiches (£1.25-£1.75) to fresh lobster salad. For fine weather there's a very pleasant patio with tubs and tables looking past the old terminal to the sea. **Bar Food** *Noon-9 (no food mid-Sept to Apr). Garden, outdoor eating area. No credit cards.*

Cape Clear Island	Paddy Bourke's	
Tel 028 39115		**P**
Cape Clear Island Co Cork		Map 2 A6

Cape Clear Island is about an hour's trip by boat from Baltimore, a journey whose highlights include great views of Fastnet Rock lighthouse (call 028 39119 for sailing times). Paddy Bourke's pub – the most southerly in Ireland – is also a vantage point for superb views, while inside it's small, snug and unspoilt. Paddy describes himself as 'old-fashioned', and that seems a good way for the natural host to be. *Open 10.30am-8pm (Sun 12-2 & 4-8 from Easter onwards). Closed Sun in winter. No credit cards.*

Caragh Lake   Hotel Ard-na-Sidhe   70%   £96
Tel 066 69105   Fax 066 69282   **H**

Caragh Lake nr Killorglin Co Kerry   **Map 2 A5**

The beautiful lakeside setting and the peace and quiet are major pluses at this splendid Victorian mansion on the edge of Caragh Lake. In the house there are 12 good-sized bedrooms furnished with antiques and a further eight rooms with private patios are available in the garden house at slightly lower rates. Sister hotel to *Hotel Europe* (Killarney) and *Dunloe Castle* (Beaufort), whose sporting facilities are available to Ard-na-Sidhe guests. ***Rooms** 20. Garden, game fishing. Closed Oct-Apr.* AMERICAN EXPRESS *Access, Diners, Visa.*

Caragh Lake   Caragh Lodge   65%   £99
Tel 066 69115   Fax 066 69316   **A**

Caragh Lake nr Killorglin Co Kerry   **Map 2 A5**

Owner Mary Gaunt is in personal charge at this Victorian fishing lodge, which stands in delightful gardens on the shore of Caragh Lake. Boating, fishing and swimming are favourite pastimes, there's a tennis court in the grounds and five championship golf courses are a short drive away. Peaceful antique-furnished day rooms. Bedrooms in main house or garden cottages. Small dogs allowed with prior notice. ***Rooms** 10. Garden, sauna, tennis, game fishing, rowing boat, bicycles. Closed mid Oct-Easter.* AMERICAN EXPRESS *Access, Visa.*

Carlingford   Jordan's Bar & Restaurant   £55
Tel 042 73223   **R**

Carlingford Co Louth   **Map 1 D3**

Harry and Marian Jordan take turns in the kitchen of their warmly decorated restaurant, but the day always starts with a baking session to produce their delicious brown soda bread and white yeast rolls. Menus are nicely balanced between the traditional and modern, and local produce is used wherever possible. They grow their own herbs and even produce their own butter. Typical dishes run from terrine of fresh salmon, pigeon breast with a herb salad and natural, baked or jellied oysters to hake with samphire sauce, crubeens (pig's trotters) and shank of lamb wrapped in puff pastry and accompanied by a rosemary sauce. Half the wines are priced at under £12.50. Seven letting bedrooms with period-style pine furniture, lough views and business facilities are due to come on stream in the summer of 1994. No smoking. ***Seats** 34. Parties 12. Private Room 16. L (Sun only) 12.30-2.30 D 7-10. Closed 25 & 26 Dec, 1st 2 weeks Jan. Set L £11.50 Set D £19.50.* AMERICAN EXPRESS *Access, Diners, Visa.*

Carlingford   P J O'Hare's Anchor Bar
Tel 042 73106   **P**

Carlingford Co Louth   **Map 1 D3**

Grocer's shop and bar share the same room at PJs, which stands right in the heart of a picturesque medieval village. Carlingford oysters are the speciality on the bar menu (£3 for 6), with smoked salmon and the day's soup among the rival attractions. It's

See over

a favourite spot with the local sailing community, and the walls
are covered with items of nautical interest. The enclosed yard
by the bar is a popular summer rendezvous. *Open (and bar food
served) 10.30am-11.30pm (Sun 12.30-2 & 4-11). No credit cards.*

Carlingford   Place of Interest
Carlingford Castle

Carne   Lobster Pot   £50
| Tel 053 31110   Fax 053 31401 | R |
Carne Co Wexford   Map 2 D5

Long and low outside, cosy and comfortable within, the Lobster
Pot is restaurant, bar and pub rolled into one. The menu sticks
mainly to familiar seafood dishes, from prawn cocktail to grilled
or poached wild salmon, pan-fried Dover sole, seafood mornay
and lobster from the tank. Also a 'landlubber's choice' of chicken,
crispy duck and various steaks. Smoking discouraged. Tables
outside in the summer. *Seats 28. Parties 16. Private Room 30.
L 12.30-2.30 (Sun only Sep-end May) D 6-9. Bar Menu all day.
Closed L Mon-Sat also L Sun Jun-Sep (except bar meals), D Tue-Sat
in winter, Good Friday, 25 Dec, all Jan.* AMERICAN EXPRESS *Access, Visa.*

Carrick-on-Shannon   Hollywell House   £46
| Tel & Fax 078 21124 | A |
Liberty Hill Carrick-on-Shannon Co Leitrim   Map 1 B3

Just across the bridge at Carrick-on-Shannon, with lovely views
down through the garden to the river, this fine period house offers
comfortable en-suite rooms furnished with antiques (two with
river views), but it is Tom and Rosaleen Maher's hospitality
which makes Hollywell outstanding. Good breakfasts, with home-
made bread and preserves, but no evening meals except by special
arrangement. No dogs. *Rooms 3. Garden, fishing.
Closed 16 Dec-10 Jan. No credit cards.*

Carrick-on-Shannon   Places of Interest
Lough Rynn Estate and Gardens   Mohill Tel 078 31427 *10 miles*
Strokestown Park House   Strokestown Tel 078 33013 *12 miles*

Carrickmacross   Nuremore Hotel   72%   £120
| Tel 042 61438   Fax 042 61853 | H |
Carrickmacross Co Monaghan   Map 1 C3

The championship-length golf course is a great attraction at this
modern low-rise hotel on the N2, and 1994 will bring a brand
new pavilion with bar, snack menu and changing facilities. Many
of the bright, airy bedrooms overlook a lake. Banqueting for up to
500, conferences for 300 theatre-style. No dogs. *Rooms 69.
Garden, indoor swimming pool, gymnasium, squash, sauna, spa bath,
solarium, tennis, golf (18), games room.* AMERICAN EXPRESS *Access,
Diners, Visa.*

Carrigaline   Pew's Bistro

£55

R

Tel 021 371512   Fax 021 371237

Main Street Carrigaline Co Cork

Map 2 B6

After working in various well-known London restaurants, local
boy Barry O'Connor has returned to create this cosy little
restaurant in the main street of town – look out for the sign above
the door depicting a hedgehog balancing a glass of wine on its
nose. Decor is dark green-painted breeze-block walls, bare-board
floor and pew seating with crisp white tablecloths adding a touch
of luxury. The wide-ranging menu, supplemented by daily
blackboard specials, might include the likes of home-made venison
sausage on a bed of pasta, snails in puff pastry with a creamy garlic
sauce and roast halibut with champagne, dill and prawn sauce
along with a couple of steak dishes. Weekday lunchtimes there is a
shorter, less expensive à la carte in addition to the regular menu.
Up to 14 different Irish cheeses (served with a glass of port) offer
an alternative to the desserts. No children under 12. *Seats 40.*
L 12.30-2.30 (to 5 Sun) D 7-11 (to 11.30 Sun). Set Sun L £9.95.
Closed D Sun (except June-Aug), all Mon & 25 Dec. Access, Visa.

Carrigtwohill   Niblicks

£38

R

Tel 021 883667

Fota Island Golf Club Carrigtwohill Co Cork

Map 2 B6

Take the Cobh turning off the N25 about five miles east of Cork
to find the club house, converted from an old farm, of a new golf
course within which, under a barn-like roof, is an informal
restaurant run by Michael Ryan (brother of Declan at *Arbutus
Lodge*). The menu makes no formal distinction between starters
and main dishes though some can be either and are dual priced.
An eclectic selection ranges from seafood chowder, a plate of tapas
and hot New York steak sandwich to fettucine with wild
mushrooms and grilled salmon with chive and white wine sauce.
Puds include the likes of millefeuille of passion fruit and cassis ice
cream, and yoghurt and cardamom cream with orange confit. The
menu gets a bit shorter after 3pm and dinner, in similar style,
is served only on Friday and Saturday. A balcony overlooking
an ornamental lake makes an ideal spot for summer eating. The
style of the menu makes it easy to eat for considerably less than the
price for two quoted above. *Seats 75. L 12.30-6 D 6.30-9.30
(Fri & Sat only). Closed D Sun-Thurs, 25 & 26 Dec. Access,
Diners, Visa.*

Cashel   Cashel House   76%

£135

HR

Tel 095 31001   Fax 095 31077

Cashel Co Galway

Map 1 A3

Standing in secluded beauty at the head of Cashel Bay, the
Victorian house is set in award-winning gardens running down
to a private beach. Dermot and Kay McEvilly have been the
welcoming, professional hosts since 1968, and their hotel won
instant renown a year later when General and Madame de Gaulle
stayed for two weeks. Turf and log fires add a cosy glow to the
gracious day rooms, where antiques and fresh flowers take the eye.
Bedrooms are individually decorated, and the Garden Suite rooms
are particularly stylish, with separate seating areas and access to the

See over

patio. Service is excellent and breakfast includes a wide range
of home-made produce, from soda bread and marmalade to black
pudding. *Rooms 32. Garden, tennis, sea & game fishing, boating,
horse riding (inc dressage). Closed 10-31 Jan.* *Access,
Diners, Visa.*

Restaurant   £70

Fixed-price five-course dinners in the sunny restaurant feature the
best of home-grown and local produce prepared without undue
elaboration or fuss. From a typical winter menu you might choose
garlic mussels, smoked salmon or veal and quail terrine to start,
then one of two soups, a sorbet, and scallop-stuffed sole, salmon
with leek sauce, lobster (£7.20 per pound supplement) or roast
sirloin of beef with béarnaise sauce. Home-made ice cream and
tarte tatin are sweet alternatives to a selection of Irish cheeses.
Lunch in the bar. *Seats 70. Parties 12. Private Room 10. L 1-2 (in
the bar) D 7.30-8.30 (Sun 7.30-9). Set D from £27.*

Cashel	Zetland House	65%	£109
Tel 095 31111 Fax 095 31117			**H**
Cashel Co Galway			Map 1 A3

On the edge of Cashel Bay, Zetland House was a sporting lodge
when built in the early 19th century. It's still a favoured base for
outdoor pursuits, notably fishing and rough shooting. Cosy sitting
rooms; most bedrooms have spectacular sea views. *Rooms 20.
Garden, croquet, tennis, fishing, snooker. Closed Nov-Easter.*
 Access, Diners, Visa.

Cashel	Chez Hans		£70
Tel 062 61177			**R**
Rockside Cashel Co Tipperary			Map 2 C5

Seafood features strongly on the menu at this former Wesleyan
chapel at the foot of the Rock of Cashel, but meat-eaters are
in no way the poor relations! Hans-Peter Matthiä puts
a contemporary stamp on classic recipes: escalope of salmon with
a lemon butter sauce, gratin of Dublin Bay prawns with
mangetout and a saffron sauce, breast of free-range chicken with
Cashel Blue cheese and leek sabayon. Other favourites, simple and
straightforward, include oak-smoked salmon, Rossmore oysters,
sole meunière and steak with a peppercorn sauce. *Seats 60. D only
6.30-10. Closed Sun & Mon, Bank Holidays, 3 weeks Jan.*
Access, Visa.

Cashel	Dowling's		
Tel 062 62130			**P**
Cashel Co Tipperary			Map 2 C5

Pat and Helen Dowling have changed the name of their pub from
Meaney's, but that's about the only change. It stands handily
on the main street and its attractions include traditional decor,
a cosy open fire and good simple snacks. But above all this is a
place for music: there are traditional Irish sessions organised
on Friday and Sunday nights (also Wednesday in summer), but
anyone with an instrument is always welcome and impromptu
sessions can get going at any time. *No credit cards.*

Cashel   Places of Interest

Cahir Castle   Cahir Tel 052 41011
GPA Bolton Library   Tel 062 61944
Thurles Racecourse   Tel 0504 22253 *16 miles*

Castleconnell   Bradshaw's Bar

Tel 061 377724	**P**
Castleconnell Co Limerick	**Map 2 B4**

The Bradshaw family bought this atmospheric 19th-century
village pub in the 1920s and since the current owner, Ger
Bradshaw, took over in 1992 he has worked hard to make
improvements while remaining true to the old traditions – so,
although an extra room has been opened up to increase space,
it has retained the authentic feeling, with bare floor, fairly spartan
furniture and an open fire. *Open from 5pm weekdays, usual pub
hours at weekends. Closed 25 Dec & Good Friday. No credit cards.*

Castledermot   Kilkea Castle   70%   £178

Tel 0503 45156 Fax 0503 45187	**HR**
Kilkea Castledermot Co Kildare	**Map 2 C4**

The oldest inhabited castle in Ireland, Kilkea was built in 1180
by Hugh de Lacy. Steeped in history, it has been renovated and
converted with skill and sensitivity that allow it to retain its
inherent elegance and grandeur. Rooms, many with wonderful
views over the formal gardens and surrounding countryside, are
splendidly furnished to incorporate modern comforts in a manner
appropriate to their age and style and the adjoining leisure centre,
although architecturally discreet, offers state-of-the-art facilities.
Outdoor sports include clay pigeon shooting, archery, tennis and
fishing on the nearby River Greese. An 18-hole championship golf
course was due to open early in 1994. **Rooms** *45. Garden, tennis,
indoor swimming pool, sauna, jacuzzi, steam room, sun bed,
gymnasium. Closed 4-5 days Christmas.* AMERICAN EXPRESS *Access,
Diners, Visa.*

De Lacy's   £75

The first-floor restaurant is appropriately grand with magnificent
views over the countryside and a bright, airy atmosphere. Scottish
chef George Smith has a distinctive style and the lengthy
descriptions on the menu give an indication of the complexity
of what is to follow. But the quality of ingredients shines through
and, in specialities such as the roast of the day, there are excellent
simpler alternatives available. Local produce features strongly,
much of it taken from the gardens below, where guests can take
coffee in summer and wander around to see the old fruit trees,
vegetables and herbs. Salads and vegetables are a speciality and
desserts beautiful and sophisticated, to match their surroundings.
Typical main-course dishes include salmon topped with a fish
mousseline, wrapped in pastry, baked and served with a crayfish
sauce, or loin of venison pan-fried with herbs, carved on rösti
glazed with game essence and served with a poached pear.
Seats *45. Parties 14. L 12.30-2.30 D 7-9.30. Closed 25 Dec.
Set L £14.95 Set D £24.50.*

Castlelyons   Ballyvolane House   £80

Tel 025 36349   Fax 025 36781   **A**

Castlelyons Co Cork   Map 2 B5

This gracious house, set in lovely wooded grounds and surrounded
by its own farmland, dates back to 1728 and was modified to its
present Italianate style in the mid-19th century. The impressive
pillared hall with its baby grand piano sets the tone but, despite
the elegance of the house and its period furnishings the owners,
Jeremy and Merrie Green, are well-known for their special brand
of informal hospitality and the atmosphere is very relaxed: well-
proportioned reception rooms are warmed by huge log fires,
residents' dinner is cooked by Merrie and taken communally
around a lovely mahogany table and stories relating to the house
abound. Bedrooms vary in size and outlook but all are warm and
comfortable, furnished with antiques and with roomy bathrooms
en-suite – one has an original Edwardian bath reached
by mahogany steps. **Rooms** 6. *Garden, croquet, fishing.*
AMERICAN EXPRESS *Access, Visa.*

Castletownbere   MacCarthy's

Tel 027 70014   **P**

Town Square Castletownbere Co Cork   Map 2 A6

One of the first drinking places to be granted a licence in Ireland,
MacCarthy's has been in the same family for 150 years (Adrienne
MacCarthy is the fourth generation). It's not only a pub, but also
a grocery which provisions the trawlers that are based in the
harbour. In the front – the grocery section – one of the last
remaining match-making booths (traditionally used by the match-
maker and the bride's and groom's parents to arrange marriage
terms) is now used as a snug, while in the back bar darts and live
music make for a very sociable ambience. *No credit cards.*

Castletownshend   Bow Hall   £50

Tel 028 36114   **A**

Castletownshend Co Cork   Map 2 B6

Americans Barbara and Dick Vickery have been running this
delightful 17th-century house overlooking the anchorage at Castle
Haven as a home-from-home for discerning guests since 1977, but
there is no sign of their enthusiasm flagging and it is not just the
high level of comfort but the warmth of their welcome that
makes a visit to their characterful and thoughtfully furnished
home memorable. Barbara is also a dab hand in the kitchen, using
produce from their lovely garden (open to the public once a year)
in imaginative meals for residents – and be sure to allow time
in the schedule for full enjoyment of a lengthy breakfast, which
includes freshly baked muffins, pancakes and home-made sausages.
No dogs. **Rooms** 3. *Garden. Closed for several days at Christmas.*
No credit cards.

Castletownshend   Mary Ann's Bar & Restaurant   £50

Tel 028 36146   Fax 028 36377   **R**

Castletownshend nr Skibbereen Co Cork   Map 2 B6

The building dates from the 11th century, but Mary Ann's has
been in business for a mere 150 years. It's best known for its bar

food (served both sessions seven days a week), which runs from
sandwiches and salads to sirloin steaks by way of soups, scallops
and chicken Kiev. Dinner in the restaurant also has a strong
following, with typical choices including seafood tagliatelle, turbot
hollandaise en croute, a hot shellfish platter, rack of lamb and fillet
of beef with a red wine sauce. *Seats* 30. *L 12.30-2.30. D from
6 (restaurant 6.30). Closed Mon Nov-Mar (except Christmas period).
Set L £13 (winter Sun only) Set D £19.50. Access, Visa.*

Castlewarren   Langton's

Tel 0503 26123	**P**
Castlewarren Co Kilkenny	Map 2 C4

A bit of a curiosity – not a real pub at all but a relic of what used
to be so common in rural Ireland – the kitchen-cum-grocery-cum-
bar. A visit here will take the traveller away from main roads
through the pleasant countryside of a little-known corner
of Ireland and back in time. A row of high stools beside the bacon
slicer at the counter and a good shelf of bottles over it are the only
real clues to the nature of the premises but, once you're ensconced,
Josie Langton, here for 25 years, will put the world to rights with
you and rustle up a bit of a sandwich in the kitchen on demand.
Pub closed Sun eve. No credit cards.

Ceanannas Mor (Kells)   O'Shaughnessy's

Tel 046 41110	**P**
Market Street Ceanannas Mor (Kells) Co Meath	Map 1 C3

A reasonably new pub, comfortably and pleasantly decorated
on an old-style theme. Unpretentious, fairly-priced bar food is the
main attraction – food like Irish stew, chicken or beef curry,
lasagne, quiches and pizzas, but better and cheaper than most.
You'll find O'Shaughnessy's just behind St Columba's Church
(where a copy of the *Book of Kells* is kept). *Bar Food 10.30-11.30
(Summer to 11, no food Sun). Closed 25 Dec & Good Friday.
Access, Visa.*

Cheekpoint   McAlpin's Suir Inn

Tel 051 82220	**P**
Cheekpoint Co Waterford	Map 2 C5

When this tiny black-and-white pub was built in 1750
Cheekpoint was the main port for the boats from England. Today
it's a quiet little backwater, although much of the seafood which
forms the bulk of the bar menu here is still landed at the quay
opposite the inn. Inside, the single bar is as neat as a new pin with
old photos and plates decorating the red walls, around which are
thinly upholstered banquettes and varnished rustic tables. The
menu offers about eight starters – shrimp cocktail (£3.95), grilled
smoked mackerel (£2.95), crab claws in garlic butter (£3.95) –
and eight main dishes – wild salmon mayonnaise (£8.95), king
scallops in cheese and white wine sauce (£8.95), curried chicken
breasts (£7.50). There's always a fruit pie made with Mrs
McAlpin's excellent pastry. *Open evening only 5.30-11.30 (6-11
in winter). Closed Mon (except July & Aug). Bar Food 6-9.30 Tues-
Sat (& Mon in July & Aug). No food Tues Oct-Easter. Access, Visa.*

Clifden   **Abbeyglen Castle**   60%   £99

| Tel 095 21201   Fax 095 21797 | **H** |

Sky Road Clifden Co Galway   Map 1 A3

Take the N59 from Galway City to Clifden, then Sky Road out
of Clifden to find the hotel, 300 yards on the left in 12 acres
of grounds. Owner Paul Hughes personally welcomes guests,
many of whom return year after year, to his crenellated hotel.
Steps lead down from the hotel to landscaped gardens and
an outdoor pool and tennis court. Public areas include a spacious
drawing room for residents and a relaxing pubby bar with open
peat fire. Refurbishment continues in the good-sized bedrooms.
No children under 10. Local fishing facilities are a major
attraction. *Rooms 40. Garden, outdoor swimming pool, sauna, tennis,
pitch and putt, snooker, table tennis. Closed 10 Jan-1 Feb.*
AMERICAN EXPRESS *Access, Diners, Visa.*

Set menu prices may not always include service or wine.
Our quoted price for two does.

Clifden   **Ardagh Hotel**   60%   £75

| Tel 095 21384   Fax 095 21314 | **HR** |

Ballyconneely Road Clifden Co Galway   Map 1 A3

Quiet family-run hotel on the edge of Ardbear Bay, a couple
of miles south of Clifden. Day rooms include a roomy and
comfortable bar, two lounges and a top-floor sun room. Golf,
fishing and riding can be arranged. No dogs. *Rooms 21. Garden,
solarium. Closed Nov-end Mar.* AMERICAN EXPRESS *Access, Diners, Visa.*

Restaurant   £55

The first-floor restaurant has lovely views to add to the enjoyment
of Monique Bauvet's imaginative way with local produce.
Farmhouse terrine with summer fruits, seafood chowder, saffron-
sauced brill, lobster (grilled fresh from the tank) and pot-roasted
rack of spring lamb show their style. Lighter meals in the bar.
Seats 50. Parties 30. D only 7.15-9.30. Set D from £19.

Clifden   **Destry Rides Again**   £40

| Tel 095 21722 | **R** |

Clifden Co Galway   Map 1 A3

Decor at the Foyles' entertaining little restaurant (named after
a Marlene Dietrich film) is predictably wacky – an old Georgian
fanlight decorates one wall and has a real skull balanced on top,
a collection of silver food domes and a variety of 'boys in the
backroom' memorabilia all create atmosphere. Dishes on the
shortish menu have a modern ring, exemplified by vermicelli
with smoked chicken and mozzarella, chargrilled halibut with
black olives and horseradish, roast Barbary duck with raspberry
and ginger, and grilled pork fillet coated in spices with hot and
sour sauce. Desserts include good home-made ices and a rich
'Lethal Chocolate Pud', made to a secret recipe. Confident, classy
cooking and great fun. Short, user-friendly, keenly-priced wine
list, with plenty available by the glass. Wheelchair facilities.
*Seats 32. Parties 16. L 12-3 D 6-10 (in winter open only for dinner
Thu-Sat 7-9). Access, Visa.*

Clifden   E J King's

Tel 095 21330

The Square Clifden Co Galway

Map 1 A3

On the square in the centre of town, a lively old bar on two
floors, retaining an essentially traditional character despite modern
touches in its atrium and striking primary colour schemes on the
upper floors. Menus lean towards local seafood, especially oysters,
crab and smoked salmon but typical blackboard specials might
include bacon and cabbage or roast beef or rack of lamb, plus
there's a choice of farmhouse cheeses. Trenchermen should head
for the fisherman's platter, complete with smoked salmon, prawns,
crab, mussels, salmon, cod, smoked trout and mackerel and salad!
Live music, mainly folk and ballads, features nightly in season,
2 or 3 times a week in winter. *Bar Food 10.30-9 (Sun from 12.30).*
Terrace. Access, Visa.

Clifden   O'Grady's Seafood Restaurant

£50

Tel 095 21450

R

Market Street Clifden Co Galway

Map 1 A3

A traditional seafood restaurant with well-spaced tables, some
in alcoves but all with a degree of privacy. Try starting with
a speciality like Jack's smoked fish bisque – smooth, creamy but
with just the right amount of texture and smokiness to be
interesting, served with a choice of good home-made white yeast
bread or wholemeal soda. Sophisticated main courses from a wide
choice, predominantly but not exclusively seafood, on the à la
carte dinner menu might include grilled fillet of turbot with
a compote of rhubarb and champagne butter cream or best end
of lamb on a jus of wild mushrooms with a hint of pesto, while
lunch offerings are simpler – marinière-style mussels, perhaps,
or braised kidneys with a creamy mushroom and pink peppercorn
sauce. Follow with 'sinful desserts' or farmhouse cheese.
An informal piano bistro serving one-plate specialities opened last
summer. Accommodation is of a high standard with eleven en-
suite bedrooms available nearby with gardens, outdoor swimming
pool, sauna and tennis. *Seats 50. Parties 20. Private Room 12.*
L 12.30-3.30 D 6.30-10. Closed mid Nov-end Feb. Set L £8.95.
AMERICAN EXPRESS *Access, Diners, Visa.*

Clifden   Rock Glen Manor   61%

£90

Tel 095 21035   Fax 095 21737

H

Ballyconneely Road Clifden Co Galway

Map 1 A3

John and Evangeline Roche have completed more than 20 years
at their 18th-century shooting lodge, which stands a mile and
a half from Clifden on the Ballyconneely road (turn right at the
pottery). Public areas include a sun room and drawing room, both
of which enjoy sea views, and a cosy bar. Well-equipped
bedrooms, fine breakfasts, plenty of sporting activity in the
vicinity. No dogs. *Rooms 29. Garden, tennis, putting green, fishing,*
snooker, croquet. Closed end Oct-mid Mar. AMERICAN EXPRESS *Access,*
Diners, Visa.

Clifden Place of Interest

Connemara National Park Tel 095 41054

Clonmel Clonmel Arms 61% £83

Tel 052 21233 Fax 052 21526 **H**

Sarsfield Street Conmel Co Tipperary Map 2 C5

Some of the bedrooms at the town-centre Clonmel Arms are
suitable for family occupation, and children under 12 can stay free
in their parents' room. There are extensive banqueting and
conference facilities, two restaurants and two bars. *Rooms 31.*
Terrace, coffee shop (10am-10pm). AMERICAN EXPRESS *Access, Diners, Visa.*

Clonmel Places of Interest

Ormond Castle Carrick-on-Suir Tel 051 40787
Clonmel Racecourse Powerstown Park Tel 052 22611

Collooney Glebe House £45

Tel 071 67787 **RR**

Collooney Co Sligo Map 1 B2

Marc and Brid Torrades rescued Glebe House from dereliction
to open it as a restaurant in 1990 and, while it does not yet have
the level of sophistication that many of the established country
houses have achieved, their warmth of hospitality and willingness
to please are likely to win the hearts of many a guest. Judging
by their performance to date, each passing year will see big
improvements. Chef Brid uses the best of local produce in hearty,
generous dishes such as duck rillettes with onion marmalade
or smoked salmon in a dill sauce topped by a featherlight fleuron
of puff pastry followed, perhaps, by paupiettes of lemon sole
stuffed with colourful julienne vegetables or a vegetarian pancake
in a light mustard sauce. Good vegetables are served up in dishes
left on the table for guests to help themselves. Classic desserts
include a surprise dessert plate; balanced selection of French and
Irish farmhouse cheeses. *Seats 35. Parties 20. Private Room 30.*
L by arrangement D 6.30-9.30. Set D £15.75. Closed 2 weeks Jan.
Rooms £30

Accommodation is available in four spacious, individually
decorated rooms, all en suite, two with baths. *Garden.*

Collooney Markree Castle 60% £97

Tel 071 67800 Fax 071 67840 **H**

Collooney Co Sligo Map 1 B2

Charles Cooper, the 10th generation of his family to live
in Markree, has made a fine job of restoring pride and splendour
to a castle which had for some years been empty and neglected.
Space and character both abound, the place is well heated (huge
fires everywhere) and there's a beautiful dining room with some
exquisite Italian plasterwork. The views are superb, and the
setting, in meadows, woods and gardens reaching to the river
Unsin, guarantees peace and quiet. They serve an excellent
afternoon tea. *Rooms 15. Garden, fishing, riding. Closed Feb.*
AMERICAN EXPRESS *Access, Diners, Visa.*

Cong	Ashford Castle	88%	£256

Cong   **Ashford Castle**   **88%**   **£256**

Tel 092 46003   Fax 092 46260   **HR**

Cong Co Mayo   Map 1 B3

With its origins dating back to the early 13th century and set amid 350 acres of magnificent parkland (including a golf course) on the nothern shores of Lough Corrib, this splendid castle has been lovingly restored – its recent history is depicted for all to see by photographic and written memorabilia displayed in various parts of the building. Throughout, there's rich panelling, intricately carved balustrades, suits of armour and fine paintings. Whether you wish to relax in the elegant drawing room, wander around the halls and galleries, or retire to the Dungeon Bar after dinner and listen to the delightful Annette Griffin singing traditional Irish folk songs and playing the harp to the accompaniment of Carol Coleman's piano, there's a unique atmosphere throughout. Managing Director Rory Murphy has been in situ for over 20 years and, with the assistance of William (Bill) Buckley, runs a truly fine hotel, backed up by excellent professional and committed staff. Spacious bedrooms (including several suites) offer attractive views and every conceivable luxury, from flowers and fresh fruit on arrival to slippers, bathrobes and Molton Brown toiletries in the splendid bathrooms; throughout the rooms you'll find period furniture, fine fabrics and superb housekeeping that includes a turn-down service. Discreet conference facilities (several EEC ministerial conferences have been held here) accommodate up to 110 theatre-style and 75 for banquets. Twenty years ago the hotel received our Gold Plate award, and it's fitting that it now becomes the first winner of our Hotel of the Year award in this new Guide to Ireland, highlighting the hotel's commitment to excellence, in standards of both service and ambience. *Dromoland Castle* in Newmarket-on-Fergus (see entry) is a sister hotel. *Rooms 83. Garden, croquet, golf (9), tennis, equestrian centre, jaunting-car, fishing, lake cruising, bicycles, boutique, snooker.* *Access, Diners, Visa.*

Connaught Room   ↑   £110

Part of the original Georgian House built in 1715, the handsome, panelled dining room with chandeliers and vast windows is only open at night and is sometimes used for theme evenings. Executive chef Denis Lenihan presides over both restaurants (see George V below) and here presents an à la carte menu with supplementary daily specials. Meat and poultry are sourced from local farms, so you can rely on the quality of raw materials, and fish comes from the West coast. A typical meal might include tartare of lightly smoked lamb fillet served with tapénade, fillet of turbot with scallops on a parsley dressing and a plate of assorted chocolate desserts. Fine selection of breads, cheeses and good coffee. Service is both caring and supremely professional. There are a few French wines quite reasonably priced for a hotel of this class, though look outside France for the best value. *Seats 40. D only 7-9.30.*

George V Room   £100

A much larger room also with handsome panelling and chandeliers. Service is again outstanding, and here fixed-price menus with several choices in each course are offered. Dinner is usually a five-course affair. Start with poached Cleggan lobster

See over

served on a truffle oil dressing, followed by carrot soup, roast rack of Connemara hill lamb and a confit of shallots, finishing with local farmhouse cheeses and a lightly frozen prune and armagnac soufflé. 15% service is added to all prices. ***Seats** 135. L 1-2.15 D 7-9.30. Set L £19 Set D £32.*

Cong Place of Interest

Ballinroe Racecourse Tel 092 41052

Cork An Spailpín Fánac

P

Tel 021 277949

28/29 South Main Street Cork Co Cork **Map 2 B6**

Food at this pleasant, low-ceilinged pub is of the simple, wholesome variety: freshly cut sandwiches, toasted Kiev and doorstep special with fries, lasagne, shepherd's pie, bacon and cabbage, Irish stew, minced beef and onion pie, a fish special. The name of the pub translates roughly as 'the jobbing traveller', recalling a once-familiar Irish character who used to keep on the move around the country in search of work. No children after 6.30pm, but they are welcome during the day. *Open 12-11 (summer to 11.30). **Bar Food** 12-3.*

Cork Arbutus Lodge 70%

£72

HR

Tel 021 501237 Fax 021 502893

Montenotte Cork Co Cork **Map 2 B6**

Considerable improvements and refurbishment have taken place in most of the bedrooms at this former home of a Lord Mayor of Cork, high above the city with views of the River Lee and the surrounding hills. The hotel gets its name from the Arbutus tree, one of the many rare trees and shrubs growing in the spectacular terraced gardens. The house is full of genuine antique furniture (note the four-poster in the Blue Room) and some marvellous art, both old and new, the modern paintings by Irish artists much in demand by galleries and museums. Declan and Patsy Ryan, here since 1961, extend a warm welcome to all their guests, ably backed up by charming staff. Whether you choose to relax in the cosy lounge or the panoramic bar with its own terrace, you'll feel at home and the cleverly designed and smartly decorated bedrooms, utilising all possible space, provide both comfort and tranquillity. Bathrooms boast quality towels, bathrobes and toiletries and you'll start the day with as good a breakfast as you'll encounter anywhere. Conference facilities for up to 120. ***Rooms** 20. Garden, tennis.* AMERICAN EXPRESS *Access, Diners, Visa.*

Restaurant ★

£80

Alongside Myrtle Allen (see entry for *Ballymaloe House*), Declan Ryan has trained and brought on more chefs in this country than anyone. Back in the kitchen from early morning until service commences, he has currently moulded together an enthusiastic young team headed by the talented Helen Ward, who is just 21! Here is a restaurant that has remained loyal to its roots – no slavish copying of French trends but a reliance on local produce including herbs and soft fruit from the hotel's own garden and traditional Cork dishes – spicy beef, tripe and drisheen. Game in season and the freshest of fish are also a feature (inspect the seafood tank in the bar) and always a fine example of the kitchen's style is the nightly-changing, seven-course tasting menu – no mini-portions, but enough to satisfy the hungriest of souls – spiced beef and mushroom filo parcels, nage of scallops and prawns, escalope of salmon on sorrel sauce, very tender roast mallard with blackcurrants, finishing with chocolate and rum log or gargantuan floating islands. Ask for the ingredients of the 'fence reducer sorbet', sometimes served as a palate cleanser! Service is as caring and professional as you'll find anywhere, the cheeseboard promotes Irish cheeses in tip-top condition, and the sweet trolley will tempt even the faint-hearted. A variety of breads is baked on the premises daily, and the wine list, as befits Ireland's Cellar of the Year, has been lovingly nurtured for three decades. Years ago, on his wine trips to France, Declan discovered several fine and relatively unknown growers from whom he still buys. *Seats 50. Parties 30. Private Room 25. L 1-2 D 7-9.30. Closed Sun, 1 week Christmas. Set L £12.50 Set D £21.50/£27.75.*

Cork   Bully's   £25
Tel 021 273555   Fax 021 273427   R
40 Paul Street Cork Co Cork   Map 2 B6

Pizzas from the wood-burning oven are one of the specialities of Eugene Buckley's popular little place. They come in a dozen varieties, top of the range being Bully's special – a half-folded version with bolognese sauce, ham, onion and mushrooms. Also on the menu are home-made pasta, grills, omelettes and seafood dishes. Also at Douglas Village, Co Cork. Tel 021 892415. *Seats 40. Parties 20. Meals 12-11.30. Closed 25 & 26 Dec, Good Friday. No credit cards.*

Cork   Cliffords   ★   £70
Tel 021 275333   R
18 Dyke Parade Cork Co Cork   Map 2 B6

As one of a select band of starred Irish restaurants, we choose Cliffords as our Restaurant of the Year, since style and quality are the keynotes here, in terms not only of cooking but also of service and decor. The building itself, once the civic library, is Georgian, but the whole place has been elegantly modernised, and Michael and Deirdre Clifford's collection of contemporary Irish art adorns the walls. The dining area is striking in its simplicity, with comfortable high-back chairs, high-quality linen and single flowers floating in glass bowls. Michael's cooking is controlled and confident, with inventive use of the best of local produce. The dinner menu changes monthly, though some specialities put in regular appearances. Typifying his style are a warm salad of grilled scallops with an aubergine mousse, Clonakilty black pudding with poached free-range egg, cabbage and smoked kassler, velouté of celeriac and wild mushrooms, monkfish tails 'en papillote' with ginger and spring onions and pan-fried fillet of beef with braised salsify and a rich Fleurie sauce. There's always a fresh fish of the day, plus game in season and some very hard-to-resist chocolate desserts. Provided you don't drink vintage first-growth clarets, the modest wine list is reasonably priced. As we went to press their small *Michael's Bistro* opened next door (4 Mardyke Street Tel: 021 276887). Average spend is around half that of the restaurant. *Seats 40. Parties 10. Private Room 50. L 12.30-2.30 D 7.30-10.30. Closed L Sat & Mon, all Sun, Bank Holidays, 2 weeks Aug. Set L £12.95 Set D £28.* AMERICAN EXPRESS *Access, Diners, Visa.*

Cork   Crawford Gallery Café

£45

Tel 021 274415

R

Emmet Place Cork Co Cork

Map 2 B6

In the city centre next to the Opera House, this is an offshoot
of the renowned Ballymaloe House at Shanagarry. Ballymaloe
desserts, ice cream or petits fours round off a meal whose
centrepiece could be chicken pie, braised lamb with colcannon
or the day's catch from Ballycotton. Snackier items include
bruschetta and open sandwiches. Also open for breakfast. *Seats 70.
Private Room 200. L 12-2.30 D 6.30-9.30. Closed D Mon, Tue &
Sat, all Sun, Bank Holidays, 1 week Christmas. Access, Visa.*

Cork   Dan Lowrey's Seafood Tavern

Tel 021 505071

P

13 MacCurtain Street Cork Co Cork

Map 2 B6

A delightfully old-fashioned pub, a perfect place to meet or eat. It's
small, with two interconnecting rooms (the one in the back with
an open fire) and is now named after a much-lamented local
theatre. The pub's history goes back to 1875 and many of the
original tavern features have been retained, including the wooden
floor and a remarkable mahogany bar unit with unusual shelving
and antique bevelled mirrors. The stained-glass windows on the
street are also of special interest, as they came from Kilkenny
Cathedral. The food is the source of justifiable pride: the bar menu
offers an above-average choice of simple soups served with home-
made bread (£1.20), salads, seafood or meat platters (£4.20 for
ham to £7.50 for wild Irish smoked salmon) and a wide selection
of sandwiches – fresh, toasted or open (£1.35-£1.50) – but it is
the emphasis on the home-made and attention to detail (such as the
freshest prawns, served only when available) which make this
place special. *Bar Food 12-3. No credit cards.*

Cork   Fitzpatrick Silver Springs   65%

£89

Tel 021 507533   Fax 021 507641

H

Tivoli Cork Co Cork

Map 2 B6

On the side of a steep hill overlooking the river and the main
Dublin road, about 2 miles out of town, the modern Silver
Springs is also a major convention centre with a large, up-to-date
facility built in 1990 a little further up the hill above the hotel
(banqueting for 750, conferences up to 800). Even further up the
hill are an extensive leisure centre and nine-hole golf course.
Within, the hotel public areas are spacious and include a large
public bar with live music from Thursday to Sunday evenings.
Recently refurbished bedrooms, all double-glazed, have lightwood
fitted furniture, good easy chairs and practical bathrooms. 'Club'
rooms are larger and there are two 'full' and three 'junior' antique-
furnished suites. 24hr room service. Children under 12 share their
parents' room at no charge. No dogs. *Rooms 110. Garden, indoor
swimming pool, gymnasium, aerobic studio, solarium, sauna, spa bath,
steam room, 9-hole golf course, squash, tennis, snooker, helipad, courtesy
coach. Closed 25 Dec.* AMERICAN EXPRESS *Access, Diners, Visa.*

Cork   Flemings

£55

RR

Tel 021 821621   Fax 021 821800

Silver Grange House Tivoli Cork Co Cork

Map 2 B6

Just a short drive from Cork on the Dublin road, Flemings
is a large Georgian family house standing in five acres of gardens.
Those acres include a kitchen garden which provides much of the
fruit, vegetables and herbs needed in the restaurant, a light,
handsome double room with marble fireplaces, comfortably
upholstered chairs and well-dressed waiters. Michael Fleming's
cooking is French, his menus sometimes fractured French with
English translations: timbale of fish and shellfish in an orange and
champagne sauce, confit of smoked chicken, pan-fried scallops
with a lemon and ginger-flavoured white wine sauce, rich venison
stew with vegetables and herbs garnished with gnocchi. Not
a lengthy wine list, but it's full of choice bottles and the best
growers. *Seats 50. Parties 22. Private Room 36. L 12.30-2.30
D 6.30-11. Set L £10.50/£12.50 Set D £19.50.
Closed Good Friday, 24-26 Dec.*

Rooms

£55

Accommodation is available in four spacious rooms, comfortably
furnished in a style appropriate to the age and graciousness of the
house. All have en-suite bathrooms. *Garden.*

See the 'Listing in County Order' section (highlighted by
colour pages) at the back of the Guide for instant comparison
of establishments in a particular area.

Cork   Forte Travelodge

£42

H

Tel 021 310722   Fax 021 310707

Jct South Ring Road/Kinsale Road Cork Airport Blackash Co Cork

Map 2 B6

1½ miles south of Cork city centre on the main airport road,
1 mile from it. The room rate of £32 (without breakfast) could
include up to 3 adults, a child under 12 and a baby in a cot.
Rooms 40. *Access, Visa.*

Cork   The Gingerbread House

R

Tel 021 276411

Frenchchurch Street Cork Co Cork

Map 2 B6

In a pedestrianised lane off St Patrick's Street, Barnaby Blacker's
little bakery and tea shop is just the place to take a break from the
hectic day's shopping. Home-baked cakes like carrot, traditional
chocolate, French chocolate (with rum and almonds), praline and
lemon (all at £1 a slice) satisfy the sweet-toothed, with sausage
rolls (£1.80) quiche (£2.60) and delicious Cornish pasties (£2.60)
for those with more savoury tastes. The latter are baked fresh each
morning and are then available until they are all gone. They all
come with a garnish of tomato relish (from Ballymaloe House) and
slices of pickled cucumber. Everything is available to take
away, including a selection of their own home-made jams and
preserves. There are four pavement tables for summer eating.
Good cafetière coffee. Unlicensed. No smoking. *Seats 14. Open
9-6.30 (Fri to 7pm). Closed Sun. No credit cards.*

Cork   Imperial Hotel   66%   £121

Tel 021 274040   Fax ext 2507   **H**

South Mall Cork Co Cork   Map 2 B6

On the main commercial and banking street of town the
Imperial's neo-classical facade conceals something of a mixture
of styles. The marble-floored lobby and some of the bedroom
corridors, which feature a number of fine antiques, retain their
original 19th-century grandeur, the cocktail bar (with nightly
pianist) and restaurant have been given a 1930s' theme and the
public bar remembers Cork's history as a shipbuilding centre.
Bedrooms, apart from a few that are furnished with antiques
in traditional style, are determinedly modern with white fitted
units, glass and chrome coffee tables and contemporary lights.
About half the rooms have novel wall-mounted 'clothes grooming
cabinets' that are designed to deodorise and dewrinkle garments.
12 of the bathrooms have shower and WC only. Room service
is available but not advertised. A recent acquisition is secure
covered parking for about 80 cars, three minutes' walk from the
hotel. *Rooms 101. Closed 1 week at Christmas.*  *Access,
Diners, Visa.*

Cork   Isaacs   £35

Tel 021 503805   **R**

48 MacCurtain Street Cork Co Cork   Map 2 B6

An 18th-century warehouse has been carefully adapted into a fine
restaurant serving an eclectic menu conceived by chef Canice
Sharkey. Lunchtime brings some snacky items (French bread with
ham, cheese and pickle; selection of patés and terrines) but
otherwise a fairly similar selection to the evening, including
perhaps salad of smoked chicken with apples and home-dried
tomatoes, salmon and potato cakes, grilled king prawns and sirloin
steak with rosemary and garlic potatoes. Sauternes and olive oil
cake with winter fruit salad is an intriguing dessert. Short
vegetarian menu. *Seats 90. Parties 30. L 12-2.30 D 6.30-10.30
(Sun to 9). Closed L Sun, 3 days Christmas. Access, Visa.*

Cork   Ivory Tower Restaurant   £55

Tel 021 274665   **R**

35 Princes Street Cork Co Cork   Map 2 B6

Situated in the first-floor front of a period office building just off
one of Cork's main shopping streets. The atmosphere is friendly
and informal – bare-board floor, unclothed tables, work of local
artists on the walls – and chef/patron Seamus O'Connell's cooking
is certainly individualistic. A cassoulet of smoked chicken seemed
to have been crossed with Irish stew being full of chunks of root
vegetable and arriving in an appetite-challenging bowlful. Mussel,
saffron and orange soup was well judged with the orange element
nicely subdued; other dishes included peppered shark with
ratatouille; sauerkraut of smoked salmon sausages, scallops and
prawns with red ónion beurre blanc; and venison and blackberry
osso buco. There are always several vegetarian options. Lunch
prices are lower than in the evening. Two or three home-made
breads vary from day to day. *Seats 36. L 12-4 D 6.30-11.
Set D varies, from £13. Closed D Mon & Tues, all Sun.
No credit cards.*

Cork   Jacques

£55

R

Tel 021 277387   Fax 021 270634

9 Phoenix Street Cork Co Cork

Map 2 B6

Jacques has recently been modernised and extended, and table
service has replaced the previous self-service arrangement.
Nothing has changed on the food side, so the evenings still bring
a good choice of dishes both traditional and modern, from
garlicky crab claws, warm scallop salad and lamb's kidneys with
grapes and croutons to roast duck, bacon-wrapped pheasant, pork
Dijon and Eastern-style shark kebab. The simpler lunchtime menu
– bruschetta, crostini, soup, open sandwiches, fish cakes, half-a-
dozen desserts – is also offered at the owners' new acquisition
Jacques at the Triskel in the Arts Centre (Tobin Street). *Seats 60.
Parties 20. L 12-4 D 6-10.30. Closed D Mon, all Sun, Bank
Holidays, 10 days Christmas. Set L £4.90 Set D £22.50.*
 Access, Diners, Visa.

Cork   Jurys Hotel   66%

£133

H

Tel 021 276622   Fax 021 274477

Western Road Cork Co Cork

Map 2 B6

Modern low-rise riverside hotel about half a mile from the centre
of town on the Killarney road. Public areas include a choice
of two bars, both with live music nightly: the convivial, pubby
Corks Bar that is popular with locals and a cocktail bar with
waterfall feature in the open-plan, split-level restaurant area. Decor
in the well-kept bedrooms is gradually being changed from
abstract to more appealing floral patterns with matching curtains
and quilted bedcovers. TVs are multi-channel with the remote
controls rather annoyingly wired to the bedside units. Extras
include fruit and mineral water. Good, well-lit bathrooms all have
vanity units, sometimes in white marble, offering good shelf space.
Room service is 24 hours and beds are turned down at night.
*Rooms 185. Garden, indoor swimming pool, children's splash pool,
keep-fit equipment, sauna, spa bath, squash, tennis.*
Access, Diners, Visa.

Cork   Lovetts

£72

R

Tel 021 294909   Fax 021 508568

Churchyard Lane off Well Road Douglas Cork Co Cork

Map 2 B6

The Lovett family's comfortable, confident restaurant is situated
in a fashionable residential area to the south of the city (convenient
for the airport) and has a loyal local following. Portraits
by an unknown 19th-century Cork artist provide a perennial
talking point and a lively background for Margaret Lovett and
Marie Harding's imaginative cooking. Seafood is its main strength,
but the best of all local seasonal produce features throughout the
menus: wild salmon even comes straight from the rod. Start,
perhaps, with black pudding mousse with a grain mustard sauce
or grilled Galway Bay mussels with garlic butter, followed
by main courses such as escalopes of salmon with lemon or white
wine sauce, other daily fresh fish options and classic meat dishes.
Diverse wine list. *Seats 45. Private Room 24. L 12.30-2 D 7-10.
Closed L Sat, all Sun, Bank Holidays. Set L £14.50 Set D £21.*
 Access, Diners, Visa.

Cork Metropole Hotel 58% £85

Tel 021 508122 Fax 021 506450 **H**

MacCurtain Street Cork Co Cork Map 2 B6

Recent refurbishment has given the 100-year-old 'Met' a new lease
of life. That the hotel is the epicentre of Cork's annual jazz festival
is reflected in the numerous photos and sketches of the stars who
have performed here displayed in the bar. On the bedroom front
it is only those on the top two floors that we recommend, those
being the ones that have been refurbished, partly with dark
stained pine furniture (some retain the old units revamped); they
all have good bathrooms that although brand new are given
a period feel by the tiling, wood-panelled tub and generously
sized, chunky wash basins. Bedroom size and shape varies
considerably and the view from some is a bit grim. The best have
views over the River Lee as it flows through the centre of town.
24hr room service. Banqueting for 300, conference facilities for
500. *Rooms 108.* AMERICAN EXPRESS *Access, Diners, Visa.*

Cork Morrisons Island Hotel 68% £119

Tel 021 275858 Fax 021 275833 **H**

Morrisons Quay Cork Co Cork Map 2 B6

Overlooking the River Lee, in Cork's business district, this 'all-
suite' hotel – in France it would be called a *hotel résidence* – is
designed for the business person with each suite having a separate
lounge (with kitchenette): ideal for meeting or entertaining.
Actually four are junior suites (large rooms with separate sitting
area) without the kitchenette and there are four larger penthouse
suites with balconies and completely separate kitchens, two with
two bedrooms. Decorwise it's fairly simple with lightwood units
in the bedrooms and darkwood in the sitting rooms with tweedy
soft furnishings. Downstairs there's a smart marble-floored lobby
and cosy bar that with several sofas doubles as a lounge area.
Room service is 24hr, as is porterage, and there is free secure
parking. *Rooms 40. Closed 4 days at Christmas.* AMERICAN EXPRESS
Access, Diners, Visa.

Cork O'Keeffe's £65

Tel 021 275645 **R**

23 Washington Street West Cork Co Cork Map 2 B6

A hospitable restaurant, run since 1990 by Marie and Tony
O'Keeffe. Their à la carte menu changes every month and offers
the likes of pork and spinach terrine with onion marmalade,
boned pig's trotter stuffed with a mousse of Clonakilty white
pudding and rolled in garlic breadcrumbs or tomato, onion and
anchovy tart with mozzarella chesse to start, followed by prawn
and scallop stir-fry, tripe and onions with fried polenta,
or noisettes of venison with a port and cranberry sauce. Small
choice of desserts or Irish cheeses to finish. Sauces are a strength,
presentation is good and portions are generous; Marie's culinary
influences are wide-ranging, with fresh local ingredients taking
pride of place in the kitchen. *Seats 33. L by arrangement D 6.30-10.
Closed Sun, Bank Holidays, 10 days Christmas.* AMERICAN EXPRESS *Access,
Diners, Visa.*

Cork   Quay Co-op

Tel 021 317660

R

24 Sullivan's Quay Cork Co Cork

Map 2 B6

A former priest house by the River Lee near the city centre, this
vegetarian restaurant occupies several period rooms on the two
floors above a wholefood shop – the stairway walls acting
as a notice board for events and organisations in the city. Work
by local artists features on the peach-coloured walls and there are
bare board floors. From opening there's tea, coffee (including
espresso), cakes and croissants until 12.30 when the lunch counter
opens. This features a selection of pizzas (£3.40), lasagne (£3.90)
and daily specials, which are often quite exotic, like Thai chili and
rice or tofu vegetable gado gado (steamed vegetables and tofu
in peanut butter sauce – both £3.90), all served with a selection
of salads. Soups might include lentil and apricot or drunken
mushroom (both £1.40) and come with organic wholemeal
bread. For the sweet-toothed there's chocolate cake, lemon sponge,
apple pie and the like. From 6pm the mood changes and there
is table service from a printed menu – tempura vegetables
(£2.70), nachos (£2.50), traditional nut roast with chestnut
stuffing and gravy (£5.90), spinach and ricotta cannelloni (£4.90)
and pear and almond tart with coconut-ginger cream (£2)
demonstrate the range. Children can have smaller portions
at reduced prices – there is just a single high-chair. About a dozen
wines are offered (just the house wine by the glass) or you can
bring your own for a corkage charge (£1.80). Two of the three
rooms are non-smoking. *Seats* 80. *Meals 9.30am-10.30pm (from
1pm Sun). Closed 25 & 26 Dec, Good Friday, Easter Sunday.
Access, Visa.*

Cork   Reidy's Wine Vaults

Tel 021 275751

P

Lancaster Quay Western Road Cork Co Cork

Map 2 B6

Imaginatively converted from a wine warehouse (and
conveniently situated just opposite the entrance to *Jury's Hotel*),
Reidy's is quite large and stylish, with vaulted ceilings, a minstrel's
gallery housing country antiques, dark green and terracotta
paintwork, traditional black-and-white tiles and a pleasing mixture
of old and new furnishings. The focal point is the main bar fixture
– a massive mahogany piece, complete with a London clock,
bevelled mirrors, stained glass and all the original Victorian
details. Bar food is prepared to a high standard by Noelle Reidy,
starting with bread and quiches baked on the premises in the early
morning and with choices noted on the blackboard as the day
progresses. The menu dishes might typically include steak and
kidney pie, savoury pancakes and seafood platter (£8). *Open usual
weekday pub hours, Sun 10.30am-11pm. **Bar Food** 10.30-10.30.
Closed 25 Dec, Good Friday.* AMERICAN EXPRESS *Access, Visa.*

Cork   Rochestown Park Hotel   67%

£85

Tel 021 892233   Fax 021 892178

H

Rochestown Road Douglas Cork Co Cork

Map 2 B6

Take the south ring road to Douglas and keep a sharp lookout for
the hotel's signs (they're small and brown) to find the bright

See over

yellow building. Public rooms are in the original Georgian house, formerly a seminary for trainee priests and once home to the Lord Mayors of Cork, with bedrooms in modern extensions. Standard bedrooms have been designed with the business person very much in mind and have practical fitted furniture including a well-lit desk with a second phone. Extras include mineral water, bowl of fruit, mints and towelling robes in bathrooms that all boast bidets. 20 Executive rooms are very large and have spa baths. Public areas include comfortable sitting areas off the marble-floored lobby, a bar with rattan-furnished conservatory and a snug residents' bar for late-night drinkers. The hotel's pride and joy is a most impressive leisure centre. *Rooms 63. Garden, indoor swimming pool, children's splash pool, gymnasium, solarium, sauna, spa bath, steam room, hydro-massage pool, aerobics studio, thalassotherapy clinic.* AMERICAN EXPRESS® *Access, Diners, Visa.*

We do not accept free meals or hospitality – our inspectors pay their own bills.

Cork	Seven North Mall	£60
Tel 021 397191 Fax 021 300811		**A**
7 North Mall Cork Co Cork		Map 2 B6

This elegant house dating from 1750 belongs to the family of Cork city architect Neil Hegarty and is run by his wife, Angela, who offers guests tea on arrival. It's centrally situated on a tree-lined south-facing mall overlooking the River Lee. Rooms are all spacious, individually furnished in a pleasingly restrained style in keeping with the house itself and with bathrooms cleverly added to look as if they have always been there. Some rooms have river views and there is a ground-floor room especially designed for disabled guests. Excellent breakfasts. A nice touch is the personalised map of the city centre given to guests, which shows clearly all the best restaurants, pubs, museums, galleries and theatres, mostly reassuringly near. *Rooms 5. Closed 18 Dec-6 Jan. Access, Visa.*

Cork   Places of Interest

Tourist Information   Tel 021 273251
The Queenstown Story   Cobh Tel 021 813591
Jameson Heritage Centre   Midleton Tel 021 613594
Triskell Arts Centre   off South Main Street Tel 021 272022
Crawford School of Art and Gallery   Emmet Place Tel 021 966777
GAA Athletic Grounds   Pairc Chaoimh Tel 021 963311
Cork City Gaol   Tel 021 542478
Church of St Francis   Liberty Street
St Finbarre's Cathedral   Sharman Crawford Street
St Colman's Cathedral   Cobh
Everyman Palace   MacCurtain Street Tel 021 501673
Opera House   Emmet Place Tel 021 270022
    Historic Houses, Castles and Gardens
Blarney Castle House and Gardens   Tel 021 385252
Dunkathel   Glanmire Tel 021 821014 *4 miles*
Riverstown House   Glanmire Tel 021 821205 *4 miles*
Fota Wildlife Park   Carrigtwohill nr Cobh Tel 021 812678

Crookhaven   O'Sullivan's

Tel 028 35200   **P**

Crookhaven Co Cork   Map 2 A6

One of the most popular traditional pubs in Ireland, sited beside
the delightful little sandy-beached harbour at 'Crook'. O'Sullivan's
has been family-run for 20 years and nowadays it's run by Billie
O'Sullivan, who somehow successfully combines the function
of providing a proper local for the lobster fishermen and the kind
of pub dreams are made of for families on holiday. The stone-
flagged bar is practical for sandy feet and parents can easily keep
an eye on castle-builders when the tide is right. Angela O'Sullivan
looks after the food herself, making soups and chowders, bread
and good, simple dishes based on local seafood – fresh and smoked
salmon, smoked mackerel, crab or shrimp – and moreish home-
made ices, apple crumble and, if the mood is on her, a special
chocolate saucepan cake. Six tables are almost on the water's edge.
*Bar Food 12-9 (Sun 12.30-2 & 4-9). Closed Monday afternoons
in winter. No credit cards.*

Crosshaven   Cronin's Bar

Tel 021 831207   Fax 021 831829   **P**

Crosshaven Co Cork   Map 2 B6

Lots of wood, soft furnishings in country prints and selected
bric-a-brac create a homely atmosphere at this welcoming bar
overlooking the marina, but the real point of interest is a great
collection of pictures, prints and photographs of local interest,
notably maritime history. Excellent food is made on the premises
by owner Sean Cronin's Dutch wife, Thecla, from snacky
sandwiches and salads to seafood specials (large prawns are very
popular), pies and steaks. Children are welcome and there's
a dining area at the back especially suitable for family meals.
*Bar Food 12.30-8.30 (L only in winter except Sat when served
6-9). No food Sun.*

Crossmolina   Enniscoe House   63%   £88

Tel 096 31112   Fax 096 31773   **A**

Castlehill nr Crossmolina Ballina Co Mayo   Map 1 B3

Generations of the same family have lived here on the shores
of Lough Conn since the 17th century and the mature woodland,
antique furniture and family portraits all contribute to today's
enjoyment of Irish hospitality and country house life. The current
owner, Susan Kellett, has established a Research and Heritage
Centre in converted yard buildings behind the house. One service
offered by the Centre is tracing family histories. The main
bedrooms have four-posters or canopied beds and fine views
of park and lake. *Rooms 6. Garden, game fishing. Closed mid
Oct-end Mar.* AMERICAN EXPRESS *Access, Visa.*

Culdaff   McGuinness's

Tel 077 79116   **P**

Culdaff Inish Owen Co Donegal   Map 1 C1

Just the kind of place the traveller might hope to happen upon,
this traditional country pub has been in the same family for three
generations and always has a welcoming turf fire burning in the

See over

public bar. This is simply furnished in a pleasant way with plain
furniture, old prints, plates and notices of local interest. Next door,
a comfortable lounge bar has great appeal, with homely chintzy
sofas, cushioned chairs and a nice old-fashioned conservatory with
a few more tables leading on to a small back garden. Food
requirements other than very simple snacks are dealt with
in a practical way – by telephoning orders to the village
restaurant, which is under the same ownership. The bar also acts
as an off-licence, so a variety of wines can be served by the glass.
Well-behaved children are welcome during the day. *Garden.*
No credit cards.

Dalkey   The Queens

Tel 01 285 4569   Fax 01 285 8345   **P**

Castle Street Dalkey Co Dublin   **Map 2 D4**

One of South Dublin's most famous pubs, The Queens
is a characterful and extremely professionally-run operation, with
open fires, old pine and whiskey jars creating atmosphere and
friendly, efficient staff dispensing the good food and drink which
has earned it so many awards. The bar menu features sandwiches
(closed or open), ploughman's salads, paté and a very popular
seafood chowder and garlicky mussels. There's also an Italian
restaurant, La Romana. **Bar Food** *12-6 (Sun brunch menu 12.30-
2.30). Children allowed in bar to eat. Access, Visa.*

Dalkey   Il Ristorante   £60

Tel 01 284 0800   **R**

108 Coliemore Road Dalkey Co Dublin   **Map 2 D4**

Italian owner-chef Roberto Pons is the power in the kitchen
of this intimate little restaurant with just six tables in a pretty, rag-
painted room above 'The Club' pub/bar. The classical North
Italian cooking is enlivened by attractive modern presentation
in dishes like gnocchi with spinach, pine nuts and Parmesan,
polenta with wild mushrooms, pasta e fagioli soup, fillets of brill
with creamed leeks, osso buco topped with gremolata and wild
boar with juniper berry sauce. There's a good selection of both
home-made pasta and desserts served from a trolley. Roberto's
Irish wife Celine provides a charming welcome. Not really
suitable for small children. *Seats 26. Parties 22. D only 7.30-10.30.
Closed Sun, Mon, Bank Holidays, 1 week Christmas, end Jan-mid
Feb. Access, Visa.*

Dalkey   Place of Interest

James Joyce Tower   Sandycove Tel 01 280 9265

Delgany   Glenview Hotel   63%   £70

Tel 01 287 3399   Fax 01 287 7511   **H**

Glen o' the Downs Delgany Co Wicklow   **Map 2 D4**

New owners have now been in situ for two years and continue
to make major improvements to this hotel that nestles beneath
Sugarloaf Mountain. There are 30 acres of gardens and dramatic
views of the Glen o' the Downs. Redecoration has been completed
throughout and the building now encompasses a conference area
with state-of-the-art facilities (catering for up to 300) at one end
and extra bedrooms at the other. Well-equipped bedrooms have

tea and coffee-making facilities, hairdryer and trouser press as standard and children under 5 stay free in parents' room. A new leisure centre with swimming pool, gymnasium, steam room and jacuzzi was due to be finished by mid-1994. *Rooms 42. Garden.* AMERICAN EXPRESS® *Access, Visa.*

Delgany   The Wicklow Arms

Tel 01 287 4611 Fax 01 287 3878	**P**
Delgany Co Wicklow	Map 2 D4

A friendly, well-maintained pub that's a popular weekend spot with Dubliners and visitors alike. Practicalities are well thought out, with a sensibly designed car park backing on to an attractively planted seating area which leads down to the back bar. Inside, the atmosphere is comfortable no-nonsense, with plenty of space to relax and enjoy generous, unpretentious food from the lounge menu such as open sandwiches served with loads of salad, paté, seafood chowder, garlicky mussels or mushrooms, and hot main courses served with chips (boiled potatoes or side salad for calorie-counters). A long wine list includes 20 half bottles. *Pub hours 6-close (Sat from 2, Sun noon-11). **Bar Food** 7-10.15 (Sat from 6), (Sun & Bank Hols 1-9). **Restaurant Meals** 12.30-3 (Sun only) 7-9.30 (except Sun & Mon). Children allowed in bar to eat but not in restaurant for Sunday lunch.* AMERICAN EXPRESS® *Access, Diners, Visa.*

Hotel sporting facilities are highlighted in the Quick Reference lists for easy comparison.

Dingle   Beginish Restaurant   £55

Tel 066 51588 Fax 066 51591	**R**
Green Street Dingle Co Kerry	Map 2 A5

Two lofty rooms provide the main seating here, while a small conservatory overlooking the lovely garden can be used as a private room. The restaurant takes its name from one of the Blasket islands and is a comfortable spot for enjoying the talents of Pat Moore. Her menu leans heavily towards seafood, the final choice depending on the day's catch and her own inspiration. Typical items on the dinner carte run from smoked mackerel paté and mussels beurre blanc to poached lobster, turbot with olive oil-scented potato pureé and a chive sauce, and pan-fried medallions of monkfish with a fennel confit and tomato basil sauce. Some meat choices, too, and delicious desserts like choux puff with fresh fruit or rhubarb soufflé tart. Good farmhouse cheese selection. *Seats 52. Private Room 18. L 12.30-2.15 D 6-9.30. Closed Mon, mid Nov-Mar.* AMERICAN EXPRESS® *Access, Diners, Visa.*

Dingle   Dick Mack's

No Telephone	**P**
Green Lane Dingle Co Kerry	Map 2 A5

Amazingly unspoilt shop-bar, once a cobbler's, now selling modern leather items and wellington boots. Basic bar, no pretensions. The cashier's booth remains as a snug and all is as it should be. *No credit cards.*

Dingle   Dingle Skellig Hotel   61%   £86

Tel 066 51144   Fax 066 51501   **H**

Dingle Co Kerry   Map 2 A5

Pleasant, practical and comfortable behind its unprepossessing 60s'
facade, the Dingle Skellig is a popular place with families
on holiday. Children are very well looked after, and there's also
plenty to keep grown-ups active and amused. The sea views are
quite a feature, and there's special anti-glare glass in the
conservatory restaurant. Bedrooms are of a reasonable size, with
several designated for family occupation. No dogs. *Rooms 115.*
Garden, indoor swimming pool, sauna, solarium, beauty & hair salon,
tennis, games room, snooker, deep-sea fishing. Closed mid
Nov-mid Mar. American Express *Access, Diners, Visa.*

Dingle   Doyle's Seafood Bar & Townhouse   £50

Tel 066 51174   Fax 066 51816   **RR**

4 John Street Dingle Co Kerry   Map 2 A5

Local seafood is the main attraction at this family-run restaurant
with flagstone floors and old pine furniture. Menus are made
up daily according to the catch landed by the Dingle boats, and
lobster, selected from a tank in the bar, is a speciality. Cooking
is straightforward, emphasising the freshness of the product. Start,
perhaps, with sweet and sour marinated herrings, crab cocktail (or
soup), millefeuille of warm oysters with Guinness sauce or home-
cured gravad lax. Main courses include another wide selection
of fish and seafood – from grilled mussels with garlic stuffing
to turbot served on the bone with *sauce ravigote*; twice-baked
cheese soufflé and rack of lamb may be the only alternatives
to seafood. Finish with a homely dessert such as raspberry
meringue cake or choose from a small selection of Irish farmhouse
cheeses. Shorter-choice, simpler set-price dinner menu served from
6 to 7pm only. The wine list is strong on whites and includes
a sensibly priced Australian selection. *Seats 50. Parties 12. D only*
6-9. Closed Sun, also mid Nov-mid Mar. Set D to 7pm £13.50.
Access, Diners, Visa.

Rooms   £62

High-quality accommodation includes a residents' sitting room
and eight stylish bedrooms furnished with antiques and luxurious
bathrooms. Breakfasts include "boiled real eggs" and the
restaurant's own fine smoked salmon (also available for take-away)
served with scrambled eggs – they wouldn't dream of letting you
go on your way without a proper breakfast.

Dingle   Greenmount House   £70

Tel 066 51414   **A**

Greenmount Dingle Co Kerry   Map 2 A5

John and Mary Curran's neat modern guesthouse is handy
to everything but has enough height to afford views over Dingle
– and an enviable reputation for hospitality, comfort, excellent
housekeeping and outstanding breakfasts, which are served
in a stylish conservatory overlooking the harbour. Individually
decorated rooms all have new bathrooms (shower only), direct-
dial telephones and many thoughtful touches including electric

blankets, TVs, clock radios, hairdryers, fresh fruit and flowers.
No children under 8 years. No dogs. Own parking. **Rooms 8.**
Garden. Closed 22-28 Dec. Access, Visa.

Dingle	**The Half Door**	**£55**
Tel 066 51600 Fax 066 51206		**R**
John Street Dingle Co Kerry		**Map 2 A5**

Cosy and welcoming, with a genuine cottage atmosphere
enhanced by exposed stone walls, copper pots and original white
tiles around the chimney breast. There's a sunny conservatory area
to the rear. Denis O'Connor's menu majors on seafood, so the
choice varies with the season and the catch. Seafood bisque,
steamed mussels, or sautéed oysters masked with a chive sauce
could be your starter, followed perhaps by grilled brill, salmon
en croute or baked fillet of plaice with a mustard sauce. Good
simple sweets. No youngsters after 8pm. **Seats 50. Parties 12.**
*Private Room 20. L 12.30-2.30 D 6-10. Closed Tue, also early
Jan-Easter.* AMERICAN EXPRESS *Access, Diners, Visa.*

Dingle	**The Islandman**	
Tel 066 51803 Fax 066 51273		**P**
Main Street Dingle Co Kerry		**Map 2 A5**

Bar, café, restaurant and bookshop – a versatile establishment even
by Irish standards! The menu is very varied: soups, marinated
herrings (£3.75) and smoked salmon to start, burgers, steaks,
seafood tagliatelle, crab claws, tarragon-sauced chicken, home-
made ice cream, whisky fruit cake (£2.75). One-plate satisfying
snacks include beef chili in pitta bread, baked potato topped with
ham and cheese (£4) and the all-day Celtic breakfast of sausages,
bacon, egg, mushrooms, chips, tea or coffee (£5.50). **Bar Food &**
Restaurant Meals *10-10.* AMERICAN EXPRESS *Access, Visa.*

Dingle	**James Flahive**	
Tel 066 51634		**P**
The Quay Dingle Co Kerry		**Map 2 A5**

Down by the harbour near the marina, this comfortable,
welcoming and most friendly of pubs has been run by James and
Peggy Flahive for 30 years. It's a great favourite of sailing people.
Photographs of distinguished visitors adorn the walls but none
is more proudly displayed than that of Dingle's best-loved resident,
Fungie the dolphin. *Open 10.30am-11.30pm, Sun 12-2 & 6-11.30.
No credit cards.*

Dingle	**Lord Baker's Bar & Restaurant**	**£60**
Tel 066 51277		**R**
Main Street Dingle Co Kerry		**Map 2 A5**

Tom Baker – businessman, councillor, auctioneer and poet, and
affectionately known as Lord Baker – acquired these premises
in 1890 and they've gradually developed from general supplier
and function caterer to a popular and thriving restaurant and bar.
Locally made tapestries are an eye-catching display in the main
eating area, beyond which is a conservatory extension leading into
the garden. Choose between the full restaurant menu and the less
formal bar menu, which offer similar choices from seafood soup,

See over

garlic prawns and chicken liver paté to seafood mornay and steaks.
Particularly favoured for Sunday lunch. *Seats 85. Parties 25.
L 12.30-2.30 D 6-10. Closed 25 Dec. Set L (Sun) £9.90
Set D £13.50.* AMERICAN EXPRESS *Access, Visa.*

Dingle   O'Flaherty's

Tel 066 51461   **P**

Bridge Street Dingle Co Kerry   **Map 2 A5**

Large square room, high-ceilinged, with flagstones, a stove, barrel
tables, an old piano and masses of old shelving for a collection
of antique signs and local bric-a-brac. Traditional Irish music is the
main attraction, with regular sessions in summer, other
impromptu sessions and occasional bursts on any instrument you
can imagine by landlord Fergus O'Flaherty. Access to the harbour
from the back of the bar. *Open 10.30am-11.30pm, Sun 12-2 & 4-
11. No credit cards.*

Dingle   Place of Interest

Great Blasket Island   Tel 066 13111

Dromahair   Stanford's Village Inn

Tel 071 64140   **P**

Dromahair Co Leitrim   **Map 1 B2**

Situated just south of Lough Gill on the ever beautiful Yeats
country route, Stanford's has been in the McGowan family for
five generations and, despite recent renovations, the front bar
remains, as it will always, as a testament to the Irish country pub
of yesteryear – not a sentimental reconstruction, but the real thing.
Elsewhere in this fisherman's hideaway, there are comfortable bars
with fires and good, simple fare (salads from £3, sandwiches from
80p) and a 32-seat restaurant (3-course lunch £6, 4-course dinner
£12) for those who prefer to sit square at a table. Straightforward
accommodation (with shared bathrooms) in five rooms is also
offered. *Bar Food 11am-10pm. Restaurant Meals 1-2.30, 7-9.
Children allowed in bar to eat, children's menu. Patio. Closed 25 Dec,
bar closed Good Friday. Access, Visa.*

Drumcliffe   Yeats Tavern

Tel 071 63117   **P**

Drumcliffe Co Sligo   **Map 1 B2**

Efficiently run, sympathetically modernised Yeats country pub
whose restaurant has recently been doubled in size. The bar menu
holds few surprises, but there's plenty of variety, from vegetable
soup, garlic mushrooms and barbecue ribs to home-made burgers,
omelettes, chicken (breaded, Kiev, Maryland, curry), cod, plaice,
salads and omelettes. Also snacks of sandwiches and filled baked
potatoes. Children's menu. More sophisticated restaurant menu.
Bar Food 12.30-10. Children allowed in bar to eat, children's menu.
AMERICAN EXPRESS *Access, Diners, Visa.*

Drumcliffe   Place of Interest

Lissadell House   Tel 071 63150

Dublin	Aberdeen Lodge	£60
Tel 01 283 8155 Fax 01 283 7877		**A**
53 Park Avenue Ailesbury Road Dublin 4		Map 4 C2

Located in a smart, peaceful south Dublin suburb, Aberdeen Lodge
stands on an avenue lined with well-established trees. The Halpins
have converted two substantial Edwardian properties to create
a discreet, comfortable private hotel. There's a simple lounge
on the ground floor along with an attractive and spacious
breakfast/dining room (dinner is available to residents by prior
arrangement). Bedrooms, their windows double-glazed, are
identically furnished, each with custom-built modern pieces; rear
ones overlook a cricket and rugby ground. The usual comforts
like trouser presses and hairdryers are provided and bathrooms
have full facilities, showers being quite powerful. Enjoyable
breakfasts include the likes of scrambled eggs and smoked salmon.
No dogs. ***Rooms* 16.** AMERICAN EXPRESS *Access, Diners, Visa.*

> Many hotels offer reduced rates for weekend or out-of-season
> bookings. Always ask about special deals.

Dublin	Anglesea Town House	£60
Tel 01 668 3877 Fax 01 668 3461		**A**
63 Anglesea Road Dublin 4		Map 3 B2

A fine, creeper-clad south Dublin Edwardian residence run with
enormous dedication and flair by Helen Kirrane with the help
of her charming daughters. The minute you enter, the heady
perfume of pot pourri greets and all around are beautiful
ornaments and furnishings. A drawing room is the epitome
of cosy homeliness with its fine, comfortable seating and
numerous books and yet more tasteful ornaments. Bedrooms
feature lacework, heavy drapes and a comforting, motherly decor.
Bathrooms, some with shower only, are spotless, like the rest
of the house. Bedding has a wonderful 'all-through' freshly
laundered smell. In the mornings guests are treated to what
is without doubt the most stunning breakfast in the British Isles.
To begin, a large bowl of fresh fruit salad is brought, then a bowl
of dried fruit compote and one of baked fruit in creamy yoghurt.
Next comes a bowl of warm baked cereal (oats, fruits, nuts soaked
in orange juice overnight then freshly baked with cream). You
help yourself to all these along with a glass of freshly squeezed
orange juice. The main course follows – specialities are kedgeree
and Anglesea omelette (a soufflé omelette with smoked salmon
and three different cheeses). Other options include kidneys, sole,
plaice, salmon or trout as well as more usual offerings.
To accompany, hot buttered toast, home-baked breads and
limitless amounts of good tea or coffee. To finish, a selection
of small dainty cakes such as a moist frangipane tart. A quite
extraordinary place. No dogs. ***Rooms* 7.** *Garden.* AMERICAN EXPRESS
Access, Diners, Visa.

Dublin   Ariel House   £63

Tel 01 668 5512   Fax 01 668 5845   **A**

52 Lansdowne Road Ballsbridge Dublin 4   Map 6 H2

A substantial listed Victorian mansion, built in 1850, has for the
past 34 years been home to the O'Brien family. It has also been
one of Dublin's most charming private house hotels. Unusually for
such premises there's a cosy bar close to the reception desk where
a selection of wines can be enjoyed. The drawing room and
bedrooms, in the original house, are furnished with beautiful
pieces of Victorian furniture. Rooms are spacious and well-
equipped and each has its own character. There is, however,
a wing of ten standard bedrooms at rear which are modern and
more functional in style and overlook the neat, well-tended
garden. All bedrooms have full tub facilities (both bath and
shower). Each also has a trouser press with iron and board,
a hairdryer and an array of useful extras. Breakfast is served in a
pretty conservatory on highly polished mahogany tables. Smoking
discouraged. Free parking. No dogs. *Rooms 28. Closed 2 weeks
Christmas.* AMERICAN EXPRESS *Access, Visa.*

Dublin   Ashtons

Tel 01 283 0045   **P**

Clonskeagh Dublin 6   Map 3 B2

Behind a frontage which can only be described as a cross between
those old country garages with facades disguising Nissen huts and
a glossy Chinese restaurant, all shiny marble, black and gold, lies
a large pub on a number of levels – one of Dublin's most
surprising pubs. It descends down to the River Dodder and
as many tables as possible are positioned to take advantage of the
river view with its ducks and waterfowl, the occasional swan
foraging among the reeds and locals pottering along the banks.
Inexpensive bar snacks include excellent home-made soups and
brown bread with walnuts and hazelnuts, but it is the lunchtime
buffet for which they are famous. There's always a roast joint and
a selection of hot dishes plus an imaginative cold buffet and salad
bar, where a whole dressed salmon takes pride of place surrounded
by dressed crab, crab claws, prawns and other freshly cooked
seafood as available. From a varied choice of desserts the house
speciality is banoffi pie – and the recipe is a closely guarded secret.
After the lunchtime buffet is cleared a separate bar snack menu
operates until 8pm. A full à la carte dinner menu is served
downstairs in the restaurant. *Bar Meals L 12.30-2.30 (7 days),
snacks 3.30-8 (Mon-Sat). Restaurant Meals D 6-10 (Sun to 9.30).
Children allowed to eat in the bar.* AMERICAN EXPRESS *Access, Diners, Visa.*

Dublin   Ayumi-Ya Japanese Steakhouse   £40

Tel 01 662 2233   Fax 01 662 0221   **R**

132 Lower Baggot Street Dublin 2   Map 6 G2

One section of the menu at this informal basement restaurant,
an offshoot of the Blackrock original, is given over to teppanyaki
– beef, chicken, salmon, prawns, tofu, Tokyo burger – griddled
and served with a choice of sauces. Other favourites include
tonkatsu (deep-fried breadcrumbed pork), mixed vegetable stir-fry
and egg noodles with meat, seafood or vegetables. The evening

evening selection is more extensive. *Seats 40. Parties 20.*
L 12.30-2.30 D 6.30-11.30. Closed L Sat, all Sun. Set L & D from
£6.95. AMERICAN EXPRESS *Access, Visa.*

Dublin	Berkeley Court	76%	£191
Tel 01 660 1711 Fax 01 661 7238			**H**
Lansdowne Road Dublin 4			Map 6 H1

The flagship of the Doyle Hotel Group, the luxurious Berkeley
Court has an impressively large split-level lobby-lounge with
mirrored columns, brass-potted parlour palms and reproduction
furniture in a mixture of styles. There are two bars – the Royal
Court and the popular Conservatory – and two restaurants. The
Court Lounge is a civilised spot for afternoon tea. Ballroom,
boardroom and several suites provide function facilities for
up to 275 people. Accommodation includes a proportion
of spacious Executive suites with classic furnishings and the
sumptuously appointed Penthouse Suite. One floor of rooms (29)
is designated non-smoking. *Rooms 207. Indoor swimming pool,
sauna, solarium, hair salon, news kiosk, boutique.* AMERICAN EXPRESS
Access, Diners, Visa.

Dublin	The Bleeding Horse		
Tel 01 475 2705			**P**
24 Upper Camden Street Dublin 2			Map 5 F1

Family-owned and partly family-run on sound, traditional
principles of service and efficiency, the Bleeding Horse is lofty
and impressive, with vast dark timbers and a huge fireplace in the
smaller bar. A balcony runs right around the centre, giving
an almost medieval feel. Trendy young staff serve a simple
selection of food, basically soup, home-made bread sandwiches,
salads and desserts such as rhubarb tart or pavlova. *Bar Food from
12.30. Children allowed in bar to eat. No credit cards.*

Dublin	Blooms Hotel	60%	£121
Tel 01 671 5622 Fax 01 671 5997			**H**
Anglesea Street Dublin 2			Map 5 F3

Modern city-centre hotel near Trinity College and Dublin Castle.
An alternative to the pubby bar is a small cocktail bar integrated
to the restaurant (newly decorated in bright yellow); otherwise
the only sitting area is a rather shabby lounge off the marbled
lobby. Bedrooms, by contrast, are pleasant and well-kept with
triple-glazed windows and extras like a complimentary quarter
bottle of wine and evening newspaper. Bathrooms are a little
dated but generally of good size and quite adequate; all have low
stools and telephone extensions and some have bidets. No dogs.
Rooms 86. Night club. Closed 24, 25 & 26 Dec. AMERICAN EXPRESS
Access, Diners, Visa.

Dublin	The Brian Boru		
Tel 01 308514			**P**
5 Prospect Road Glasnevin Dublin 9			Map 3 A4

Named after an 11th-century High King of Ireland, this smartly
maintained pub is also known as *Hedigan's* after owner Peter
Hedigan. Original Victorian themes – mahogany, stained glass

See over

and, especially, very fine tiling – have been carried through
faithfully as alterations have been made through the years,
everything is neat and clean and the eye is drawn past
an abundance of strong tables and seating, to a patio/beer garden
at the back, also furnished with comfortable eating in mind.
It comes as no surprise that the Brian Boru has been in the same
family since 1904. Bar food is best described as traditional with
an original twist. *Garden. Access, Visa.*

Dublin	Burlington Hotel	70%	£154
Tel 01 660 5222 Fax 01 660 8496			**H**
Upper Leeson Street Dublin 4			Map 6 G1

Part of the Doyle Hotel Group, the Burlington is Ireland's largest
hotel and always bustles with commercial business. Public rooms
are on a grand scale, with large chandeliers in the main
lobby/lounge area, a convivial bar (Buck Mulligan's) and a disco.
Bedrooms are thoughtfully designed and well-equipped, with
good working space for the business guest and neat tiled
bathrooms with ample shelf space and bathrobes. The Burlington
has a good reputation for banquets and has conference facilities for
up to 1,000. No dogs. *Rooms 450. Hair salon, kiosk, boutique.*
AMERICAN EXPRESS *Access, Diners, Visa.*

Dublin	Central Hotel	57%	£139
Tel 01 679 7302 Fax 01 679 7303			**H**
1 Exchequer Street Dublin 2			Map 5 F3

Privately owned hotel whose plus points include a central
location, nightly live music (traditional Irish and folk) in the
newly themed Molly Malone's Tavern, the owner's collection
of contemporary Irish art around the walls and free use of a
nearby office car park overnight (7.30pm-8.30am) and
at weekends. Bedrooms vary widely in size and shape but all are
furnished in similar style with functional lightwood units; wall-
mounted TVs are too high up near the ceiling and housekeeping is
less than perfect. About half the bathrooms have shower and
WC only and there is often no usable shelf space. 24hr room
service. Children under 12 stay free in parents' room. No dogs.
Rooms 70. Closed 25 & 26 Dec. AMERICAN EXPRESS *Access, Diners, Visa.*

Dublin	Chapter One		£70
Tel 01 873 2266 Fax 01 873 2330			**R**
18/19 Parnell Square Dublin 1			Map 5 F4

A characterful vaulted cellar restaurant underneath the Dublin
Writers Museum. Menus lean slightly towards Russian/
Scandinavian themes, offering starters like warm salads, baked
goat's cheese and duck livers with garlic croutons alongside blinis
and gravad lax; main courses might include roast duck with
apricot sauce and endives, or griddled calf's liver with black olives,
rosemary, red onion and a balsamic vinegar gravy. Good pastry
dishes among the desserts. Concise wine list. The Museum Coffee
Shop, upstairs, serves more informal food all day. *Seats 100.
Private Rooms 16-40. L 12-2.30 D 5.45-11. Closed L Sat, all Sun,
Bank Holidays (except coffee shop).* AMERICAN EXPRESS *Access,
Diners, Visa.*

Dublin   Chicago Pizza Pie Factory

Tel 01 478 1233 Fax 01 478 1550	**R**
St Stephen's Green Centre Dublin 2	Map 5 F2

In a dimly-lit basement with deep-red-painted walls, Chicago-related memorabilia – flags, road signs, pictures, number plates and what have you – create an entertaining backdrop to read while waiting for the delivery of your chosen deep-pan pizza, burger, salad or other delight. Cheerful American-style service, a genuinely friendly atmosphere and fresh, wholesome cosmopolitan food fast-cooked to order. Gooey desserts might undo all the good of what went before, but you don't see anyone complaining – it's fun. Special value weekday lunch menus and family entertainment on Sundays. *Seats 90. Meals 12-11.30 (Sun from 12.30). Closed 25 & 26 Dec, Good Friday.*   *Access, Visa.*

Dublin   The Chili Club   £45

Tel 01 677 3721	**R**
1 Anne's Lane South Anne Street Dublin 2	Map 5 F2

Just off bustling South Anne Street, in Dublin's most fashionable shopping area, this intimate, low-ceilinged restaurant provides an oasis of serenity. Anna, the Thai chef, cooks the hot and spicy food of her homeland to be 'as traditional as the market will allow'. Satays, sweet and sours and even most of the curries are easy on the palate, but the soups have the expected Thai kick. *Seats 42. Parties 15. Private Room 16. L 12.30-2.30 D 7-11. Closed L Sat, all Sun, Bank Holidays. Set L £7.95 Set D £17.50.* Access, Diners, Visa.

Dublin   Clarence Hotel   60%   £50

Tel 01 677 6178 Fax 01 677 7487	**H**
6 Wellington Quay Dublin 2	Map 5 E3

Built in 1890 and recently purchased by the rock band U2, the Clarence is undergoing a very major transformation into a top-grade hotel. This has always been the traditional stopping place for country folk 'coming to town' as it's down the road from Heuston station. This staid image is gradually being changed. By the summer of this year a brand new nightclub, The Kitchen, will have opened in the basement and a new residents' lounge off the lobby. On the first floor will be the hotel restaurant. At the rear of the ground floor there is already a smart all-day brasserie, the Tea Room. The hotel's bar also to the rear of the ground floor is another area to undergo refurbishment by the summer. Work on the currently quite cramped bedrooms will begin in the autumn and may lead to their complete closure for a thorough rebuild with reopening scheduled for late 1995. Children under 12 share parents' room at no charge. 24hr room service. No dogs. *Rooms 66. Closed 25-28 Dec.* Access, Diners, Visa.

Dublin   The Commons Restaurant   £85

Tel 01 475 2597 Fax 01 478 0551	**R**
Newman House 85/86 St Stephen's Green Dublin 2	Map 5 E2

Situated in the basement of Newman House, the original home of University College Dublin and one of Europe's finest historic

See over

18th-century town houses, this spacious restaurant opens out at the
back on to a large courtyard, with further access to some five acres
of private gardens. There's some interesting Irish art on the walls
and the setting is undeniably elegant, not always matched
by Gerard Kirwan's cooking, which though using the best of Irish
produce, is sometimes prone to slight lapses. Both a four-course
table d'hote and carte are offered. From the latter, a starter of of
two tiny quail breasts on braised lentils was minimal in the
extreme, followed by the dated practice of a palate-cleansing
sorbet, often acceptable but not when flowery, sweet and rather
fruity as in a spearmint offering. The grilled turbot, on the other
hand, with braised fennel and a dill cream sauce, was perfectly
cooked, as were the accompanying vegetables and potatoes, which
included *macaire* (baked and filled with fried mash). Other starters
might include foie gras terrine and a salmon and chive roulade;
main courses – breast of pheasant with traditional bread sauce
or cannon of lamb flavoured with honey and thyme. For dessert,
perhaps a warm pear strudel with crème anglaise or dark chocolate
terrine with a Baileys sauce. Good Java coffee rounds off the meal,
which attracts an automatic, not inconsiderable, 15% service
charge. The wine list has several notable wines, but would benefit
from a more constructive order/grouping. *Seats 60. Parties 12.
Private Room 26. L 12.30-2.15 D 7-10. Closed L Sat, all Sun, Bank
Holidays, 25 & 26 Dec. Set L £16 Set D £27.50.* AMERICAN EXPRESS
Access, Diners, Visa.

Dublin	Hotel Conrad	75%	£217
Tel 01 676 5555 Fax 01 676 5424			**H**
Earlsfort Terrace Dublin 2			Map 5 F2

Opposite the National Concert Hall, just off St Stephen's Green,
the Conrad is very much a modern international-style hotel with
an impressive array of business facilities, earning the accolade
of Business Hotel of the Year. It caters largely to a corporate
clientele – although concessions to the locality include Alfie
Byrne's bar, themed along the lines of a traditional Dublin pub.
Bedrooms, while decoratively uninspiring, are eminently
comfortable and well planned with large beds, good easy chairs,
decent work space, three telephones (including sockets for fax),
and every modern comfort. Excellent marble bathrooms have
large tubs with good showers above them, comprehensive
toiletries and ample towelling with generously-sized bathrobes.
Levels of service are high, from free valet parking and
comprehensive 24hr room service to a proper turn-down service
in the evenings, when a bottle of mineral water and a hand-made
Irish chocolate are left at the bedside. Breakfast is the best meal
of the day. Banqueting for 150, conference facilities for 300.
Conrad is the international branch of Hilton USA, which is not
to be confused with the now British (Ladbroke-owned) Hilton
chain. No dogs. ***Rooms** 191. Hair salon, news kiosk, brasserie (7am-
11.30pm).* AMERICAN EXPRESS *Access, Diners, Visa.*

Dublin	Cooke's Café	↑	£65
Tel 01 679 0536 Fax 01 679 0546			**R**
14 South William Street Dublin 2			Map 5 F3

A heart-of-the-city restaurant that has deservedly been
a phenomenal success ever since opening in mid-1992. Johnny

Cooke's the chef and he heads a dedicated team who work in a
tiny, open-plan kitchen separated from an equally none-too-large,
very informal dining room by a tall screen which features a mural
in the same 'distressed' classical Italianate style as the rest of the
room. Tables are close and there are several sittings, so the timing
of bookings, which are essential, can be critical. The menu will
be familiar to those conversant with the current vogue for new-
wave cooking. Here it is mostly Italian. Presentation too forms
an integral part of the experience, as in delicious lightly fried squid
rings served in the middle of an extra large plate and sitting
on a square of spicy arrabbiata sauce with roasted garlic (although
on a recent visit the promised hot spiciness was lacking).
To accompany, if required, a small wicker basket overflowing
with superb home-baked breads is offered along with an olive oil
dip. A cream of red bell pepper soup garnished with goat's cheese;
mussels steamed with garlic, wine, leeks, herbs and butter and
Caesar salad are all typical starters. Main dishes are quite diverse,
ranging from tortelloni with Parmesan, gorgonzola cream and
melted appenzeller cheese to calf's liver with a sage and pancetta
butter and a plump, tender partridge roasted and served
on a creamy celeriac purée and surrounded by a delicately fragrant
lemon thyme butter. Simply prepared, very fresh vegetables are
available separately. Desserts include good home-made ice creams
and such sugary delights as honey chocolate cake or a very similar
chocolate marzipan cake and pecan tart. In fine weather there are
tables outside on the pavement. Service does its best to cope with
the often crowded conditions. No children under 3 after 6pm.
According to the menu, discretionary gratuities cannot
be processed on credit cards. *Seats 40. Parties 12. Private Room 40.*
Meals 12.30-3.30 & 6-12 (May-Sept 8am-midnight). Set L £12.95.
Closed Bank Holidays. *Access, Diners, Visa.*

Dublin	Le Coq Hardi	★	£95
Tel 01 668 9070 Fax 01 668 9887			R
35 Pembroke Road Ballsbridge Dublin 4			Map 6 H1

John and Catherine Howard run a classic restaurant in a classic
Georgian building at the end of a terrace. Inside are high ceilings
and handsome mirrors, brasswork and ornate plasterwork, and the
immaculately set tables put the seal on a setting that's entirely
fitting for John's serious French-based cooking. Many of his dishes
are from the traditional repertoire – terrine of foie gras with
brioche, cod boulangère, Venetian-style lamb's liver, entrecote
with a shallot and bone marrow sauce. 'Le Coq Hardi' is a breast
of chicken filled with potato, wild mushrooms and herbs,
wrapped in bacon, oven-roasted and finished with Irish whiskey
sauce. Other dishes are more contemporary in style, such as warm
salad with game, pink grapefruit and pine nuts, strudel
of vegetables on a light curry sauce with mint, or darne of salmon
steamed with tomato, black olives, olive oil and sea salt. Bread-
and-butter pudding with Irish whiskey custard is a favourite
dessert. Particularly famous for its Bordeaux cellar, which includes
an 1870 Chateau Mouton Rothschild for the modest sum
of £5000+, do not ignore the exceptional selection of cognacs and
armagnacs, nor the rest of the list that has plenty of good wines
from outside France; really, though, this is a connoisseur's list
to drool over. *Seats 50. Private Room 34. L 12-2.30 D 7-11.*

*Closed L Sat, all Sun, Bank Holidays, 1 week Christmas, 2 weeks
Aug. Set L £14.50 Set D £24.50.* AMERICAN EXPRESS *Access,
Diners, Visa.*

Dublin	The Davenport Hotel	76%	£177
Tel 01 661 6800 Fax 01 661 5663			**H**
Merrion Square Dublin 2			Map 6 G3

The original, imposing neo-classical facade of architect Alfred
G Jones's Merrion Hall fronts one of Dublin's most elegant hotels,
opened last year. Only a stone's throw from Trinity College and
the National Gallery, the impressive exterior of The Davenport
is carried through into the marble-pillared lobby, an atrium
encircled by Georgian windows which soars up through six
storeys to the domed roof and cupola. Rooms beyond are
on a more human scale, with relatively low ceilings creating
an unexpectedly intimate atmosphere throughout the hotel.
Colour schemes tend to be bold, giving each area a specific
character – the Presidents Bar is masculine, club-like, for example,
the restaurant lighter and more feminine – with stylish drapes and
quality materials, notably marble and a variety of woods, used
throughout. Although not individually decorated there
is considerable variety among the bedrooms (some Lady Executive
designated), which tend to have a homely, almost country
atmosphere which is emphasised by the irregular shapes in some
rooms and (well-furnished) bathrooms. Nice touches include a safe
as well as trouser press, air-conditioning, good American over-bath
showers and an attractive Irish-made range of toiletries. 24hr room
service. Private 24hr valet parking. Banqueting/conference
facilities for 400/300. ***Rooms** 120.* AMERICAN EXPRESS *Access,
Diners, Visa.*

Our inspectors **never** book in the name of Egon Ronay's
Guides. They disclose their identity only if they are
considering an establishment for inclusion in the next
edition of the Guide.

Dublin	Davy Byrnes		
Tel 01 677 5217 Fax 01 677 5849			**P**
21 Duke Street Dublin 2			Map 5 F3

At the heart of Dublin life (and immortalised in James Joyce's
Ulysses), Davy Byrnes is not only a mecca for literary-minded
tourists, but also a pleasant, well-run and conveniently central
place well used by Dubliners in town on business, shopping
in nearby Grafton Street or simply having a day out. Decor-wise,
it is in a 1920s' time-warp and is likely to remain so through
future redecorations as it has done in the past; however, for such
a famous pub, it is remarkably unselfconscious. It has always had
a good reputation for food. At its simplest, sandwiches are
invariably fresh and there's a good choice of moderately-priced hot
dishes (£3.95-£5.95) on a blackboard every day. They take pride
in seafood, particularly oysters, with fresh crab or king prawn
salads (around £6.95) featuring as the most expensive lunchtime
dishes, and poached salmon steak with hollandaise (£5.95)
appearing among additional hot dishes in the evening. Sunday
brunch £5.50. ***Bar Food** 12-10 (Sun 12-2, 4-11). Access, Visa.*

Dublin   Dillons Restaurant

Tel & Fax 01 677 4804	**R**
21 Suffolk Street Dublin 2	**Map 5 F3**

Central, and especially well-located for shoppers in the Grafton
Street area, Dillons is meeting the growing demand for traditional
Irish food. The long, narrow, high-ceilinged room has a non-
smoking area at the back and a deli counter at the door and
is decorated with memorabilia, including a butcher boy's delivery
bike. Good old-fashioned cooking at reasonable prices offers
a wide range of old favourites, including everything from
crubeens (pig's trotters) to corned beef or bacon and cabbage, from
oysters to Irish stew or Dublin coddle – and you can even round
it off with Guinness cake. *Seats* 110. *Meals 12-12. Set L from £5.50
D £9.95. Closed 25 & 26 Dec.* AMERICAN EXPRESS *Access, Diners, Visa.*

CLOSED

Dublin   Doheny & Nesbitt

Tel 01 676 2945 Fax 01 676 0655	**P**
5 Lower Baggot Street Dublin 2	**Map 6 G2**

Only a stone's throw across the road from *Toners*, Doheny &
Nesbitt is another great Dublin institution, but there the similarity
ends. Just around the corner from the Irish parliament, this solid
Victorian pub has traditionally attracted a wide spectrum
of Dublin society – politicians, economists, lawyers, business
names, political and financial journalists – all with a view to get
across, or some scandal to divulge, so a visit here can often
be unexpectedly rewarding. Like the *Shelbourne Hotel* down the
road, which has a similar reputation and shares the clientele, half
the fun of drinking at Nesbitt's is anticipation of 'someone'
arriving or 'something' happening, both more likely than not.
Apart from that it is an unspoilt, very professionally run bar with
a traditional emphasis on drinking. No children allowed in bar.
Access, Visa.

Dublin   Doyle Montrose Hotel   65%   £106

Tel 01 269 3311 Fax 01 269 1164	**H**
Stillorgan Road Dublin 4	**Map 4 C2**

A major facelift has given the Montrose a smart modern
appearance. Located alongside the N11, a few miles south of the
city centre, it now also has an attractive 'old Ireland' themed pub
with its own entrance. Spacious public areas include a large open-
plan bar and lounge. Bedrooms are furnished in an identical smart,
contemporary style with Executive rooms differing only in being
larger. A good selection of amenities includes an iron and ironing
board. Acceptable breakfasts are cooked to order – quite a rarity
in a large hotel. *Rooms* 179. *Beauty salon, hair salon, news
kiosk/shop.* AMERICAN EXPRESS *Access, Diners, Visa.*

Dublin   Doyle Tara Hotel   61%   £106

Tel 01 269 4666 Fax 01 269 1027	**H**
Merrion Road Dublin 4	**Map 4 C2**

Formerly the *Tara Tower*, the hotel has recently undergone some
major changes (with more planned as we went to press). On the
ground floor, the spacious lobby and open-plan bar are due for
refurbishment, while at the rear there are now 32 splendid new

See over

Executive rooms decorated in a smart, modern style. All rooms
have the same amenities but the standard rooms at the front enjoy
the best views over Dublin Bay. The hotel is very convenient for
the Dun Laoghaire ferry. *Rooms 114. News kiosk/shop.*
AMERICAN EXPRESS *Access, Diners, Visa.*

Dublin	L'Ecrivain	£70
Tel 01 661 1919 Fax 01 661 0617		**R**
112 Lower Baggot Street Dublin 2		Map 6 G2

As the name implies, this unpretentious little basement restaurant
serves French food and has a writers' theme, with portraits
of famous Irish writers by local artist Liam O'Neill hanging on the
terracotta-painted walls. A tiny reception lounge with a comfy
sofa welcomes diners, who can look forward to fresh seasonal
produce, especially the fish that comes from south and west Cork
on the day the catch is landed; everything is expertly cooked
by chef/patron Derry Clarke and his small team in the kitchen.
Seasonal vegetarian and à la carte menus are supplemented
by good-value set lunch and dinner offerings with a selection
of five starters and main courses to choose from. Look out for
dishes such as pan-fried black and white puddings with pureéd
mash and jus, grilled goat's cheese with a crisp salad and pesto in
a filo basket and west coast mussel broth with smoked bacon,
followed by steamed brill with lemon grass, rosemary, roasted
sweet peppers and aged balsamic vinegar, or generous slices
of tender rib of beef with mushrooms and light tarragon puffs.
Desserts, recited at the table, could include pear and almond tart,
crème brulée and Paris-Brest. Excellent Irish farmhouse cheeses,
generous cups of various coffees and intimate service from Sally-
Anne Clarke and her team. The decent wine list has the added
benefit of wines costing £20 or more not attracting the service
charge – a commendable practice that more restaurants should
follow. *Seats 40. L 12.30-2 D 6.30-11. Closed L Sat, all Sun.
Set L £13.50 Set D £21.95.* AMERICAN EXPRESS *Access, Diners, Visa.*

Dublin	Ernie's	£80
Tel 01 269 3260 Fax 01 269 3969		**R**
Mulberry Gardens Donnybrook Dublin 4		Map 3 B2

The Evans family has owned this elegant south-city restaurant
since 1984 and its most remarkable feature is the late Ernie Evans's
personal collection of paintings (mostly of Irish interest and many
of his beloved Kerry), which take up every available inch of wall
space – closely followed by the pretty little central courtyard
garden which makes an especially attractive feature when floodlit
at night. The interior was extensively refurbished last year. Chef
Sandra Earl is very much in control in the kitchen, producing
refreshingly updated versions of the classics. Feuillette of mussels
with smoked bacon and dill, warm parcel of crab and mozzarella,
and pan-fried medallions of monkfish with tagliatelle, wild
mushrooms and seed mustard sauce are all typical of her style and
desserts include comfort food like apple and prune tart with
Calvados ice cream as well as elegant concoctions appropriate to a
grand finale. *Seats 60. L 12.30-2.30 D 7.15-10.15. Closed Sun &
Mon, Bank Holidays, 1 week Xmas. Set L £13.50 Set D £22.50.*
AMERICAN EXPRESS *Access, Diners, Visa.*

Dublin   Les Frères Jacques   £80

Tel 01 679 4555   Fax 01 679 4725   **R**

74 Dame Street Dublin   **Map 5 E3**

The decor, the atmosphere, the staff and many of the customers
are French, and the menu adds Gallic twists to prime Irish
produce. Ragout of game and duck livers with port wine sauce,
roast leg of lamb with ratatouille, chicken supreme in a light curry
and mango sauce are other favourites, and among the desserts you
might find tarte tatin, poached pear with praline ice cream and
warm rice pudding with apricot and red fruit mousseline. The
restaurant is in two sections, either of which may be used for
a private party. One room is designated non-smoking. There's live
piano music three nights a week. *Seats 55. Private Rooms 15/40.
L 12.30-2.30 D 7.30-10.30 (Fri & Sat to 11). Closed L Sat, all Sun,
Bank Holidays, 25-29 Dec. Set L £13 Set D £20.*
Access, Visa.

Dublin   Furama   £75

Tel & Fax 01 283 0522   **R**

88 Donnybrook Road Dublin 4   **Map 3 B2**

Like eating inside a gleaming black lacquered box, with the
dining area reached via a small wooden bridge over an ornamental
pool with goldfish. Furama offers a selection of familiar Cantonese
as well as a few Szechuan dishes, capably cooked and served
by hardworking, very pleasant staff. There's a special fish menu
offering scallops, mussels, black sole, sea bass and lobster; the
scallops may come sliced in a black bean sauce, while the sole can
be steamed with ginger and scallions. Sweets – like much of the
menu – are aimed at Western palates with various ices dominating
the choice. *Seats 60. Parties 20. L 12.30-2 D 6-11.30 (Fri & Sat
to 12, Sun 1.30-11). Set D £15. Closed 24-26 Dec.*
Access, Diners, Visa.

Dublin   Georgian House   56%   £83

Tel 01 661 8832   Fax 01 661 8834   **H**

20 Lower Baggot Street Dublin 2   **Map 6 G2**

Bedrooms in the original building have character and charm
while those in the recently built separate bedroom extension at the
rear are more modern and functional. Conveniently close to the
city centre, the hotel also has direct access to its own pub,
Maguire's, next door. Children up to 4 stay free in parents' room.
24hr room-service. No dogs. *Rooms 33.* Access,
Diners, Visa.

Dublin   George's Bistro & Piano Bar   £70

Tel 01 679 7000   Fax 01 679 7560   **R**

29 South Frederick Street Dublin 2   **Map 5 F3**

In a side street between the Dail and Trinity College, a bistro
popular with the post-theatre crowd. Straightforward menu
of dishes based on top-quality ingredients, correctly cooked. Steaks,
racks of lamb and Dover sole are favourite main courses, with
something like avocado with crab or garlic mushrooms to start.
The other attraction is live music (piano with female vocal),
which tends to inhibit conversation but fuels the late-night buzz.   *See over*

Note that it's no longer open at lunchtime. *Seats 90.*
Private Room 50. D only 5-1am. Closed Sun & Mon, Bank Holidays,
1 week Christmas. Set D £18.50. AMERICAN EXPRESS *Access, Diners, Visa.*

Dublin   Glenveagh Town House   £50

Tel 01 668 4612   Fax 01 668 4559   A

31 Northumberland Road Ballsbridge Dublin 4   Map 6 H2

A large Georgian house within comfortable walking distance
of the city centre (it has off-street parking – a very useful feature).
Bedrooms are pleasantly decorated and sport duvets and remote-
control TVs. Bathrooms have excellent showers. Breakfasts are
available from 8am though earlier meals can be arranged. The
selection is a familiar one but includes black and white pudding
among its offerings. There's a comfortable drawing room at the
front. Friendly, caring staff. No dogs. *Rooms 11. Closed 21-27 Dec.*
Access, Visa.

Dublin   The Goat

Tel 01 298 4145   Fax 01 298 4687   P

Goatstown Dublin 14   Map 3 B1

"Dublin's Sporting Pub" is a real city landmark. Big, with an even
bigger car park (complete with house mini-bus to ferry customers
home safely), it has its own clock tower and would be unmissable
even without its current coat of pink paint. Inside, despite its size,
it is a friendly sort of place where families are made especially
welcome. The lounge menu offers sandwiches, omelettes, steaks
and salads, and there's a more formal restaurant. *Bar Food 12-3,*
3.30-9. Children allowed in bar to eat, children's menu. Patio & garden.
AMERICAN EXPRESS *Access, Diners, Visa.*

Dublin   Good World   £40

Tel 01 677 5373   R

18 South Great George's Street Dublin 2   Map 5 F3

A city-centre restaurant much favoured by Dublin's Chinese
community, who flock here at lunchtime for an excellent selection
of carefully prepared dim sum. These come in steamer baskets
of stainless steel rather than bamboo but this is no way affects their
quality. Mixed meat dumplings and char siu buns are noteworthy
as are the long, slippery rice-flour envelopes of the various cheung
funs. The regular menu features a standard selection of classic
Cantonese dishes, but it's the dim sum that are primarily
of interest here. No smoking in the downstairs dining room.
Seats 95. Parties 40. Private Room 20. Meals 12.30pm-3am.
Closed 25 & 26 Dec. AMERICAN EXPRESS *Access, Diners, Visa.*

Dublin   Gotham Café

Tel 01 679 5266   Fax 01 679 5280   R

8 South Anne Street Dublin 2   Map 5 F3

Right in the heart of the city, off Grafton Street, Gotham Café
is bright, buzzy and new. Walls are lined with framed Rolling
Stone magazine covers and the menu features New York-
influenced Italian new-wave cooking. Thus penne come with
a chili sauce and Creole sausage (£6.50) and tagliatelle with
chicken breast and broccoli (£7.50). Excellent value is found

in the selection of gourmet pizzas, for example the Central Park
(£4.85 regular, £7.50 large); this has a topping of tender giant
prawns (thoughtfully deveined), roast sweet peppers, zucchini,
garlic and mozzarella; Harlem (£4.25 and £6.50) features sun-
dried tomatoes, roast peppers, garlic and a mix of goat's and
mozzarella cheeses. Wine licence only. *Seats 68. Parties 12. Meals
11am-midnight (Sun from noon). Closed 3 days Christmas, Good
Friday. Access, Visa.*

Dublin	Gresham Hotel	64%	£140
Tel 01 874 6881 Fax 01 878 7175			H
Upper O'Connell Street Dublin 1			Map 5 F4

A prime position on Upper O'Connell Street and free, secure valet
parking are major attractions of this famous north-city hotel. The
comfortably furnished, chandelier-lit lobby/lounge is a popular
meeting place, especially for morning coffee or afternoon tea, and
Toddy's Bar (named after an illustrious former manager) is an all-
day eating spot. Front bedrooms are best, with smart modern
bathrooms, and there are nine full suites. Banqueting/conference
facilities for 200/325. *Rooms 200. Closed 25 & 26 Dec.*
AMERICAN EXPRESS *Access, Diners, Visa.*

> If we recommend meals in a hotel a **separate**
> entry is made for its restaurant.

Dublin	Grey Door		£50
Tel 01 676 3286 Fax 01 676 3287			RR
22 Upper Pembroke Street Dublin 2			Map 5 F2

Conveniently close to the main south city-centre shopping and
business areas, the Grey Door is discreetly set in a fine Georgian
terrace near Fitzwilliam Square. Russian influences feature
strongly, especially in the dinner menu of the cosy, small-roomed
ground-floor restaurant decorated in classical pale grey and
primrose yellow. Starters include blinis with mushrooms, smoked
salmon or caviar. Seafood *moskova* is a mixture of poached turbot
and salmon wrapped in spinach and served with a tomato and
basil vinaigrette. Main dishes range from planked steak *Hussar*
(a sirloin steak cooked on oak planks, served with garlic butter,
duchesse potatoes and sweet pickle) to a chicken breast,
breadcrumbed and fried after being stuffed with vodka and garlic
butter. Fish dishes could be monkfish *nantaise* – the fish pan-fried
and marbled with roast vegetables and served on a mushroom
butter sauce. Lunchtime sees a simple 3-course set menu; in the
basement *Blushers* bistro offers simpler evening fare. *Seats 50.
L 12.30-2.15 D 7-11 (Bistro 6-11.30). Set L £14.50. Closed L Sat,
all Sun & Bank Holidays.* AMERICAN EXPRESS *Access, Diners, Visa.*

Rooms £99

Seven bedrooms are spacious and appointed to a high standard,
with mahogany furniture and fine fabrics in pale blues and reds;
thoughtfully designed bathrooms have powerful over-bath
showers and generous towels. There is an elegant, period drawing
room for residents' use, traditionally furnished with a marble
fireplace and antiques. Staff are friendly and helpful.

Dublin   Hibernian Hotel   70%   £135

Tel 01 668 7666   Fax 01 660 2655   **HR**

Eastmoreland Place Ballsbridge Dublin 4   Map 6 G1

A Victorian redbrick building, once a nurses' home, tucked away
in a quiet residential area. Handy for the centre of Dublin, though
not quite as central as the fondly-remembered *Royal Hibernian*
(now the site of a shopping mall on Dawson Street). The public
areas, including two reception lounges, can double up to receive
small conferences/receptions; they are cosy, with open fireplaces
and well furnished with decent pictures and plenty of comfortable
seating as well as pretty floral arrangements. The hotel's trademark
is a huge glass bowl of liquorice allsorts and jelly babies on the
reception counter, a theme carried through to the bedrooms,
where it becomes a novel alternative to fresh fruit. Bedrooms,
by no means lavish but quite adequately furnished, offer remote-
control TV, trouser press, hairdryer, bathrobe, slippers; quality
Crabtree & Evelyn toiletries (plus emergency shaving kit and
dental care) are to be found in the compact bathrooms, though the
towels are on the small side. Third-floor bedrooms can be subject
to strange sounds – extraneous noises from either the lift
mechanism or water storage tanks can invade a night's sleep.
Super-friendly staff provide just the right level of service, which
includes a nightly bed turn-down service; an added bonus is that
of real loose-leaf tea for a refreshing breakfast drink. Children
under 12 stay free in their parents' room. Under the same
ownership as *Grey Door* (see entry). Secure parking. ***Rooms 30.
Patio garden.*** AMERICAN EXPRESS®, *Access, Diners, Visa.*

Restaurant   £55

Relaxing dining in an elegantly appointed room decorated in deep
terracotta, dark green and cream or under stylish cream parasols
on the terrace – an oasis of tranquillity in the city. French chef
Frederic Souty produces limited but lively daily-changing à la
carte and table d'hote menus; the former may offer a choice
of about four first and main courses, typically artichokes and wild
mushrooms tossed in garlic or gratin of mussels and raspberry
vinegar followed by soup and sorbet at dinner. Well-balanced
main courses might include confit of goose with morel and
cognac essence or roast noisettes of venison with a redcurrant jus.
French cheeseboard. ***Seats 40. Parties 15. Private Room 25.
L 12.30-2.30 D 6.30-10 (Fri & Sat to 11). Set D £19.95.
Closed L Sat, Good Friday, Christmas.*** AMERICAN EXPRESS® *Access,
Diners, Visa.*

Dublin   Imperial   £40

Tel 01 677 2580   Fax 01 671 9127   **R**

13 Wicklow Street Dublin 2   Map 5 F3

Smartly decorated Chinese restaurant with pink and gold marble
effect walls and much polished brass in evidence, creating
a smartly upmarket interior. An ornamental pool has golden carp
(not on the menu). A few items are missing on Thursdays and
Fridays – notably the yam croquettes and egg custard tarts (it's
their chef's day off). However the char siu buns and slippery
cheung fun are always available and are unmissably delicious. The
regular menu features a familiar selection of mainly Cantonese

dishes. Lunchtime and especially on Sundays there's a good selection of dim sum available. Standards of service are excellent. *Seats 180. Parties 50. Private Room 70. Meals 12.30pm-11.45pm. Set L £6 Set D £30.* AMERICAN EXPRESS *Access, Visa.*

Dublin	Ivy Court		£55
Tel 01 492 0633 Fax 01 492 0634			**R**
88 Rathgar Road Dublin 6			Map 3 A2

Swiss chef Joseph Frei cooks an eclectic and imaginative range of dishes in his delightful restaurant almost due south of the city centre. Walls have large Breughel-inspired murals while the menu offers such varied starters as quick-fried ribbons of squid, surprisingly mildly flavoured with garlic and chilis, or traditional black pudding with onion jam and redcurrant jelly. Main dishes include enjoyable pasta dishes as well as sole fillets creole served with fried banana, rice and a mild curry sauce; half a roast boned and stuffed duckling with a raspberry coulis or veal emincé with Swiss-style rösti potatoes. There's an attractive courtyard, out front, used for fine-weather dining. No smoking in downstairs dining room. Children welcome before 8pm. *Seats 80. Parties 12. Private Room 26. D only 5.30-11.30. Closed 25 Dec, Good Friday. Access, Diners, Visa.*

Dublin	Jurys Christchurch Inn	55%	£56
Tel 01 475 0111 Fax 01 470 4888			**H**
Christchurch Place Dublin 8			Map 5 E3

Budget hotel within walking distance of the city centre run on the same lines as sister hotel *Jurys Galway Inn* (see entry, Galway). Spacious rooms, some with views over Christchurch cathedral and its environs, accommodate up to four people for a flat-rate room tariff. Basic requirements are well provided for, with good-sized beds, neat bathrooms with over-bath showers, decent towels and toiletries, direct-dial phone and colour TV. One floor of rooms is designated non-smoking. Children up to 14 stay free in parents' room. No room service. Multi-storey car park nearby. *Rooms 183. Closed 24-26 Dec.* AMERICAN EXPRESS *Access, Diners, Visa.*

Dublin	Jurys Hotel and Towers	76%	£162
Tel 01 660 5000 Fax 01 660 5540			**H**
Pembroke Road Ballsbridge Dublin 4			Map 6 H1

Close to Lansdowne Road rugby ground and the Royal Dublin Society showgrounds, this lively modern hotel has extensive banqueting/conference facilities (for 600/850 guests respectively), two restaurants, a coffee shop, two bars and a popular nightly cabaret (the last is a 2½hr dinner show, which runs from May to October and has played to over 2 million people in 30 years). For the quieter life, The Towers is a hotel within a hotel with its own security access, hospitality room, library and boardroom in addition to 100 Executive bedrooms (£224). Throughout the hotel, rooms are spacious, very comfortable and well-equipped with good, well-planned bathrooms and a well-selected range of toiletries. Free parking for 280 cars. The hotel has earned a special European commendation for its disabled guest facilities. Children under 14 stay free in their parents' room. No dogs.

See over

Rooms 400. *Garden, indoor & outdoor swimming pools, spa bath, beauty & hair salon, masseuse, coffee shop (6.30am-4.30am), gift shop, airline desks.* *Access, Diners, Visa.*

Dublin   Kapriol   £64

Tel 01 4751235	**R**
45 Lower Camden Street Dublin 2	Map 5 F1

A popular Italian restaurant near the famous *Bleeding Horse* pub and within walking distance of many of the main hotels. Egidia and Giuseppe Peruzzi provide a warm greeting, a very friendly atmosphere and a menu of traditional Italian dishes which has barely changed in 20 years. Pasta is all home-made, and main-course specialities include sea trout baked in foil, chicken involtini, veal escalopes stuffed with chopped fillet steak and casseroled, and venison in a rich wine sauce (Oct-Mar). *Seats 30. D only 7.30-12. Closed Sun, Bank Holidays, last 2 weeks Aug.* AMERICAN EXPRESS *Access, Diners, Visa.*

Dublin   Kavanagh's

No Telephone	**P**
Prospect Square Glasnevin Dublin 9	Map 3 A4

An entertaining, unselfconscious pub that's been in the Kavanagh family since 1833. It's known locally as the 'Gravediggers Arms' because of its location at the back of Dublin's largest cemetery. It's a small place, with a stone floor, rather rickety woodwork breaking up the bar, and fittings and decorations which are simple, original and authentic. Pints of Guinness are the main liquid sustenance. *No credit cards.*

Dublin   Kielys

Tel 01 283 0209	**P**
22/24 Donnybrook Road Donnybrook Dublin 4	Map 3 B2

Kielys is a Donnybrook landmark with its long, impressive frontage. Inside, it's rather sober – a masculine image that does nothing to prepare the first-time visitor for the contrast inside, where art nouveau decorations writhe around the mirrors, especially at the impressive mahogany bar area, creating a feminine feeling. This unexpectedly fin de siècle atmosphere is reinforced by the use of traditional mahogany tables on curvaceous wrought-iron bases, stained-glass windows at the back (although clear glass at the front lets in the midday sunshine and allows a refreshing view of the little green across the road) and a semi-snug, the size of a domestic sitting room, which creates the feeling of a club within the pub. Typical lunchtime meals from the blackboard might include pan-fried lamb chops or duck with orange which, like lighter food later in the day, is ordered from the bar and served to your table. Another surprise awaits the curious – at the back there is another pub, *Ciss Madden's,* a very traditional old Dublin spit'n'sawdust kind of a place; it has a separate entrance but can also be reached through Kielys bar. The locals clearly think all this quite normal. Furthermore, there's an Italian restaurant, *La Finezza,* upstairs (Tel 01 283 7166, open from 5pm, bar and restaurant menus). *Bar Food 12.30-2.30 (Sun to 2), 3-8 (Fri & Sat to 7, Sun 4-8). Children allowed in the bar to eat.* AMERICAN EXPRESS *Access, Visa.*

Dublin   Kilkenny Kitchen

Tel 01 677 7066	**R**
Massan Street Dublin 2	**Map 5 F3**

Situated on the first floor of a modern, purpose-built shop, over the famous Kilkenny Shop with its Irish crafts and woollens, this self-service restaurant is a favourite spot for local workers and shoppers alike, thanks to its wholesome, inexpensive all-day food. Although the menu is quite wide-ranging (it includes a good choice of hot and cold lunch dishes), it is for refreshing salads and, even more, home-made breads, cakes and biscuits (to eat or take home), that the Kilkenny Kitchen is best known. Always busy, so expect to share a table, the best of which overlook the playing fields of Trinity College. *Seats 170. Private Room 40. Open 9-5 Mon-Sat. Closed Sun, Bank Holidays, 25-27 Dec.* AMERICAN EXPRESS *Access, Diners, Visa.*

Dublin   Kitty O'Shea's Bar

Tel 01 660 8050 Fax 01 668 3979	**P**
23/25 Upper Grand Canal Street Dublin 4	**Map 6 G2**

One of Dublin's best known and best loved pubs, a favourite meeting place before or after a rugby match at Lansdowne Road and a popular spot for a snack or a meal. Typical dishes on the luncheon menu include chicken liver paté (£1.75), prawn cocktail, lasagne, roast pork and devils on horseback (£4.75, lamb's liver stuffed and wrapped in bacon). Similar evening choice, with apple pie a dessert always in demand. Live traditional entertainment each night. No small children after 5. Saturday and Sunday brunch (£3.65) a speciality. *Bar Food 12-2.30 & 6-10 plus snacks at other times.* AMERICAN EXPRESS *Access, Visa.*

Dublin   Langkawi Malaysian Restaurant

	£40
Tel 01 668 2760	**R**
46 Upper Baggot Street Dublin 4	**Map 6 G1**

Decorated throughout with a batik theme, Langkawi offers a selection of far eastern dishes with Malay, Chinese and Indian influences. Chef Alexander Hosey brings street crediblitiy to his mee goreng 'hawker' style (£8.95) – the type of popular food sold cheaply in outdoor markets in Malaysia and Singapore – as well as subtlety to some of his more exotic dishes. range from mild satay to 'devil's curries' for fireproof palates: ayam (chicken breast) and daging babi (pork). The inspiration for the latter comes from "a blending of locally produced spices and seasoning of Portuguese influence in the region of the city of Malacca". *Seats 50. L 12.30-2 D 6-12. Closed L Sat & Sun.* AMERICAN EXPRESS *Access, Diners, Visa.*

Dublin   Little Caesar's Pizza

Tel 01 671 8714	**R**
5 Chatham House Balfe Street Dublin 2	**Map 5 F2**

Well-placed opposite the entrance to the Westbury Hotel, this great meeting place occupies a buzzy little ground-floor and basement premises with considerable chic – mirrors and murals work miracles in minuscule spaces. The menu may hold no surprises but it is honest fare, cooked to order before your very eyes, and its popularity bears witness to a high level of consistency.

See over

Minestrone will be thick, rich and served with lots of crisp, finger-licking garlic bread, thin, crisp-crusted pizza ripiena comes laden with ham and bubbling mozzarella, parmesan and ricotta cheeses while creamy spaghetti carbonara is just dead-on classic and side salad is Sicilian style, heady with olive oil. House specials include charcoal-grilled chicken and steak; reasonably priced wines. *Seats 60. Meals Noon-12.30am. Closed 25 & 26 Dec and Good Friday.* AMERICAN EXPRESS *Access, Diners, Visa.*

Dublin **Lobster Pot**	**£70**
Tel 01 668 0025	**R**
9 Ballsbridge Terrace Dublin 4	**Map 6 H1**

A welcoming and comfortable first-floor dining room with a cosy ambience and very genial, long-serving staff. A tray of the day's fresh fish is brought to the table – Galway oysters, mussels, Dublin Bay prawns, plaice, monkfish, black soles and lobster are among the selection. Although specialising in fish they also have an extensive choice of meat dishes including wild duck and excellent steaks. Cooking is soundly classical and traditional and is none the worse for it. Results are extremely enjoyable as in scampi, deliciously moist under their crisp breadcrumb coating and accompanied by a well-made tartare sauce. Salmon and turbot are poached or grilled; plaice and sole grilled on the bone, the latter also available *bonne femme.* Individual preferences are well catered for too. The sweet trolley, too, can be admired for its simplicity; typically, a blackcurrant mousse is a perfect blend of light, smooth egg and cream mixture, the blackcurrant glaze providing the correct balance of sweet tartness. *Seats 40. Parties 7. L 12.30-2.30 D 6.30-10.30. Closed L Sat, all Sun, Bank Holidays & 1 week Christmas.* AMERICAN EXPRESS *Access, Diners, Visa.*

Dublin **Locks**	**£85**
Tel 01 543391 Fax 01 538352	**R**
1 Windsor Terrace Portobello Dublin 8	**Map 5 F1**

Generous portions of imaginative food are served in Claire Douglas's restaurant down by the canal in the residential Portobello district. Bouillabaisse, ravioli of spinach with prawns in a blue cheese sauce, roast duck with pineapple sauce and suckling pig with apples and horseradish show the style. Steaks are the popular simpler choice. *Seats 47. Private Room 30. L 12.30-2 D 7.15-11. Closed L Sat, all Sun, Bank Holidays, 1 week Christmas. Set L from £12.95 Set D from £18.95.* AMERICAN EXPRESS *Access, Diners, Visa.*

Dublin **Marine Hotel** **64%**	**£84**
Tel 01 832 2613 Fax 01 839 0442	**H**
Sutton Cross Dublin 13	**Map 4 C4**

Standing right at Sutton Cross at the isthmus of Howth some 10kms from the city centre, the Marine has a large car park at the front while at the rear lawns lead right down to the waters of Dublin Bay. Public rooms include a delightful sun lounge overlooking the lawns and an attractive bar with brass fittings and gilt-edged furniture. Both bedroom floors have just been completely refurbished. Decor is appealing with richly coloured floral fabrics and smart darkwood furniture. All are well equipped (hairdryer, trouser press, remote TV, hot drink facilities). Bathrooms, too, are neat, all with showers, some with shower/WC only. Friendly and helpful staff. *Rooms 26. Garden, indoor swimming pool, sauna, tennis. Closed 25 & 26 Dec.* AMERICAN EXPRESS *Access, Diners, Visa.*

Dublin	McCormack's Merrion Inn	
Tel 01 269 3816		**P**
188 Merrion Road Dublin 4		**Map 4 C2**

They take their lunch and its comfortable consumption seriously at this well-established pub. Despite its considerable age – and more than a passing nod to tradition where serious matters such as service, friendliness and efficiency are concerned – a modern hand has been at work with the decor, but the unexpectedly bright colours work surprisingly well to create a cheerful atmosphere, with various styles of seating and a generous distribution of tables and bar space to enjoy food and drink in comfort. Soup and sandwiches are available at the bar and there is a hot and cold buffet at the back. Choices on the blackboard change daily, but there is always a roast, typically roast beef with roast potatoes and a selection of five other vegetables (£5.95), a traditional casserole such as beef and Guinness (£4.95), chicken Kiev (£5.45) – a range of salads and good desserts (all £1.50) like pear and chocolate tart or sablés. Sunday brunch £4.95. Children welcome at lunchtimes and until 6pm on Sunday. No parking, use the hospital's car park over the road. *Bar Food 12-3 only. Garden. Closed 25 Dec, Good Friday.* AMERICAN EXPRESS *Access, Diners, Visa.*

Dublin	Merrion Hall	£45
Tel 01 668 1426 Fax 01 668 4280		**A**
56 Merrion Road Ballsbridge Dublin 4		**Map 3 B3**

The recent addition of the adjacent property has doubled the capacity of this charming, immaculately maintained, family-run guesthouse on the main ferry road just south of the city centre. The main sitting room is very comfortable, encapsulating perfectly the friendly and homely ambience generated by the Sheeran family. There's now an additional sitting room identical in size to the original one. It is used primarily in the busier summer months. Bedrooms are pretty and well equipped. Four are triple rooms while a further four have both a double and a single bed. The excellent breakfast selection features a self-service buffet including home-made yoghurt, poached fruits, fresh fruit salad and a cheeseboard. No dogs. *Rooms 15. Closed 2 weeks from 21 Dec. Access, Visa.*

Dublin	Le Mistral ★	£80
Tel 01 478 1662 Fax 01 478 2853		**R**
16 Harcourt Street Dublin 2		**Map 5 F2**

Opened approximately a year ago in an attractive, cosy, cellar-like basement just off St Stephen's Green, Ann and Philippe Misischi's restaurant offers a true taste of Provence. Along with their head chef Serge Mangin, who hails from Toulouse, they have created a menu whose dishes not only tempt but, even better, thrill the palate. Philippe scours the markets daily to compile short, imaginative menus of the freshest and best-quality produce

See over

available. Before choosing from the menu, however, take time
to note the tray laden with prime fish and shellfish that is brought
to your table. Scallops, for instance, plump and glistening, are
briefly sautéed and served with a delicate chive butter that
complements their seafresh sweetness. Other typical starters are
a feuilleté of snails with garlic coriander butter, a timbale of fresh
and smoked salmon with a grelette sauce or a papeton (mousse)
of aubergines with a red pepper cream. Main dishes are superb
examples of the chef's culinary skills with a rack of Wicklow
lamb, cooked just pink and extremely tender, arranged along
with the natural juices around paper-thin sliced courgettes with a
fresh plum tomato confit. A side-plate of vegetables complements
the flavours on the plate – a baked half tomato topped with
gremolata, a delicate puff-pastry bouchée filled with creamy
duxelles and a roundel of gratin dauphinois, each
mouthwateringly good in its own right. Other main dishes could
include fillet of beef with a Chambertin sauce and glazed shallots,
and medallions of roast monkfish with a navarin of fennel and
tapénade. Last, but by no means least, are exquisite desserts like
a warm pithiviers, freshly baked and filled with a moist almond
mixture and served with a honey-scented crème anglaise of the
lightest consistency. Tarte tatin and rich chocolate cake with
a sherry sauce are other equally desirable options. Splendid service
and worthy Newcomer of the Year. *Seats 60. Parties 16.
Private Room 40. L 12.30-2.30 D 7.30-11 (Fri & Sat to 11.30).
Set L £12.95 Set D £18.95. Closed L Sat, all Sun, Bank
Holidays & 5 days Christmas.* AMERICAN EXPRESS *Access, Diners, Visa.*

Dublin	Mont Clare Hotel	66%	£146
Tel 01 661 6799 Fax 01 661 5663			H
Merrion Square Dublin 2			Map 6 G3

Sister hotel to the *Davenport* (qv) across the road and with
a similar clubby feel although a little less grand and more intimate
in style. The bar is a fine example of a traditional Dublin pub
complete with bare-board floor, enough mahogany to stock a rain
forest and lots of atmosphere. The only other sitting area is in
a small alcove off the smart marble-floored lobby. Bedrooms are
generally not large but have warm decor in stylish dark reds and
blues with darkwood furniture, air-conditioning and telephones
at both desk and bedside with a third in the good marble
bathrooms. Guests have use of the private Riverview Racquets and
Fitness Club at members' rates. Free valet parking. *Rooms 74.*
AMERICAN EXPRESS *Access, Diners, Visa.*

Dublin	National Museum Café	
Tel 01 662 1269		R
Kildare Street Dublin 2		Map 5 F2

Before or after a stroll around the exhibits of Ireland's heritage, the
café offers a counter service selection of savoury and sweet foods.
The setting is a grand one – a fine mosaic floor, with a beautiful
crystal chandelier overhead. Tables are of pink granite and the
range of food encompasses light snacks such as scones, biscuits and
banana bread. At lunchtime, daily-changing hot specials might
include chicken and vegetable soup served with a scone and butter
(£1.65), followed by beef stroganoff and rice (£4.50) or seafood
smokies with vegetables (£5.25). Cold fare and vegetarian dishes

also, plus a good choice for the sweet-toothed. A no-smoking area
was planned as we went to press. *Seats 60. Meals 10-5 (Sun 2-5).
Closed Mon, 25 Dec & Good Friday.* AMERICAN EXPRESS *Access,
Diners, Visa.*

Dublin   No 31   £68

Tel 01 676 5011 Fax 01 676 2929 ·	A

31 Leeson Close off Leeson Street Lower Dublin 2   Map 5 F2

In a small mews close to the city centre (and most Dublin
restaurants and nightlife), the Bennetts have opened up their
stylish home to offer charming and exclusive bed and breakfast
accommodation. You press an intercom at heavy, varnished light
oak doors set in a high perimeter wall to gain admittance. The
instant you enter, the impression is of a well-designed modern
house. It was built by the architect Sam Stephenson and was his
home for 30 years. Here he entertained celebrities of politics and
culture. Cool white, with good use of light and space, typifies the
decor. The lounge, with a mirror mosaic-lined bar in the corner,
features an eye-catching square sunken seating area, black leather
upholstery contrasting with the white. Around the walls are
numerous works of art. Upstairs, there's a large refectory table
where Mary Bennett produces excellent breakfasts between 8.30
and 10. These include vegetarian options, freshly baked scones,
home-made preserves and freshly squeezed fruit juices. Bedrooms
are bright, simply appointed and homely, one with its own patio.
Remote-control TVs, radio-alarms and hot drink facilities are
standard. Secure, locked parking is also provided, as is a laundry
service. *Rooms 5. Patio. Closed 25 Dec. Access, Visa.*

Dublin   O'Dwyer's

Tel 01 676 3574 Fax 01 676 2281 AMERICAN EXPRESS	P

Mount Street Dublin 2   Map 6 G2

This large, bustling pub in pseudo-Victorian style always has
a good buzz – well supported at lunchtime and early evening
by a thriving local business and professional community. The
Night Train night club later attracts a younger crowd especially
appreciative of the famous O'Dwyer's pizzas. Professionally run,
cheerful, central. AMERICAN EXPRESS *Access, Diners, Visa.*

Dublin   Oisíns   £95

Tel & Fax 01 475 3433	R

31 Upper Camden Street Dublin 2   Map 5 F1

The menu at this modest little first-floor restaurant is rendered
in both Irish and English, listing a short but interesting selection
of dishes with a traditional provenance: Dublin coddle (a stew
of bacon, sausages, potatoes and onions), crubeens (pig's trotters),
Irish stew with dumplings, carrageen moss. Friendly service,
regular live music. The wine list has an Irish table wine from
Mallow. *Seats 40. D only 6.30-10.30. Closed Sun & Mon in winter,
Bank Holidays, 24 Dec-end 1st week Jan. Set D £35 plus 15%
service.* AMERICAN EXPRESS *Access, Diners, Visa.*

Dublin   Old Dublin Restaurant
£60

Tel 01 542028   Fax 01 541406

R

90/91 Francis Street Dublin 8

Map 5 F3

An evening à la carte has increased the menu options at this
welcoming, comfortable restaurant, whose various rooms feature
marble fireplaces and good pictures. Eamonn Walsh's cooking
takes its main influences from Russia and Scandinavia: gravlax,
borsch, blinis with salted salmon, prawns, herrings or mushroom
salad, chicken Kiev, Georgian lamb kebabs. House specialities such
as prawn-stuffed turbot Odessa, salmon coulibiac and planked
sirloin Hussar carry a supplement on the fixed-price menu. Good
cheeseboard; all desserts home-made. *Seats 65. Parties 30.
Private Room 16. L 12.30-2.30 D 6-11. Closed L Sat, all Sun, Bank
Holidays, 3 days Christmas. Set L from £12.50 Set D from £19.*
AMERICAN EXPRESS *Access, Diners, Visa.*

Dublin   The Old Stand

Tel 01 677 7220

P

37 Exchequer Street Dublin 2

Map 5 F3

A sister pub to *Davy Byrnes* (see entry), The Old Stand
is a comfortable, old-fashioned place, attractive in a strong, sensible
way with black paint outside and dark mahogany inside, good
detail behind the bar and a loyal local following. The food
is simple but good – they are famous for their steaks, from 6oz
(£5.30) right up to 14oz; there is a daily roast special (keenly
priced at only £3.95 and always the most popular dish, whatever
it is), plus grills, omelettes, salads and sandwiches. A well-run,
gimmick-free pub. *Bar Food 12.30-3 & 5-9.30. (Sat 12-8.30, Sun
12.30-2 & 4-8, Bank Holidays 12-6). Access, Visa.*

Dublin   101 Talbot
£32

Tel 01 8745011

R

101 Talbot Street Dublin 1

Map 5 F4

Upstairs in a busy shopping street, close to O'Connell Street and
the Abbey and Gate Theatres, this bright, airy restaurant has
a rather arty cheap and cheerful atmosphere which harmonises
well with the wholesome Mediterranean-influenced and spicy
Eastern food. Pasta, vegetarian, fish and meat dishes all appear
on the menu: tagliatelle with pesto, hazelnut rissoles, Chinese-style
stir-fried vegetables, poached salmon, baked haddock with
avocado/hollandaise sauce, pan-fried lamb's liver, medallions
of pork with an orange and rum sauce. Open all day for tea,
coffee, soup, pasta and snacks. *Seats 60. L 12-3 D 6.30-11 (light
meals 10am-11pm). Closed D Mon, all Sun, Bank Holidays.*
AMERICAN EXPRESS *Access, Visa.*

Dublin   Pasta Fresca
£30

Tel 01 679 2402

R

2-4 Chatham Street Dublin 2

Map 5 F2

Bustling Italian restaurant/wine bar/deli just off the smart Grafton
Street shopping area. Friendly waiting staff serve an all-day
selection of straightforward food – pasta, pizza, salads, burgers and
a few more substantial meat dishes. *Seats 85. Meals 8am-11.30pm.
Closed Sun, Bank Holidays. Set L £4.95 Set D £8.50. Access, Visa.*

Dublin   Patrick Guilbaud   ★↑   £100

| **Tel 01 676 4192   Fax 01 660 1546** | **R** |

46 James Place off Lower Baggot Street Dublin 2   Map 6 G2

Approaching this purpose-built restaurant, you might wonder if you are in the right street, so unprepossessing does the building look from a distance. But once inside there's no mistake – a comfortable reception lounge with several striped sofas, lots of greenery in both the plant-filled atrium and high-ceilinged dining room, decent art (mostly abstract paintings), and, above all, very smartly attired and professional staff. For well over a decade this has been *the* place in which to enjoy classical French cuisine with a light, modern approach. The seemingly ageless Patrick is on hand to offer advice on the menus as well as engaging customers in conversation, whether on golf – one of his passions – or France's chances in the Five Nations rugby championship, especially against Ireland at Lansdowne Road! For an eponymous restaurant, somewhat unusually Patrick is not the chef/patron – the cooking is left to a team of French chefs, led by Guillaume Le Brun (visible in a glass-fronted kitchen); indeed, most of the staff are French. The ingredients, naturally, are mostly Irish, notably as in seafood dishes, such as pan-fried king scallops served with seasonal salad and bacon, Dublin Bay prawns in crisp pastry cases served with mango and capers, or steamed sea bass on a saffron purée with red pepper oil. Also highly recommended as starters are the home-made lemon pasta with salmon and hot lobster tourte with chive sauce, while game dishes in season (roast wild venison with sauce poivrade and morello cherries or roast breast of pheasant with parcels of mushrooms) are eagerly awaited by regulars. The table d'hote lunch and dinner menus (both exclusive of a service charge of 15%, as is the à la carte) are particularly good value, and though (at time of writing) there's no choice at dinner (four courses and coffee), lunch offers four selections among both starters and main courses. And for a table whose occupants cannot make up their minds, why not try the *menu surprise* (£45 per person)? Desserts (a tart lemon mousse, berry cheesecake or poached pear in red wine) and French cheeses are quite splendid, as is the variety of breads offered, the amuse-gueule, the coffee and petits fours. Service is impeccable. As you would expect, the wine list is predominantly French, but not exclusively so, and – for a restaurant of this class – prices are reasonable; note the old classics in the 'Specialist Cellar'. **Seats 50. Parties 20.**
Private Room 30. L 12.30-2 D 7.30-10.15. Closed Sun & Mon, Bank Holidays. Set L £15.50 Set D £25 & £45. AMERICAN EXPRESS *Access, Diners, Visa.*

Dublin   The Pembroke

| **Tel 01 676 2980   Fax 01 676 6579** | **P** |

31 Lower Pembroke Street Dublin 2   Map 6 G2

A warm, welcoming city-centre pub with a cosy, real coal fire and exceptionally fine etched mirrors behind the bar, highlighting the mainly 1920s' decor. Dark mahogany woodwork and small, snug-like seating areas confirm this impression of intimacy and it comes as a pleasant surprise to find that you do not have to leave the premises to find good bar food at a fair price, and even outside normal meal times they will run up a tasty snack. The cellar

See over

Buffet Bar serves salads and a hot food buffet at lunchtimes; fancier evening fare. *Bar Food 12.30-8 (Sat to 3). Pub closed Sun.* AMERICAN EXPRESS *Access, Diners, Visa.*

Dublin   Periwinkle Seafood Bar

| Tel 01 679 4203 | **R** |

Unit 18 Powerscourt Townhouse Centre South William Street Dublin 2   Map 5 F3

Established over 12 years in a ground-floor corner of a colourful, bustling 'artsy crafty' shopping mall, Periwinkle has the simplest of decors – split-level quarry-tiled floors, varnished pine tables and counters with low or high stools depending on where you choose to sit. Blackboard menus proclaim the day's offerings of which the most popular item is seafood chowder, thick and warming, available in a mug-size portion (£1.15) or bowl-size (£1.75), both with freshly baked Irish brown bread. Excellent salad garnishes accompany most dishes too. Each day as well as the perennial seafood salads and platters there's a changing fish dish of the day, for example cod niçoise (£3.95), a hot fish special such as a deliciously cheesy soufflé-topped plaice (£5.95) or crab claws in garlic butter (£6.95). Hot food becomes available at 11.30am and continues until closing time. *Seats 55. Meals 10.30-5. Closed Sun & Bank Holidays. No credit cards.*

Dublin   Pizzeria Italia   £25

| Tel 01 677 8528 | **R** |

23 Temple Bar Dublin 2   Map 5 F3

A tiny one-room pizza-bar and restaurant run since 1986 by the Alambi family. Efficient, humorous staff and delicious, herby aromas set the tone: traditional minestrone is convincingly home-made and pizzas and classic pasta dishes feature alongside steaks and the likes of *pollo cacciatore* (chicken cooked in red wine with mushrooms, onion, tomato and oregano) and crème caramel. *Seats 20. Meals 12-11. Closed Sun & Mon, Bank Holidays, 2 weeks June, 2 weeks from 24 Dec. No credit cards.*

Dublin   Il Primo   £45

| Tel 01 4783373 | **R** |

16 Montague Street Dublin 2   Map 5 F2

Simply appointed little Italian restaurant opposite the Children's Hospital (Harcourt Street). Dishes are colourful and big on flavour, from hot garlic crostini with sun-dried tomatoes and basil, Roman salad with cold meats and duck liver terrine with roasted peppers to perky salads, pizzas and pasta (ravioli with meat or fish of the day, tagliatelle with spicy sausage, pappardelle with roasted chicken pieces or mixed vegetables in walnut sauce). Any wine under £30 is available by the glass. *Seats 44. Parties 30. L 12-3 D 6-11 (Fri, Sat to 11.30). Closed Sun, Bank Holidays.* AMERICAN EXPRESS *Access, Diners, Visa.*

Dublin   Raglan Lodge   £77

| Tel 01 660 6697   Fax 01 660 6781 | **A** |

10 Raglan Road Ballsbridge Dublin 4   Map 6 H1

Built in 1861 and epitomising the grand Victorian town-house style, the lodge stands in a select tree-lined avenue off one of the main routes to the city centre. Helen Moran has been here just over two years and has created a charming, hospitable environment. Thirteen white granite steps lead up to the main door, painted a distinctive and cheering sunshine yellow. There's a lounge on the lower ground floor, though it is little used, while on the ground floor there's a fine breakfast room wherein to enjoy the likes of slices of smoked salmon bordered by soft scrambled eggs. The seven high-ceilinged bedrooms are spotlessly maintained and feature creature comforts like sweet-smelling warm bedding, thick towels, good soaps and crystal-clear reception of all the major television channels. No dogs. **Rooms** 7. *Garden. Closed 1 week Christmas.* AMERICAN EXPRESS *Access, Diners, Visa.*

Set menu prices may not always include service or wine.
Our quoted price for two does.

Dublin	Rajdoot	£48
Tel 01 679 4274		**R**
26 Clarendon Street Westbury Centre Dublin 2		Map 5 F3

Part of a small UK chain (although the latest branch is on the Costa del Sol) of reliable restaurants specialising in tandoori and North Indian Moghlai cooking. The latter tends to produce mild and subtly spiced dishes like chicken pasanda – the breast stuffed with flaked almonds, mint and cherries with a sauce of cashew nuts and almonds. Luxurious, somewhat exotic decor. **Seats** 92. *L 12-2.30 D 6.30-11.30. Set L from £6.95 Set D from £14.50. Check closures.* AMERICAN EXPRESS *Access, Diners, Visa.*

Dublin	Roly's Bistro	£50
Tel 01 668 2611 Fax 01 660 8535		**R**
7 Ballsbridge Terrace Ballsbridge Dublin 4		Map 6 H1

Roly Saul and his chef Colin O'Daly run a lively and popular French-style bistro offering a winning combination of good food and kind prices. Inspiration for the menu comes from near and far: Clonakilty black pudding with sweet potatoes and apple, terrine of wild mushrooms with tarragon and Marsala, stir-fry vegetables and noodles, Cajun chicken breast, baked fillet of salmon trout with lime and nut butter sauce, grilled fillet of beef Burgundy. The wine list includes a dozen house selections at under £10 a bottle. An increased choice of bread will be available in the restaurant with the opening of their bakery next door. **Seats** 120. *Parties 12. Private Room 65. L 12-3 D 6-10 (Sun to 9). Closed Good Friday, 25 & 26 Dec. Set L £9.50.* AMERICAN EXPRESS *Access, Visa.*

Dublin	Royal Dublin Hotel	63%	£99
Tel 01 873 3666 Fax 01 873 3120			**H**
40 Upper O'Connell Street Dublin 1			Map 5 F4

A modern hotel on Dublin's most famous street, with practical overnight accommodation, an all-day brasserie and a business centre with full facilities. Children under 12 stay free in parents' room. Secure parking for 35 cars in a basement garage. **Rooms** 117. *Brasserie (7am-midnight).* AMERICAN EXPRESS *Access, Diners, Visa.*

Dublin Ryans of Parkgate Street

Tel 01 677 6097	**P**
28 Parkgate Street Dublin 8	**Map 3 A4**

One of Dublin's finest Victorian pubs, Ryans of Parkgate Street has been in the same family for three generations – the present building is a reconstruction dating from 1896 and retains many original features, including two snugs at the back, a magnificent carved oak and mahogany central bar (its centrepiece a double-faced mechanical clock), brass gas lamps and an outstanding collection of antique mirrors. Bar fare runs from simple light snacks to traditional hot dishes, with slightly more variety in the evening. There are also different menus at lunchtime and in the evening (lunch £13, dinner à la carte). *Bar Food 12.30-2.30 (Sat & Sun L soup and sandwiches only), 5.30-7.30.* AMERICAN EXPRESS *Access, Visa.*

Dublin Sachs Hotel 62% £98

Tel 01 668 0995 Fax 01 668 6147	**H**
19-29 Morehampton Road Donnybrook Dublin 4	**Map 3 B2**

The night club at this small hotel in a Georgian terrace is a popular attraction, and a different kind of exercise is available (free to residents) at a leisure centre a short drive away. Bedrooms are individually appointed in period style, and double-glazing keeps things peaceful at the front. Conference/function facilities. *Rooms 20. Closed 25 Dec.* AMERICAN EXPRESS *Access, Diners, Visa.*

Dublin Señor Sassi's £58

Tel 01 668 4544	**R**
146 Upper Leeson Street Dublin 4	**Map 6 G1**

Busy, bustling restaurant with densely packed marble-topped tables and currently fashionable Mediterranean/Californian style dishes; salad of warm squid with ginger and soy, loin of lamb with aubergine and balsamic vinegar jus, fillet steak with caramelised onions and mash, paillard of salmon with wilted greens and herb salsa, bruschetta of chargrilled vegetables. The daytime menu is in brasserie style with dishes ranging from £1.90 (for country broth with hot bruschetta) to £7.50 (steak with red wine jus and braised cabbage). *Seats 75. Private Room 30. Meals Noon-11.30 (Fri & Sat till midnight, Sun 5.30-10.30). Set L £9.50. Closed L Sun, 25 & 26 Dec, 1 Jan.* AMERICAN EXPRESS *Access, Diners, Visa.*

Dublin Shalimar £50

Tel 01 671 0738 Fax 01 677 3478	**R**
17 South Great George's Street	**Map 5 F3**

Smart, comfortable restaurant opposite the Central Hotel serving standard Indian fare in friendly fashion. *Seats 110. L 12-2.30 (Sun to 3) D 6-12 (Fri & Sat to 12.30, Sun 5-11). Closed L Sat, 25 & 26 Dec, Muslim Holidays. Set L £6.95.* AMERICAN EXPRESS *Access, Diners, Visa.*

Dublin   Shelbourne Hotel   74%   £223

Tel 01 676 6471   Fax 01 661 6006   **H**

St Stephen's Green Dublin 2   **Map 5 F2**

Situated on St Stephen's Green, Europe's largest garden square, the
Shelbourne has been at the centre of Dublin life since opening its
doors early in the 19th century. The Irish Constitution was
drafted in what is now one of the many function rooms. The hotel
has retained much of its original grandeur, with a magnificent
faux-marbre entrance hall and a sumptuous lounge where
morning coffee and afternoon tea are taken. The famous
Horseshoe Bar and the newer Shelbourne Bar are among the
favourite gathering places for Dubliners, especially on a Friday
night, and many a scandal has originated from their walls.
Spacious, elegantly furnished superior and de-luxe rooms and
suites have traditional polished wood furniture and impressive
drapes, while standard rooms in a newer wing are smaller. All
rooms are well appointed, with bathrobes, mini-bars and three
telephones as standard. Valet parking. 12 function rooms can cater
for up to 500 for a reception. Children up to 16 stay free
in parents' room. As we went to press, a major refurbishement
programme was nearing completion. Forte Grand. *Rooms 164.*
Beauty salon, hairdressing, news kiosk. AMERICAN EXPRESS® *Access,*
Diners, Visa.

Dublin   The Stag's Head

Tel 01 679 3701   **P**

1 Dame Court Dublin 2   **Map 5 F3**

Although small by comparison with the vast drinking emporiums
being built today, The Stag's Head remains one of Dublin's most
impressive old pubs – a lofty, spacious bar and one of the few
with its original late-Victorian decor more or less untouched. Sit
at the long granite bar and regret the absence of hand pumps
which used to grace it, but enjoy the acres of original mahogany
and admire its hand-worked detail. Some of it frames the
marvellous bevelled mirrors that soar up to finish in curvaceous
arches over the panelling and original fittings behind the bar.
Open usual pub hours but only 7-11pm on Sunday and Bank
Holidays. *No credit cards.*

Dublin   La Stampa   £55

Tel 01 6778611   Fax 01 6773336   **R**

35 Dawson Street Dublin 2   **Map 5 F2**

Noisy (but unobtrusively), bustling, lively and frenetic – just how
a restaurant of this *genre* should be. Sited in a spacious high-
ceilinged room with large mirrors and plain wood floor, there's
a Renaissance feel about the place, which also has a fully licensed
bar where drinks can be enjoyed while waiting for a table. What's
more, the staff smile and besides being genuinely cheerful are
efficient as well; combine this with decent food at fair prices, and
you have a winning and successful formula, as here. Chef Paul
Flynn spent several years working in top London restaurants, and
though the dishes on the menu are altogether more rustic and
substantial than served in those establishments, his background and
pedigree stand him in good stead. Starters include freshly made

See over

pasta strips with a chunky tomato sauce, chopped Toulouse sausage
and coriander (also available as a main course), an authentic Caesar
salad, or a spicy terrine of duck with onion compote, while main
courses might feature roast monkfish with basil purée, tomato and
pepper olive oil, boiled bacon with traditional Irish colcannon
(curly kale and mashed potato) and a caper and parsley sauce,
or herb-crusted roast rack of lamb served with Provençal tomatoes
and potato dauphinois in a light garlic sauce. Desserts are no less
abundant in the true sense of the world – try the sticky toffee
pudding or chocolate truffle cake, pronounced "wicked" by two
adults on a recent visit. Fine coffee and very drinkable house wines
on an inexpensive wine list. *Seats 160. Parties 12. Private Room 40.
L 12-2.30 D 6.30-11.30. Closed Sun, Good Friday, 2 days Christmas.
Set L £12.50 D £16.50.* AMERICAN EXPRESS *Access, Diners, Visa.*

Dublin   The Station House

| Tel 01 313772 | **P** |

3-5 Station Road Raheny Dublin 5   **Map 4 C4**

Outside may be deceptively like any other fairly traditional
Dublin pub, but inside, the Station House has surprising Spanish-
style decor – heavy, rustic furniture upholstered in warm, 'aged'
tapestry and carpet-bagging fabrics sit comfortably around tile-
topped tables on hard wooden floors enlivened by the occasional
trompe l'oeil 'rug' strategically placed to trip the unwary.
Traditional bar food from the carvery is freshly cooked and
wholesome: roast rib of beef £4.95, hot meat rolls £2.70, seafood
dieppoise £4.75, bacon and cabbage £4.75. A la carte menu (with
a few children's favourites) during the afternoons and evenings.
Staff are friendly and helpful and there's a walled garden at the
back. Barbecues most weekends (weather permitting). *Bar Food &
Meals carvery 12-2.30 (Sun 12.30-2), à la carte 2.30-9 (Sun 4-8).
Children allowed to eat in the lounge until 7.30, children's menu.
Garden, outdoor eating. Access, Visa.*

> We welcome bona fide complaints and recommendations on
> the tear-out pages at the back of the Guide for readers'
> comments. They are followed up by our professional team.

Dublin   Stauntons on the Green   £62

| Tel 01 478 2133   Fax 01 478 2300 | **A** |

83 St Stephen's Green South Dublin 2   **Map 5 F2**

The front bedrooms of Stauntons on the Green overlook the
beautiful St Stephen's Green while the rear-facing rooms have
almost equally attractive views over the hotel's private gardens
and Victorian Iveagh Gardens beyond. Recently acquired, this
mid-terrace Georgian property comprises three houses of fine
classical proportions. It is gradually undergoing a major
programme of upgrading which will lift it from its current
guesthouse status. Completion is due sometime in 1995. Currently
there's a traditional rear-facing sitting room while upstairs,
bedrooms are fitted with simple units and have tea/coffee facilities
and remote-control TVs. Bathrooms, all with showers, have good
toiletries. No dogs. *Rooms 30. Garden. Closed 25 & 26 Dec.*
AMERICAN EXPRESS *Access, Diners, Visa.*

Dublin   Stephen's Hall Hotel   65%   £143

Tel 01 661 0585   Fax 01 661 0606   **HR**

14/17 Lower Leeson Street Dublin 2   **Map 5 F2**

Situated in a thriving business and tourist area just off St Stephen's
Green and run on the same lines as *Morrison's Island* in Cork (see
entry), this is Dublin's first all-suites hotel. Each suite has its own
lobby and kitchenette in addition to a dining area and sitting
room. Suite types range from studios (double bed, kitchen,
bathroom) to three townhouses each with two single and a double
bed, two bathrooms, sitting room, kitchen, dining room, balcony
and private entrance to the street. All are well furnished in a
pleasingly understated modern Irish style, with thoughtfully
planned bathrooms and well-designed furniture. In addition to full
room service and 24-hour porter service, a special shopping service
is available for guests who wish to cook in their suite; all meals,
including breakfast, can also be taken in the restaurant. *Rooms 37.
Free secure parking. Closed 1 week Christmas, but ring to confirm.*
 Access, Diners, Visa.

The Terrace Bistro   £45

The semi-basement restaurant is bright and warmly decorated,
with formal white-clothed tables. Well-balanced menus show
a variety of influences and a fine dash of originality: tossed salad
of salami with roast peppers, olives and a marjoram dressing;
steamed mussels with lemon and basil sauce; coulibiac of cod with
a fresh herb sauce; chicken satay with pecan rice; tournedos
of beef with caramelised shallots and a bourbon sauce. *Seats 48.
Parties 12. Private Room 40. L 12.15-2.30 D 6.15-9.30.
Closed L Sat, all Sun. Set L from £9.50 Set D £14.50.*

Dublin   Ta Se Mohogani Gaspipes   £45

Tel 01 679 8138   **R**

17 Manor Street Stoneybatter Dublin 7   **Map 3 A4**

A nonsense name for a stylish little American restaurant featuring
live jazz on Friday and Saturday. Lunchtime brings pizzas, pasta,
omelettes, burgers and New York strip sirloin steak, while in the
evening there's pasta plus specialities like chicken cutlet milanese
or oriental-style sautéed pork medallions. Also daily fish,
international and dessert specials ("your waitperson will inform
you"). Vegetarian dishes, too. *Seats 40. Parties 16. L 12-3 D 7-11
(Fri & Sat to 2.30 am). Closed Sun & Mon, 2 weeks end July, Bank
Holidays. Access, Diners, Visa.*

Dublin   Toners Pub

Tel 01 676 3090   **P**

139 Lower Baggot Street Dublin 2   **Map 5 F2**

Situated only a few hundred yards from the *Shelbourne Hotel* and
St Stephen's Green, this rare survivor of a style of pub which has
all but disappeared in Dublin is now fiercely resistant to change.
Owners, regulars and visitors alike blossom in its dimly-lit
interior, where pints are drunk in the hard-benched little snug,
or on high wooden stools at the bar with its rackety old combed-
wood divisions. Journalists from offices across the road discuss the

See over

issues of the day, actors on location in the city come to share the buzz and everyone enjoys the genuine charm of Toners. Totally Irish, great crack... "you couldn't change this place". *No credit cards.*

Dublin   Tosca

Tel 01 679 6744 Fax 01 677 4804	**R**
20 Suffolk Street Dublin 2	Map 5 F3

The rear of Tosca's bar, most unusually, features a significant section of the blackened hull of a ship. Wrought out of papier maché instead of steel, it looks authentic, however, complete with rivets and portholes. In its centre is a gleaming brass espresso machine. All this strikes you immediately you enter and it sets the tone for what is a stylishly modern restaurant serving suitably fashionable new-wave Italian food plus pizzas. Tomato crostini (£2.95), delicious crunchy country bread topped with fresh tomato, a few anchovies, garlic and just-melted mozzarella; black pudding salad (£3.25); pesto chicken (£8.50) – breast of chicken with sun-dried tomato and pesto – are all typical of the imaginative and enjoyable cooking on offer here. *Seats 70. Parties 30. Private Room 15. Meals 11.30am-midnight (to 1am Thur-Sat). Closed 25 & 26 Dec.* AMERICAN EXPRESS *Access, Diners, Visa.*

Dublin   The Westbury   79%   £180

Tel 01 679 1122 Fax 01 679 7078	**H R**
Off Grafton Street Dublin 2	Map 5 F3

Part of the Doyle Hotel Group since 1985, the Westbury is located within walking distance of many Dublin landmarks. The major shops are also close at hand, and the hotel has its own shopping mall. Among the day rooms are the Terrace Bar and the Sandbank Seafood Bar. Pinks and blues are key colours in the bedrooms, which offer a high standard of comfort and accessories; they range from modernised singles to luxury penthouse suites. Business gatherings and banquets (to a maximum of 180) are accommodated in elegantly furnished boardrooms and function suites. Here, as elsewhere, the Westbury has the atmosphere of a top-class hotel with legions of staff providing a good level of service. *Rooms 203. Gymnasium, beauty & hair salon, news kiosk, coffee shop (10am-10pm, Sun to 3pm).* AMERICAN EXPRESS *Access, Diners, Visa.*

Russell Room   £85

The traditional French menu holds few surprises, though the cooking is sound and both service and surroundings suitably stylish. Seafood makes a strong showing, and flambéed crepes Suzette is a completely apposite dessert for the setting. A three-course table d'hote lunch (four courses at dinner) offers a choice of five or so dishes at each course. *Seats 100. Parties 40. L 12.30-2.30 D 6.30-10.30 (Sun to 9.30). Set L £14.50 Set D £18.50.*

Dublin   The Yacht

Tel 01 336364 Fax 01 333009	**P**
73 Clontarf Road Dublin 3	Map 4 C4

This old-established local is known variously as 'The Yacht' and 'Tobin's,' and is like a great white steamer looking over to the port. Within, decorative buff 'sails' soften the height of the light, airy bar and a mixed collection of maritime bric-a-brac – some of it genuinely old and including artefacts from the much-loved old back bar 'the Tiller Room' – combine old and new to create a lively atmosphere which goes far beyond the usual 'theme decor'. Bar food at this friendly, well-run pub is unpretentious, wholesome, good value – and predictably popular, and luckily there is plenty of counter and table space for a fair crowd to eat in comfort. Everything is home-made, roast beef from the carvery is good value (£4.95) and comes with two styles of potato and four other fresh vegetables; Pavlova (£1.30) is the favourite dessert. The wide pavement is popular for alfresco relaxation in summer, despite the traffic. **Food** *carvery 12.30-3. Bar Food 3-8.30 (Sun 12.30-2 only). Children allowed in bar to eat, children's menu. Patio, outdoor eating. Access, Visa.*

Dublin   Yellow House

Tel 01 932994	**P**
Willbrook Road Rathfarnham Dublin 14	**Map 3 A1**

The Yellow House is named after the unusual shade of the bricks with which it was built, and is the landmark pub of Rathfarnham. It makes a perfect rendezvous point, with no chance of confusion. Tall and rather forbidding from the outside, the warmth of the interior comes as a pleasant surprise and repays closer examination of pictures and old decorative items of local historical interest. Daily lunchtime carvery in the lounge bar; basket snacks and straightforward dishes like steak sandwich (£4.95), fresh pasta with smoked salmon and cream (£3.95) in the evening. Evening à la carte (and Sunday lunch) in the restaurant (no children after 7.30pm). **Bar Food** *Mon-Fri 5-8 (Sat 12-8). Carvery Mon-Fri 12.30-2.30. Children allowed in bar to eat, children's menu.* AMERICAN EXPRESS *Access, Diners, Visa.*

Dublin   Zen   ↑

Tel 01 497 9428	**£45**
	R
89 Upper Rathmines Road Dublin 6	**Map 3 B2**

Due south of the city centre, Zen has a most unusual setting in what was once a Church of England meeting hall. The dimly-lit interior is vast, with a lofty hammer-beam roof. This is the home of some of the capital's very best Chinese food and fully deserves our Oriental Restaurant of the Year Award. Many of the specialities are from the Szechuan region, and dishes that are particularly hot and spicy are denoted by an asterisk on the menu. Dumplings, for instance, filled with a delicious minced pork mixture, are served in a Szechuan sauce strongly flavoured with ginger, garlic and chili – a tastebud-enlivening sensation that begins the meal with more than just a tingle. Flavours are keen and often wonderfully intense and are an indication of the precision and care taken at each stage of preparation. Hot and sour soup, the classic Szechuan soup, is here also available in an extremely good vegetarian version, thick with finely cut vegetables and egg threads and topped with lightly toasted, crunchy whole yellow beans. Prawns are carefully deveined before being lightly cooked to retain their tender succulence; they appear fried with cashew nuts or crispy with scallions. Smoked duckling, another Szechuan speciality, is one of the few dishes from this

See over

region that isn't highly seasoned as is sweet and sour pork
Szechuan style. Special crispy duck (Beijing-style) dinner for two
requires 2 days notice. Service is charming. *Seats 85. Parties 12.
Private Room 14. L 12.30-2.15 D 6-11.30. Closed L Mon-Wed
& Sat, 25 & 26 Dec, Good Friday. Set D from £16.50.*
AMERICAN EXPRESS *Access, Diners, Visa.*

Dublin   Places of Interest

Tourist Information   Tel 01 284 4768
Dublin Airport   Tel 01 844 5387
Bank of Ireland   College Green Tel 01 661 5933
Trinity College (Book of Kells) and Dublin Experience   University of
   Dublin Tel 01 677 2941
The Curragh   Co Kildare Tel 01 289288
Dublin Zoo   Phoenix Park Tel 01 677 1425
Fairyhouse Racecourse   Ratoath Tel 01 825 6777
Irish Whiskey Corner   Bow Street Distillery Tel 01 872 5566
Leopards Town   Fox Rock Tel 01 893607
Gaelic Athletic Association (GAA)   Tel 046 23638
Croke Park Football Ground   Hurling and Gaelic Football
   Tel 01 836 3222
Irish Rugby Union   Tel 01 668 4601
Lansdowne Road Rugby Ground   Baub Bridge Tel 01 668 4601
   Theatres and Concert Halls
Abbey and Peacock Theatres   Lower Abbey Street Tel 01 878 7222
Andrew's Lane Theatre   Exchequer Street Tel 01 679 5720
Gaiety Theatre   South King Street Tel 01 677 1717
Gate Theatre   Cavendish Row Tel 01 874 4045
Olympia Theatre   Dame Street Tel 01 677 7744
Tivoli Theatre   Francis Street Tel 01 454 4472
National Concert Hall   Earlsfott Terrace Tel 01 671 1888
Point Depot (Exhibitions and Concerts)   North Wall Quay
   Tel 01 836 6000
Irish Film Centre   Eustace Street Tel 01 679 3477
   Museums and Art Galleries
Dublinia, Christchurch   Tel 01 475 8137
Chester Beatty Library and Gallery of Oriental Art   Shrewsbury Road
   Tel 01 269 2386
Civic Museum   South William Street Tel 01 679 4260
Dublin Writer's Museum   Parnell Square North Tel 01 872 2077
Fry Model Railway Museum   Malahide Castle Tel 01 845 2758
Irish Museum of Modern Art/Royal Hospital   Kilmainham
   Tel 01 671 8666
Guinness Brewery   James's Gate Tel 01 453 6700 *ext 5155*
Hugh Lane Municipal Gallery   Parnell Square Tel 01 874 1903
National Gallery of Ireland   Merrion Square West Tel 01 661 5133
National Museum of Ireland   Kildare Street Tel 01 661 8811
National Wax Museum   Granby Row, Parnell Square Tel 01 872 6340
Natural History Museum   Merrion Street Tel 01 661 8811
   Historic Houses, Castles and Gardens
Ashtown Castle   Phoenix Park Tel 01 661 3111
Drimnach Castle   Longmile Road Tel 01 450 2530 *4 miles*
Dublin Castle   Dame Street Tel 01 677 7129
Joyce Tower   Sandycove Tel 01 280 9265
Kilmainham Gaol   Kilmainham Tel 01 453 5984
Malahide Castle   Malahide Tel 01 845 2655
Marsh's Library   St Patrick Close Tel 01 454 3511
National Botanic Gardens   Glasnevin Tel 01 837 7596
Newbridge House   Donabate Tel 045 31301
Newman House   St Stephen's Green Tel 01 475 7255
Number Twenty Nine   Lower Fitzwilliam Street Tel 01 702 6165

Powerscourt Townhouse   South William Street Tel 01 679 4144
Royal Hospital   Kilmainham Tel 01 671 8666
  Cathedrals & Churches
Christ Church Cathedral   Christ Church Place Tel 01 677 8099
St Patrick's Cathedral   Patrick's Close Tel 01 475 4817
Whitefriar Street Carmelite Church   Aungier Street Tel 01 475 8821
Pro Cathedral   Marlborough Street Tel 01 287 4292

Dublin Airport	**Forte Crest**	**57%**	**£129**
Tel 01 844 4211 Fax 01 842 5874			**H**
Collinstown Dublin Airport Co Dublin			**Map 3 B4**

Conference facilities for 150, 8 meeting rooms, ample car parking
and 24hr room service in a modern hotel within the airport
complex. Some non-smoking rooms, some of family size (children
up to 16 stay free in parents' room). *Rooms 192. Closed 25 Dec.*
Access, Diners, Visa.

Dun Laoghaire	**Chestnut Lodge**	**£45**
Tel 01 280 7860 Fax 01 280 1466		**A**
2 Vesey Place Monkstown Dun Laoghaire		**Map 4 D1**

Built in 1844, the building is a very fine example of classical
Regency architecture. From its position almost at the end of a row
of similar houses on a hillside, there are glimpses of the sea visible
through the chestnut trees which were planted in a small park
across the road at the front. This is very much a family home with
breakfast taken communally at a beautiful highly polished
mahogany dining table in the drawing room. Here, after a very
comfortable night's sleep in one of the spacious, warm and well-
appointed bedrooms, you can enjoy freshly squeezed orange juice,
a choice of fresh fruit salad, yoghurts, stewed fruits and cereals
before tucking into a delicious traditional Irish cooked breakfast
finished off by oven-warmed croissants and home-made preserves.
Very usefully located close to the Dun Laoghaire/Holyhead ferry
terminal. No dogs. *Rooms 4. Access, Visa.*

Dun Laoghaire	**Restaurant na Mara**	**£75**
Tel 01 280 0509 Fax 01 284 4649		**R**
1 Harbour Road Dun Laoghaire Co Dublin		**Map 4 D1**

Railway buffs will be fascinated by this elegant harbourside
restaurant, as it is the old Kingstown terminal building and   *See over*

is owned by Irish Rail Catering Services. In 1970 a preservation order was issued by the local authority. The interior has classical decor throughout in soft soothing tones. French-influenced menus are a mixture of traditional and modern styles, with a strong emphasis on the sea in dishes like lobster bisque, seafood sausage, oysters raw or served warm with smoked salmon and paloise sauce, grilled black sole, brill Grand Duc and Dublin Bay prawns in garlic butter, mornay or curried. Flambéed specialities feature and there is a short choice of meat and vegetarian dishes. Well-chosen wines (mostly French) at fair prices, with some helpful notes; several good champagnes. *Seats 80. Private Room 36.* *L 12.30-2.30 D 7-10.30. Closed Sun, 1 week Christmas. Set L from £11 Set D £23.* AMERICAN EXPRESS *Access, Diners, Visa.*

Dun Laoghaire   Royal Marine Hotel   64%   £85

Tel 01 280 1911   Fax 01 280 1089   **H**

Marine Road Dun Laoghaire Co Dublin   Map 4 D1

Imposing Victorian hotel set in four acres of grounds overlooking the ferry port yet just moments from the main street of town. Grand day rooms feature faux-marble columns, high ceilings and elaborate coving. Upstairs, it's a hotel of two halves with the best rooms, off broad chandelier-lit corridors in the original building, having nice lightwood furniture and smart bathrooms; eight of the rooms here are particularly large, with four-poster beds, antique furniture and spacious bathrooms boasting chunky Victorian-style fittings. The remaining bedrooms are in the 1960s Marine Wing and offer ageing shelf-type fitted units and a textured finish to the walls. Foodwise, only the substantial cooked breakfast can be recommended. No dogs. *Rooms 104.* *Garden.* AMERICAN EXPRESS *Access, Diners, Visa.*

Dun Laoghaire   Places of Interest

Tourist Information   Tel 01 280 6984/5/6
National Maritime Museum   Haigh Terrace Tel 01 280 0969

Dundalk   Ballymascanlon House   59%   £75

Tel 042 71124   Fax 042 71598   **H**

Ballymascanlon Dundalk Co Louth   Map 1 D3

Two miles out of Dundalk on the Belfast road, this Victorian mansion is set in 130 acres of parkland. Bedrooms vary considerably in size, the largest being arranged around a glass-domed circular landing. There is a well-planned leisure complex, good golf course and conference facilities for 250. *Rooms 36.* *Garden, indoor swimming pool, gymnasium, squash, sauna, solarium, floodlit tennis, golf (9). Closed 24-27 Dec.* AMERICAN EXPRESS *Access, Diners, Visa.*

Dundalk   Places of Interest

Tourist Information   Tel 042 35484
Basement Gallery   Town Hall Tel 042 32276
Dundalk Racecourse   Dowdallshill Tel 042 34419
Moyry Castle
Kilnasaggart Pillar Stone

Dunderry — Dunderry Lodge Restaurant — £75

R
Tel 046 31671
Dunderry Navan Co Meath
Map 1 C3

Although set in a comfortably furnished, characterful old stone building, formally set tables with white linen and fine glasses create a sense of occasion at this well-known country restaurant. Owner-chef Paul Groves uses home-grown and local produce to good effect in menus which are imaginative without being pretentious. Both table d'hote (a small choice at each of three courses, or four with soup) and carte are offered. From the latter, start with a turntable of Oriental appetisers (for two), including satay, wun tuns, spring rolls, chili prawns, tandoori fish and sushi rice, a grilled game sausage with sweet and sour red cabbage and a juniper jus or ravioli of oysters on a light thyme sauce; continue with puff pastry-wrapped, pan-fried scallops with parsley, bacon and garlic, fried wild mallard on creamed celeriac and a Madeira sauce or Parma ham-wrapped teal filled with pistachio. Leave room for the famous dessert trolley that groans with a wide range of temptations – from floating islands and chocolate mousses to ices set in a bowl of hazelnut meringue gateau. Sunday lunch offers exceptional value. Interesting and unusual selection of wines. No children under 6. *Seats 40. Parties 12. L Sun 1-2 (also open L Sat May-Aug, other days by arrangement) D 7-9.30. Closed D Sun, all Mon, Bank Holidays, 2nd week Jan, 1st week Aug. Set L £13.50 Set D £13.95/£15.95.* AMERICAN EXPRESS, *Access, Diners, Visa.*

Dundrum — Dundrum House — 66% — £84

H
Tel 062 71116   Fax 062 71366
Dundrum Cashel Co Tipperary
Map 2 B5

The Crowe family take great pride in their hotel, a large Georgian house set in 150 acres through which a trout-filled river runs. Public rooms include a lofty reception hall, a comfortable drawing room furnished with wing chairs and, in the old chapel, a bar with live music every night in summer. Spacious, simply decorated bedrooms are furnished with antiques. The 150-acre County Tipperary Golf and Country Club is incorporated within the extensive grounds. *Rooms 55. Garden, tennis, riding, golf (18), fishing, snooker.* AMERICAN EXPRESS *Access, Diners, Visa.*

Dunkineely — Castle Murray House — 69% — £44

HR
Tel 073 37022   Fax 073 37330
Dunkineely Co Donegal
Map 1 B2

Since they opened in September 1991 some hidden force has gradually drawn the cognoscenti to Thierry and Clare Delcros' dramatically situated small clifftop hotel a few miles west of Donegal town. Overlooking the ruins of the castle after which it is named, with stunning views of the rugged Donegal coastline and crashing seas, the location is truly breathtaking – and this sturdily built and well-run establishment lives up to it. On to the original structure the Delcros have built well-judged additions including a long and comfortable stone-floored semi-conservatory along the front (imaginatively lit at night and well placed to make the most of the view) and, completed in 1993, the second phase of spacious bedrooms, furnished simply but to a high standard

See over

with pristine white-tiled bathrooms to match. A cosy bar and residents' sitting room beside the dining room are scheduled to open this year. *Rooms 10. Access, Visa.*

Restaurant   £55

The large, well-appointed dining room has tweed-curtained, double-glazed windows on two sides to take full advantage of the views and a big continental-style table-height log fire, providing an appropriate setting for Thierry Delcros' excellent French cooking. Menus change by the season, with a stronger emphasis on seafood in summer, and pricing by choice of main course allows semi à la carte flexibility of choice with set menu economy, but their understated language does nothing to prepare the diner for the richly imaginative treats Thierry has in store – or for his sure-handed skill in the execution in, typically, mussels in garlic butter finished unexpectedly with melted cheese and served fiercely hot with a crispy seaweed garnish. In addition to a wide range of seafood, main courses might offer an unusual combination like kebabs of duck fillet, wrapped in bacon, tightly packed on wooden skewers and served on a little bed of crisp cabbage. Pretty desserts, a mixed French and Irish farmhouse cheese selection and good coffee. *Seats 45. Parties 15. L Sun only 1-2.30 D 7-10. Set Sun L £13.50. Closed Mon & Tues Oct to mid-June, 24 & 25 Dec.*

Dunlavin	**Rathsallagh House**	67%	£110

Tel 045 53112   Fax 045 53343   **AR**

Dunlavin Co Wicklow   Map 2 C4

Joe and Kay O'Flynn's delightful, rambling country house (built in the former stables of a Queen Anne house which burned down in 1798) has an award-winning walled kitchen garden, 280-acre farm and seemingly endless rolling parkland. Fishing and deer-stalking are easily arranged (also hunting in season) and the new 18-hole golf course is a further attraction – or you can simply catch up with your reading by the fireside in the delightfully lived-in drawing room. Rooms are generally spacious and quite luxurious in an understated way, with lovely country views; some smaller, simpler rooms in the stable yard have a special cottage charm. There is a completely separate private conference facility for up to 50 theatre-style (25 boardroom-style) in a courtyard conversion at the back. Outstanding breakfasts are served in the traditional way from a huge sideboard. No children under 12. *Rooms 14. Garden, croquet, indoor swimming pool, tennis, golf (18), practice golf, snooker, helipad. Closed 23-26 Dec.* AMERICAN EXPRESS® *Access, Diners, Visa.*

Restaurant   £65

Take in the easy-going atmosphere in the old kitchen bar while reading the menu, then settle down in the traditional dining room and enjoy the evening shadows falling on parkland and the hills beyond. Good home cooking is the order of the day, allowing the freshness and quality of prime local produce to come through. Typical offerings on the limited choice four-course menu might include mushroom and thyme soup, grilled Wexford scallops or woodland salad with quails' eggs, followed by Duncannon turbot with béarnaise or spicy bacon and garlic potatoes. Roast local beef is a speciality, also Wicklow lamb. Leave some room for a tempting dessert from the trolley, or some Irish farmhouse cheese. Snacks are also served all day in the bar. *Seats 50. Private Room 15. L by arrangement for groups, not Sun. D 7.30-9. Closed Mon in winter, 3 days Christmas, 1 week from 2 Jan. Set L £14.95 Set D £25-£30.*

Dunmore East   The Ship

Tel 051 83144	
Dunmore East Co Waterford	Map 2 C5

This well-located roadside bar/restaurant is situated high up over the bay, but is more remarkable for its atmosphere and seafood than a sea view. The solidly-built house dates back to Victorian times and, since the mid-80s, has enjoyed a national reputation under the present ownership for local seafood served in pleasantly informal surroundings. The bar area near the entrance develops gradually into a dining area, with unusual, sturdy furniture made from old barrels, darkwood walls and a strongly nautical theme – the interior is dimly atmospheric in contrast to the bright roadside patio area used for casual summer meals. They no longer serve bar food, but the à la carte menu is available lunch and dinner in summer (lunch Sun only in May & Oct, dinner in winter except Sun & Mon). *Access, Visa.*

Dunworley   Dunworley Cottage   £60

Tel 023 40314	R
Butlerstown Clonakilty Dunworley Co Cork	Map 2 B6

Katherine Norén's remote stone cottage is a haven of serious cooking, favouring organic produce and catering for special dietary needs. Many dishes have become specialities, including nettle soup, Clonakilty black or white/black pudding served with sherry sauce and lingonberries, home-made smoked salami, seafood casserole and steaks pan-fried and served with garlic butter, fried onions, mushrooms and a green peppercorn sauce. Apfel strudel, home-made ice creams and petits fours, farmhouse cheeses to finish. Children's menu (Swedish meatballs the favourite) or half-portions at half prices. *Seats 50. Private Room 20. L 1-5 D 6.30-10. Closed Mon & Tue, also Nov and Jan-Feb. Set D £18.* AMERICAN EXPRESS *Access, Diners, Visa.*

Durrus   Blairs Cove House Restaurant   £60

Tel 027 61127	R
Blairs Cove Durrus nr Bantry Co Cork	Map 2 A6

Converted from the characterful outbuildings of the 17th-century Blairs Cove House, in a lovely waterside location overlooking Dunmanus Bay, Sabine and Philippe de Mey's restaurant has been delighting guests with its unique style since 1981. The renowned buffet groans under an abundance of starters (local seafood, patés and salads), then a wide range of main courses that includes locally caught fish – warm salad of scallops, perhaps, or John Dory with vegetables, lemon and soya dressing – and specialities like rack of lamb or steak cooked over an open wood-fired grill in the restaurant. To finish, irresistible desserts and local farmhouse cheeses (deserving of the Irish Cheeseboard of the Year Award) are dramatically displayed on top of the grand piano. The loos are up a long flight of stairs. Well-equipped, self-catering

See over

188 Republic of Ireland

accommodation is available on the premises and nearby. Look for the blue entrance gate, 1½ miles outside Durrus, on the Goleen/Barley Cove road. *Seats 70. D only 7.30-9.30. Closed Sun (also Mon Sep-Jun), Nov-Feb. Set D £23.* *Access, Diners, Visa.*

East Ferry   The Marlogue Inn

Tel 021 813390	**P**
East Ferry Marina Cobh Co Cork	Map 2 B6

Despite the name, which somehow conveys the impression of an old-established hostelry, this beautifully located little waterside pub was only opened in 1992 and improvements are still ongoing, especially in the patio/barbecue area on the river side. As we went to press the pub was closed for redecoration and the style of bar food was likely to change. *Bar Food 12-3, 6-10. Access, Visa.*

Ennis   Auburn Lodge   61%

	£84
Tel 065 21247 Fax 065 21202	**H**
Galway Road Ennis Co Clare	Map 2 B4

Low-rise modern hotel on the N17 20 minutes from Shannon airport. Practical accommodation, friendly staff and versatile conference/function facilities. Ample free parking. No dogs. *Rooms 100. Garden, tennis.* *Access, Diners, Visa.*

JAMESON The Spirit of Ireland

Ennis   The Cloister

Tel 065 29521	**P**
Abbey Street Ennis Co Clare	Map 2 B4

Built right in the walls and garden of a 13th-century Franciscan abbey, this famous pub is steeped in history and the back windows of its cosy low-ceilinged rooms overlook the friary and its brilliant emerald-green grass surrounds. The main restaurant incorporates rooms from the original abbey kitchen. In winter, fires create a sense of cheer and, in the event of fine summer weather, an attractive patio garden provides an escape from the unseasonable dimness of the bar. Although well supported by locals, the reputation for good food here extends far beyond the immediate area with a compact, well-balanced à la carte restaurant menu and an £18, three-course table d'hote offering a good choice – from game and foie gras roulade to Fergus salmon with gazpacho sauce and winter's fruit pudding with brandy butter. Lunchtime sees the likes of fish pie, scrambled eggs with smoked salmon, lasagne, Irish stew, chicken pot pie along with daily fish and meat specials. After 6pm the bar menu incorporates both snacks (soup of the evening with brown bread, goat's cheese salad with port sauce) and more substantial dishes (Dijon chicken en croute, steamed Ballyvaughan mussels with garlic bread, herby rack of lamb). *Bar Food 12-4, 6-9.30 Nov-mid Mar, 12-9.30 mid Mar-end Oct. Children's menu and portions available. Patio, outdoor eating.* *Access, Visa.*

Ennis   Old Ground Hotel   66%   £99

Tel 065 28127   Fax 065 28112   **H**

Ennis Co Clare   **Map 2 B4**

This famous old ivy-clad hotel next to Ennis cathedral is handy
for Shannon Airport and a convenient base for touring Clare.
Some of the ground-floor bedrooms are suitable for disabled
guests, and conference facilities for up to 250 (banquets 180) are
provided. Children under 16 may stay free in their parents' room.
Forte Heritage. *Rooms 58.* AMERICAN EXPRESS *Access, Diners, Visa.*

Ennis   West County Inn   59%   £55

Tel 065 28421   Fax 065 28801   **H**

Clare Road Ennis Co Clare   **Map 2 B4**

"Hospitality is our strength" is the motto of this bright modern
hotel, and that extends to families, disabled guests (some rooms
expecially fitted out) and conference delegates. 1994 should see the
completion of a programme of refurbishment in the bedrooms.
There are two restaurants and a lively night club. The West
County also has a snooker room, and guests may use free of charge
the leisure centre at the sister hotel *Clare Inn* (Newmarket-on-
Fergus). *Rooms 100. Snooker.* AMERICAN EXPRESS *Access, Diners, Visa.*

Ennis   Places of Interest

Tourist Information   Tel 065 28366
Graggaunowen Bronze Age Project   Quin Tel 061 367178
Knappogue Castle   Quin Tel 061 361511

Enniskerry   Curtlestown House   £50

Tel 01 2825083   Fax 01 2866509   **R**

Curtlestown Enniskerry Co Wicklow   **Map 2 D4**

A charming country restaurant in a little farmhouse half an hour's
drive from Dublin. Colin Pielow's traditional menus change with
the seasons, game being a winter stalwart, with fish taking centre
stage in summer. Poached salmon with watercress sauce, chicken
chasseur, braised saddle of rabbit and peppered sirloin steak show
his admirably straightforward style. Sunday lunch is much more
a family affair than the evenings. One room is reserved for non-
smokers. *Seats 40. Parties 20. L (Sun only)*
12.30-2.30 D 8-10. Closed Mon. Set Sun L £11.50 Set D from
£17. Access, Visa.

Enniskerry   Enniscree Lodge   59%   £75

Tel 01 286 3542   Fax 01 286 6037   **HR**

Cloon Enniskerry Co Wicklow   **Map 2 D4**

The views are really wonderful from this friendly old inn, which
has a cosy bar for winter, a terrace for sunny weather and good
all-day bar food. Bedrooms are comfortably furnished in country
style and most enjoy the beauty of the setting; bathrooms are
slightly dated but neat and functional. A residents' lounge doubles
as a small function room. Children up to 12 may stay free
in parents' room. *Rooms 10. Closed Mon-Thur in Jan & Feb.*
AMERICAN EXPRESS *Access, Diners, Visa.*   *See over*

Restaurant £60

Chef Paul Moroney succeeds with a combination of traditional
and contemporary cuisine in this attractive restaurant overlooking
Glencree. Dishes on a winter menu included potato and parsnip
boxty with a purée of spiced apple, terrine of rabbit and pigeon,
Wicklow lamb in a mustard crust with mint chutney, and roast
pheasant with garden herb stuffing and juniper berry sauce.
*Seats 40. Parties 12. L 12.30-2.30 D 7.30-9.30 (Sat to 10, Sun to 9).
Set L £12.50.*

Enniskerry   Places of Interest

Powerscourt Gardens and Waterfall   Tel 01 286 7676
Fernhill Gardens   Sandyford Tel 01 295 6000 *3 miles*

Fahan   Restaurant St John's £55

`Tel 077 60289`   **R**

Fahan Innishowen Co Donegal   Map 1 C1

In a substantial period house overlooking Lough Swilly, Reg
Ryan's warm welcome is underlined by a glowing open fire in the
bar area and the decor throughout is comfortably unassertive,
leaving the mind clear to enjoy Phil McAfee's confident cooking
to the full. A two-tier system offers a five-course restricted choice
£16 menu, or more choice at £20. Start perhaps with smoked
chicken salad with hazelnut oil and balsamic vinegar or gravad lax
with a dill sauce, followed by a home-made soup – typically carrot
and tarragon or a chowder - then a tossed mixed leaf salad. Main
courses might include tender crisp-skinned roast duckling, cooked
on the bone but served off it, lamb with a home-made gooseberry
mint jelly or a wide choice of fish – turbot, brill, John Dory –
with fennel sauce. Details – delicious home-baked bread,
imaginative vegetables, desserts with the emphasis on flavour
rather than show, such as peaches in brandy with vanilla ice cream
and wonderful choux petits fours with spun sugar served with
freshly brewed coffee – all add up to a great dining experience.
There's a good selection of half bottles and New World wines
on the comprehensive wine list at friendly prices. *Seats 40.
Private Room 22. No smoking in rear dining room. D only 7-9.30.
Closed Sun-Tue, 2 days Christmas, Good Friday.* AMERICAN EXPRESS
Access, Diners, Visa.

Ferrycarrig Bridge   Ferrycarrig Hotel   61% £90

`Tel 053 22999   Fax 053 41982`   **H**

Ferrycarrig Bridge nr Wexford Co Wexford   Map 2 D5

All bedrooms in this well-run modern waterside hotel overlook
the Slaney estuary and there is a path leading to Ferrycarrig Castle.
Comfortably furnished public rooms include the Dry Dock bar
and two restaurants, all enjoying the views. Stylish bedrooms have
well-equipped bathrooms with plenty of shelf space. There's
conference space for up to 400, ample free parking and up-to-date
leisure facilities. *Rooms 40. Garden, tennis, gymnasium, sauna, steam
room, solarium, whirlpool bath, beauty salon.* AMERICAN EXPRESS *Access,
Diners, Visa.*

Foulksmills   Horetown House   £50

Tel 051 63771   Fax 051 63633   **R**

Foulksmills Co Wexford   Map 2 C5

Horetown House is best known as a residential equestrian centre
with a relaxed country atmosphere. Residents generally use the
dining room in the main house (where a hearty farmhouse dinner
is offered as an alternative to the more formal table d'hote).
Alternatively, the Cellar Restaurant, which is cosy and
atmospheric, with an open fire, whitewashed arches and sturdy
country furniture, is open to non-residents and very popular in the
area, especially for Sunday lunch. Proprietor Ivor Young and his
head chef David Cronin can be relied on to produce meals based
on quality ingredients, including local salmon, wild Wicklow
venison and other game in season. Afternoon teas also available.
*Seats 45. Parties 10. Private Room 30. L (Sun only) 12.30 – 2.30
D 7-9. Set L £8.95 Set D from £18.50. Closed D Sun, all Mon,
Christmas week. Access, Visa.*

Galway   Ardilaun House   66%   £94

Tel 091 21433   Fax 091 21546   **H**

Taylors Hill Galway Co Galway   Map 2 B4

The original house was built in 1840 and contains handsomely
proportioned day rooms looking out over the attractive grounds.
Sympathetic extensions have been added over the past 30 years
or so, providing unpretentious, traditionally furnished bedrooms
of various sizes, and a conference facility for up to 400 delegates.
Friendly, helpful staff. No dogs. *Rooms 90. Garden, gymnasium,
sauna, solarium, snooker. Closed 6 days Christmas.* AMERICAN EXPRESS
Access, Diners, Visa.

Galway   Brennans Yard   64%   £70

Tel 091 68166   Fax 091 68262   **H**

Lower Merchants Road Galway Co Galway   Map 2 B4

A new hotel created from stylishly converted old warehousing
in Galway city's 'Left Bank' area. First impressions are of an
attractive building with unexpectedly cramped entrance, but the
second phase of development, which will include the foyer
as originally planned, has yet to be completed. Public rooms
currently in operation include a pleasantly bright if smallish dining
room (also to be extended) and, at the back, the striking Oyster
Bar for informal meals, especially local seafood. Individually
decorated bedrooms make up in style what is lacking in space –
well-planned, clean-lined rooms have old stripped pine pieces,
locally-made pottery and neat, functional bathrooms; three rooms
have both a double and single bed; family facilities are provided.
Direct-dial phones, radio and TV, tea/coffee-making facilities,
hairdryer and toiletries included as standard. *Rooms 24.
Closed 2 weeks Christmas.* AMERICAN EXPRESS *Access, Diners, Visa.*

Galway   Casey's Westwood Restaurant   £60

Tel 091 21442/21645   **R**

Dangan Upper Newcastle Galway Co Galway   Map 2 B4

Bernie and Mary Casey have been running this popular eating
place since 1982 and the long, low building houses a number

See over

of bars and restaurant areas to suit various occasions. An evening in the main restaurant starts in the cocktail lounge, where orders are taken before you settle into a comfortable carver or banquette at a well-appointed table to enjoy son John Casey's sound cooking; there's no doubting John's commitment or his imaginative flair in the kitchen. His menus offer a wide choice – perhaps offering a timbale of smoked salmon and cream cheese with mango mayonnaise, stuffed fillet of pork with wild mushroom sauce and feuilleté of grapes with a Kirsch sabayon at lunchtime, from a three-course menu with three choices at each stage. Four-course dinners see more involved dishes, from ravioli of chicken and cheese with smoked bacon and basil sauce to half a roast pheasant served with a purée of parsnip and chocolate and raspberry sauce, and blackberry and blackcurrant délice with home-made fig and port ice cream – flavours galore! Vegetables are imaginative, desserts unusual and prettily presented and home-made petits fours are served with coffee. Low-cholesterol and vegetarian dishes available. **Seats** 120. L 12.30-2.15 D 6.30-10. *Closed Good Friday, 24-26 Dec. Set L £10.95 Set D £19.50.* *Access, Visa.*

Galway	Corrib Great Southern Hotel	68%	£123
Tel 091 755281 Fax 091 751390			H
Dublin Road Galway Co Galway			Map 2 B4

Overlooking Galway Bay, a large, modern hotel on the edge of the city, offering a wide range of facilities for both business guests and family holidays. Bedrooms vary considerably; refurbished rooms are much improved and new, spacious 'superior' rooms are well planned with good attention to detail and stylish bathrooms. Children under 2 stay free in parents' room, £20 per night for under-12s; baby-sitting arranged on request. The (smallish) swimming pool has a lifeguard at all times and, in high season and busy weekends, children's entertainment and a crèche are provided. New state-of-the-art business/convention centre has facilities for groups of 8 to 850, with banqueting for up to 700. Public areas include a cosy residents' lounge and O'Malleys Pub, a big, lively bar with sea views. **Rooms** 180. *Indoor swimming pool, steam room, whirlpool bath, snooker, helipad.* *Access, Diners, Visa.*

Hotel sporting facilities are highlighted in the Quick Reference lists for easy comparison.

Galway	Glenlo Abbey	66%	£115
Tel 091 26666 Fax 091 27800			H
Bushy Park Galway Co Galway			Map 2 B4

The summer of '93 saw the doubling of the accommodation at this 18th-century abbey conversion, and the new rooms include six suites with whirlpool baths. All the rooms have king-size beds, personal safes and roomy, well-designed marble bathrooms. There are two bars – the Kentfield for cocktails and the convivial Oak Cellar, and a variety of function rooms. An 18-hole golf course with clubhouse, two tennis courts, a gymnasium and sauna are due to come on stream as we publish. **Rooms** 43. *Garden. Closed 24-29 Dec.* *Access, Diners, Visa.*

Galway   Great Southern   69%   £113

Tel 091 64041   Fax 091 66704

H

Eyre Square Galway Co Galway   Map 2 B4

Overlooking Eyre Square right in the heart of Galway, this
historic railway hotel (built in 1845) has retained many of its
original features, and old-world charm mixes easily with modern
facilities. Refurbished public rooms are quite grand and include
O'Flahertys Pub bar as well as a cocktail lounge. Bedrooms, which
vary somewhat but are generally spacious, are traditionally
furnished with dark mahogany units, brass light fittings and smart
fabrics. Various rooms offer conference facilities for up to 450
(banquets 350). Roof-top swimming pool with magnificent views
over the city. *Rooms 116. Indoor swimming pool, sauna, steam room,
hair salon.* AMERICAN EXPRESS® *Access, Diners, Visa.*

Galway   Jurys Galway Inn   55%   £61

Tel 091 66444   Fax 091 68415

H

Quay Street Galway Co Galway   Map 2 B4

The emphasis at the Galway Inn is firmly on value for money;
run on the same lines as the new *Jurys Christchurch Inn* in Dublin,
this 'inn' offers a good standard of basic accommodation without
frills. Rooms, almost all with lovely views, are large (sleeping
up to four people) with everything required for basic comfort and
convenience – neat en-suite bathroom, TV, phone – but no extras.
Beds are generous, with good-quality bedding, but wardrobes are
open; don't expect tea/coffee-making facilities or room service,
either. Public areas include an impressive, well-designed foyer
with seating areas, a pubby bar with a good atmosphere and a self-
service informal restaurant. Obviously a good place for family
accommodation and budget-conscious travellers; booking some
way ahead is advised. *Rooms 128. Closed 24-28 Dec.* AMERICAN EXPRESS®
Access, Diners, Visa.

Galway   Places of Interest

Tourist Information   Tel 091 63081
Thoor Ballylee   Gort Tel 091 31436 *W B Yeats' home*
Coole   Gort Tel 091 31804 *Nature Reserve*
Galway Racecourse   Ballybrit Tel 091 53870
Aran Islands   Tel 091 63081

Glasson   Glasson Village Restaurant   £50

Tel 0902 85001

R

Glasson Athlone Co Westmeath   Map 1 C3

An attractive stone building (once a barracks) in a pretty village
off the main road in Goldsmith country. The atmosphere is
friendly, and the place really bustles at Sunday lunchtime. Owner-
chef Michael Brooks is something of a seafood specialist, so on the
dinner menu you might find goujons of lemon sole with garlic
butter, hot terrine of salmon and hake with a sweet red pepper
sauce, seafood soup and the fresh fish dish of the day. Other
choices could include a warm salad of spicy lamb sausages,
tandoori-style julienne of chicken with mint sauce and roast rack
of lamb *persillé. Seats 50. Parties 12. Private Room 14. L 12.30 &
2.15 (Sun only, 2 sittings) D 7-10.15. Closed D Sun, all Mon,*

See over

*3 weeks Oct, 4 days Christmas. Set L £9 Set D £16.75. Access,
Diners, Visa.*

Glasson   Grogan's

Tel 0902 85158	**P**
Glasson nr Athlone Co Westmeath	**Map 1 C3**

Grogan's is a delightfully quaint, family-run pub in the pretty and
accessible village of Glasson, near Athlone. The cosy, low-ceilinged
front bar is divided in the traditional manner, with an open fire
at one end and a fair choice of chilled or 'soft' Guinness at both.
Simon Grogan presides over the kitchen and supplies
as wholesome a range of simple bar meals as anyone could wish
for, with home-made soup and bread (£1), smoked salmon
(£2.55), fresh Dublin Bay prawn cocktail (£3.25) and oysters,
fresh or grilled with garlic butter (£3.50/£3.75), as well as salads
and snacks including speciality toasted sandwiches such as black
pudding (£1.45). There's also a larger back bar and a beer garden
where summer barbecues are held. **Bar Food** *12.30-3, 7-9 (Sun
in summer only 12-2, 4-8). Children allowed in bar to eat. Garden.
No credit cards.*

Glen of Aherlow   Aherlow House   63%   £53

Tel 062 56153 Fax 062 56212	**H**
Glen of Aherlow nr Tipperary Co Tipperary	**Map 2 B5**

Standing four miles from Tipperary in the middle of a forest,
Aherlow House was originally a hunting lodge. The decorative
inspiration is Tudor, and beyond the heavy oak doors the
atmosphere is set by darkwood beams and log fires. A large terrace
outside the bar commands views of the glen. Well-appointed,
individually furnished bedrooms include three suitable for families
(under-tens free in parents' rooms). Conference/function facilities.
No dogs. **Rooms** *10. Closed Mon-Thu Nov-mid Dec & mid Jan
to early March.* AMERICAN EXPRESS® *Access, Diners, Visa.*

Glen of Aherlow   Place of Interest

Tipperary Racecourse   Tel 062 51357

Glengarriff   The Blue Loo

Tel 027 63167	**P**
Main Street Glengarriff Co Cork	**Map 2 A6**

Philip Harrington's unusually named pub may well inspire a first
visit out of curiosity alone, but its friendliness will ensure a return.
Spick and span, with a choice of sitting indoors in a pleasant
traditional country atmosphere or at roadside tables and benches
out in the sun, it is a pleasingly simple place, with food (May-Oct)
to match – fresh crab and fresh or smoked wild salmon are the
specialities, served in open or closed sandwiches. *Open 10.30am-
11.30pm (Sun 12.30-2, 4-11). No credit cards.*

Goleen Harbour   Heron's Cove Restaurant   £35

Tel 028 35225 Fax 028 35422	**R R**
Goleen Harbour Co Cork	**Map 2 A6**

Owner-chef Sue Hill runs a tidy ship at her chameleon-like
waterside restaurant, which converts from its daytime persona as a

practical, inexpensive stop-off place with rugged wooden tables
and menus to match – hearty soups, home-made bread, home-
cooked ham, farmhouse cheeses, seafood specials and afternoon teas
– to a romantic candle-lit evening restaurant with embroidered
cloths, linen napkins and silver cutlery. As the atmosphere is
transformed, so too is the menu, now sophisticated and frequently
changing. What the two faces of Heron's Cove have in common
is the freshness of good local ingredients and a refreshing
determination to keep prices reasonable. *Seats 30. Private Room 24.
Meals 12-9.45pm. Set L (Sun) £8.25 Set D £13.50. Closed end
Sep-early June except Easter. Access, Diners, Visa.*

Rooms   **£30**

Three en-suite rooms are available for bed & breakfast throughout
the year (but booking essential Oct-Apr). Self-catering
accommodation also available. *Garden.*

Gorey	Marlfield House	81%	£140
Tel 055 21124 Fax 055 21572			**H R**
Gorey Co Wexford			Map 2 D5

Built in 1820 and standing in lovely gardens and woodland, the
mansion has been owned and run by the Bowe family since 1978.
Fine beaches and many tourist spots are within a walk or short
drive, but it's equally pleasant to 'stay put' and relax in the
sumptuous, stylish day rooms. These include a semi-circular hall
(note the splendid 18th-century marble fireplace) and an elegant
lounge. Bedrooms are individually decorated and vary from
charming smaller rooms at the top of the house – some with four-
posters and all with good facilities and beautiful bedding including
fine, broderie anglaise-trimmed, cotton sheets – to a very grand
series of six luxurious suites on the ground floor, each different
but all with elaborate use of exclusive fabrics, carefully chosen
antiques and pictures and appropriately large, well-appointed
bathrooms. Colours throughout the house are rich and subtle and
beautiful fresh flowers abound. No dogs. *Rooms 19. Garden, sauna,
tennis, helipad. Closed Dec & Jan.* AMERICAN EXPRESS® *Access, Diners, Visa.*

Restaurant   **£90**

Almost an extension of the garden, the combination of trompe-
l'oeil and real plants plus the proximity of the conservatory
extension confuses the senses in this exotic dining room. Two new
chefs have recently been appointed: David Norris and Kevin
Arundel, and with owner Mary Bowe taking a more active role
in the kitchen, the high standards of the past are certain to be
maintained. The hotel also offers bar lunches. *Seats 60. L 12.30-2
D 7-9.30. Set L £17.50 Set D £28.*

Greencastle	Kealy's Seafood Bar		£45
Tel 077 81010			**R**
Greencastle Co Donegal			Map 1 C1

Unexpected sophistication awaits the visitor to this rugged
commercial fishing port – James and Tricia Kealy's bar is more
cocktail than fisherman's and, although tables are simply laid with
paper napkins and inexpensive cutlery and glasses, it is
immediately obvious that the food is taken seriously. Wholesome
all-day snacks give way to a good value four-course dinner menu,

See over

often including popular dishes lifted out of the ordinary by giving them a new twist – avocado may come with pesto and sun-dried tomatoes, for instance, poached salmon with a wild mushroom sauce, even the ubiquitous seafood cocktail, though simply described as 'a mixture of white fish', has been known to conceal large chunks of lobster. Sirloin steak is offered as a concession to non-fish eaters, vegetables are served simply and generously on a platter and desserts range from homely and hot (apple pie, crepes suzette) to sophisticated cold (passion fruit delight); black plates are used to good effect for fish and desserts. No smoking. *Seats 40. Parties 25. Private Room 25. L 12.30-5 D 7-9.30. Closed Mon, 1 week Mar, 1 week Oct, Good Friday, 25 Dec.* AMERICAN EXPRESS *Access, Diners, Visa.*

Many hotels offer reduced rates for weekend or out-of-season bookings. Always ask about special deals.

Greystones	**The Hungry Monk**	**£55**
Tel 01 287 5759		**R**
Greystones Co Wicklow		**Map 2 D4**

On the first floor, over a building society, this characterful little restaurant is unassuming from the street and the contrast inside is remarkable: a glowing fire and candlelight – even at Sunday lunch, now sensibly extended to make a very Irish lunch ("not brunch but linner", says genial host Pat Keown!), with last orders at 8pm – add to the warm welcome. Well-appointed tables with fresh flowers, delicious home-baked bread, serious wine glasses and, of course, a plethora of monk-related pictures and bric-a-brac complete the picture. Menús, changed seasonally, keep an eye on fashions and inject popular dishes with a dash of originality – as in warm salad of garlic mushrooms or roast lamb with a herb crust and minted lamb jus – but top-quality ingredients are the vital link, including game in season and daily seafood blackboard specials, from nearby Greystones harbour. Best of all, perhaps, are the prices – value for money is a priority here and the size of the bill is often a welcome surprise. A quite splendid and very fairly-priced wine list features an inexpensive house section, and a really comprehensive world-wide selection with the New World well represented, as are Italy, Spain and Portugal. *Seats 40. Parties 20. L Sun only 12.30-8 D 7-11. Closed L Mon-Sat D Sun-Wed in winter. Set L Sun £10.95 Set D (not Sat) £14.95.* AMERICAN EXPRESS *Access, Diners, Visa.*

Hodson Bay	**Hodson Bay Hotel**	**65%**	**£90***
Tel 0902 92444 Fax 0902 92688			**H**
Hodson Bay Athlone Co Roscommon			**Map 1 C3**

Large, lively, lakeside hotel offering extensive conference and leisure facilities. Golfing is available in the Athlone Golf Club, located next to the hotel, boating and watersports on Lough Ree and River Shannon and a wide number of pursuits in the hotel's excellent leisure and activity centre. Practical en-suite bedrooms, large foyer-lounge, dining room plus self-service food area, waterside bar. *Half-board terms only. **Rooms 46.** Garden, tennis, indoor swimming pool, gymnasium, keep-fit equipment, sauna, solarium, fishing.* AMERICAN EXPRESS *Access, Diners, Visa.*

Hodson Bay   Place of Interest

Athlone Castle Athlone Tel 0902 92912

Howth   Abbey Tavern

Tel 01 390307   Fax 01 390284   **P**

Howth Co Dublin   **Map 2 D4**

Halfway up a hill above the picturesque harbour, the Abbey has
all the hallmarks of a cosy, convivial pub. Blazing fires warm the
two rooms, which are characterised by thick stone walls, flagstone
floors with converted church pews and polished darkwood
furniture adding flavours to a venue that is popular with locals
as well as visitors from the Dublin area. A major attraction is the
Irish evenings of music and song held here most nights and for
which booking is required. *Open 3pm-11pm Mon-Fri, 1pm-11pm
Sat (1pm-11.30pm in summer), 12.30pm-11pm Sun. Closed Good
Friday, 25 & 26 Dec. No credit cards.*

Howth   Adrian's   £50

Tel 01 391696   **R**

3 Abbey Street Howth Co Dublin   **Map 2 D4**

Small family-run restaurant with menus that offer interest, variety
and careful use of fresh produce. East coast chowder with freshly
baked breads is a satisfying starter, and many dishes may
be ordered as either starter or main course: "crab toes" in chili oil,
baked mussels in garlic crumb, pasta with shellfish, meat
or vegetarian sauce. From the £16 dinner menu might come
salmon ravioli, aubergine and polenta rarebit, baked cod
in a piquant sauce and haunch of venison with kale. The dish for
a real treat is Adrian's Pier Head Special (£22), a platter including
crab, prawns, scallops, mussels, soused herring, and salmon fresh
and smoked, served with potato salad and a half-bottle of wine.
*Seats 32. Private Room 36. Meals 12-10 (Sun 2-8). Set L & D (12-
3, 6-9.30) £6.50/£7.90 Set D £16.* AMERICAN EXPRESS *Access,
Diners, Visa.*

Howth   Deer Park Hotel   64%   £67

Tel 01 832 2624   Fax 01 839 2405   **H**

Howth Co Dublin   **Map 2 D4**

Located high up on the Howth peninsula and surrounded by 1200
acres that includes five golf courses (18, 9 and 12-hole par 3, 18-
hole pitch and putt, plus a new 9-hole course). Deer Park also
enjoys excellent views to the north and east with Howth harbour,
Ireland's Eye and Lambay islands in one direction, Dublin in the
other. Built in 1973, it has a fairly modern appearance. There's
a bright, airy first-floor residents' lounge with a terrace for fine
weather, while on the ground floor the bar offers excellent views
to the east and Dublin. Bedrooms are of good size, offering smart
darkwood furniture. Each has its own fridge and toaster as well
as the usual tea/coffee facilities. Bread and cereals can be provided
for those with early planes to catch from Dublin airport. Vinyl-
floored bathrooms, all with showers, have enamel baths.
Rooms 50. Garden, golf. AMERICAN EXPRESS *Access, Diners, Visa.*

Howth   Howth Lodge Hotel   65%   £63

Tel 01 832 1010   Fax 01 832 2268   **H**

Howth Co Dublin   Map 2 D4

Built 175 years ago and since considerably enlarged (but keeping
the original style), with the whole frontage painted a distinctive
black and white, Howth Lodge offers good standards
of accommodation as well as a very fine leisure centre across the
road (note that the gym is only available to fully experienced
users). On the ground floor, public areas are open-plan, featuring
a spacious lounge with bamboo furniture that leads to a cosy,
beamed bar with stripped bare floorboards at the rear. There are
13 older bedrooms in the original building, but the majority are
in a purpose-built modern block completed last year. All
bedrooms are well equipped, double-glazed and offer at least
a partial view of the sea. The new bedrooms are excellent – of
good size and very prettily decorated. Front rooms have
traditional-style darkwood furniture, while the rear rooms have
lightwood pieces. Bathrooms are bright and clean; six have bidets.
*Rooms 46. Garden, indoor swimming pool, solarium, sauna, spa bath,
steam room, gym. Closed 25 Dec.* AMERICAN EXPRESS *Access, Diners, Visa.*

Howth   King Sitric   £70

Tel 01 832 6729   Fax 01 839 2442   **R**

East Pier Harbour Road Howth Co Dublin   Map 2 D4

Howth is home to one of the largest fishing fleets in Ireland,
so King Sitric, a very well-established fish restaurant, is perfectly
placed on the harbour front. Warm salad with grilled herring,
baked crab gateau, moules marinière, poached lemon sole, queen
scallops, sole meunière or Colbert, lobster taken from the tank,
grilled or poached turbot, poached salmon, oysters from Galway
Bay... these and many more classics you'll find on Aidan
MacManus's mouthwatering menus. Lunch in the seafood bar
provides great views and excellent value for money. Joan
MacManus is a charming hostess. King Sitric is not only
an outstanding seafood restaurant but boasts one of the finest wine
lists in Ireland with excellent house recommendations,
an especially splendid selection of Chablis and Alsace, and
a comprehensive choice of other whites and red wines, many
of which are served at the restaurant's special 'wine evenings'.
*Seats 60. Private Room 22. L 12.30-3 (summer and pre-Christmas
only) D 6.30-11. Closed Sun, Bank Holidays, 10 days Christmas &
Easter. Set D £22.* AMERICAN EXPRESS *Access, Diners, Visa.*

Howth   Place of Interest

Howth Castle Gardens   Tel 01 832 2624

Inistioge   The Motte   £60

Tel 056 58655   **R**

Inistioge Co Kilkenny   Map 2 C5

Set in one of Ireland's prettiest villages, everything about Tom
Reade-Duncan and Alan Walton's intimate, characterful little
restaurant is just right – the antiques, artistic candle-lit table
settings and warm, welcoming atmosphere. The menu, which

is changed with the seasons according to availability of produce and sensibly limited to a choice of about six on each course, is interesting and chef Alan Walton follows through with style. Start, perhaps, with crab and ginger strudel, a sausage of crabmeat quite sharply scented with ginger, wrapped in filo and partnered with a mellow balsamic vinaigrette or hare terrine, followed by crisp-skinned pink-fleshed Barbary duck with a sumptuous confit of garlic and flageolet beans or fillets of plaice with a crispy herb and pine nut crust. Details are excellent: three kinds of olives to nibble over aperitifs and three kinds of bread, served with nice little chunks of butter in a pottery bowl, good choice of imaginatively presented vegetables, farmhouse cheese selection, delicious gimmick-free desserts, lovely aromatic coffee. All in all, an immaculate restaurant, fully deserving of our Best Table Presentation Award. *Seats 24. Parties 8. D only 7-10 (Sun to 9). Set D £18.50. Closed Bank Holidays, Christmas week.* Access, Diners, Visa.

Innishannon Innishannon House Hotel 63% £95
Tel 021 775121 Fax 021 775609 H
Innishannon Co Cork Map 2 B6

Built in 1720 for a wealthy farmer, Innishannon House enjoys a romantic setting in gardens and parkland on the Bandon River (fishing available here and on the Brinny). Bedrooms, all en suite, are individual in their size, shape and furnishings; some overlook the river, others the gardens. There's a cosy residents' bar (snacks served all day), a restaurant, sitting room and conservatory. Popular afternoon teas. *Rooms 13. Garden, fishing, boating.* Access, Diners, Visa.

Kanturk Alley Bar
Tel 029 50171 P
Strand Street Kanturk Co Cork Map 2 B5

A little gem of a drinking pub, run by the same family for several decades (daughter Alice has recently taken over from mother Mary). It's opposite the creamery and tucked away behind a modest grocery which is stocked with some items not held by many more glamorous shops. Look out for 'The Ballad of Ned Jones's Toyota', a true story in verse. *Open 9.30am-midnight (Sun 12.30-2.30 & 4-11.30).*

Kanturk Assolas Country House 72% £104
Tel 029 50015 Fax 029 50795 AR
Kanturk Co Cork Map 2 B5

Only an hour from Cork city, Assolas is well situated as a base for visiting West Cork and Kerry. The charming creeper-clad house goes back to the 17th century and is currently home to three generations of Bourkes, including the manager, Joe, and his wife Hazel, a very talented chef. An exceptional welcome is backed up by open log fires, elegant furnishings and antiques, excellent housekeeping and a high level of comfort throughout. Of the nine bedrooms, three in the main house are designated 'Superior' and are large, with the finest views; three are in a restored old stone building in the courtyard. Despite its undeniable elegance, Assolas has all the warmth and hospitality of a family home – best *See over* summed up, perhaps, by the collection of wellington boots in the hall for anyone who feels like seeking out the otters along the riverbank. No dogs in the house. **Rooms** 9. *Garden, croquet, tennis, fishing. Closed Nov-mid March.* ᴀᴍᴇʀɪᴄᴀɴ ᴇxᴘʀᴇss *Access, Diners, Visa.*

Restaurant ★ £65

They do things properly at Assolas and the deep red walls, polished antique furniture and neatly uniformed staff provide a fitting background for Hazel Bourke's wonderful food, much of it produce from their own beautifully maintained walled kitchen garden (in which herbs, vegetables and soft fruit grow) or from trusted local suppliers – allowing maximum variety for residents. Start, perhaps, with Union Hall prawns and scallops in a puff pastry case, typically followed by a pink grapefruit sorbet or dressed Assolas greens. Local lamb, served with a rosemary flavoured jus and Hazel's mint jelly, might tempt from a choice of five main courses, which always includes an imaginative vegetarian option. Simplest desserts are sometimes the best – superb blackcurrant ice cream or a shimmering jewel-like compote of garden fruits – and the local farmhouse cheeseboard is kept in immaculate condition. Coffee and petits fours are served beside the fire in the drawing room. There are no New World wines on an otherwise decent wine list that features many top growers. No children under 7. **Seats** 25. *Private Room 20. D only 7-8.30. Set D £27.*

Kanturk   The Vintage

Tel 029 50549	**P**
O'Brien Street Kanturk Co Cork	Map 2 B5

Stephen Bowles has owned this pleasant, well-run riverside pub since 1985 and it is well worth a visit, whether for a quiet pint or a bite to eat. The interior is pleasingly traditional and comfortably furnished. Suitable for just a quick snack or a complete meal; choose from traditional dishes like bacon and cabbage or Irish stew, T-bone steak or a traditional roast on Sundays. Daily-changing blackboard specials always include a vegetarian main dish. *Open 10.30am-11.30pm Mon-Sat, 12.30-2 & 4-11 Sun.* **Bar Food** *12.30-9.30 Mon-Sat, 12.30-2 & 6-9.30 Sun. Access, Visa.*

Kenmare   Dromquinna Manor Hotel   60% £70

Tel 064 41657 Fax 064 41791	**H**
Blackwater Bridge nr Kenmare Co Kerry	Map 2 A6

About three miles out of town and beautifully situated in extensive grounds leading down to the private foreshore and a little quay and newly built marina (the setting for their informal summer Old Boathouse Bistro restaurant), this Victorian manor boasts a unique tree-house apartment as well as many more orthodox attractions, including a Great Hall with original oak panelling. Generously proportioned bedrooms are individually decorated, all en suite, some with four-poster or brass beds. A generally relaxed atmosphere pervades the hotel. **Rooms** 28. *Garden, keep-fit equipment, games room, tennis, mooring, fishing.* ᴀᴍᴇʀɪᴄᴀɴ ᴇxᴘʀᴇss *Access, Diners, Visa.*

Kenmare	The Horseshoe	£32
Tel 064 41553		**R**
3 Main Street Kenmare Co Kerry		Map 2 A6

Behind its unassuming exterior The Horseshoe hides a pleasantly
rustic old-fashioned bar. Behind this again, there's a cosy, informal
restaurant with open fire, oil-clothed tables, (real) cattle stall
divisions and an unpretentious menu backed up by owner-chef
Irma Weland's simple, wholesome food. Old favourites like deep-
fried mushrooms with garlic mayonnaise take on a new lease
of life in Irma's hands (crisp, light, very hot and full of contrasts),
and, while steaks and fish are reliable, a vegetarian main course
such as tagliatelle with creamy leek, mushroom and garlic sauce
can be memorable. Good desserts may include a moreish
caramelised apple and pear flan. Tables outside in summer.
Seats 35. Parties 8. Private Room 30. Meals 12-10pm.
Closed Tues in winter. No credit cards.

Kenmare	The Old Bank House	£70
Tel 064 41589 Fax 064 41589		**R**
Main Street Kenmare Co Kerry		Map 2 A6

Matthew d'Arcy moved across the road from the *Park Hotel*
in 1992 to set up in this converted bank and his wife Aileen
provides a warm welcome. There's a real fire glowing where the
main banking hall used to be and the vault at the back is opened
up on busy nights. Staff are informal and friendly and the menu
longish and ambitious. Ravioli of prawn mousse with a sweet
pepper-scented butter or leek and chicken timbale could start your
meal, with rolled fillet of black sole (accompanied by a spinach
mousse and sea urchin sauce) or stuffed guinea fowl to follow.
Desserts include an excellent orange and Cointreau soufflé. A table
d'hote menu will be introduced in the summer of 1994. *Seats 40.*
Private Room 25. D 7-9 (from 5 to 10.30 high season).
Closed Mon & Tues in winter, 25 Dec, 2 weeks Feb.
Access, Diners, Visa.

Kenmare	Packie's	£45
Tel 064 41508		**R**
Henry Street Kenmare Co Kerry		Map 2 A6

Owner-chef Maura O'Connell Foley packs in the crowds with
cooking that's short on pretension and long on flavour. The sunny
influences of California and the Med combine with domestic
traditions on a menu typified by smoked salmon with red onion
and caper sauce, grilled crubeens (pig's trotters) with mustard
pickle, fillet of brill with carrot and wine sauce and warm fish
mousse with oysters and chive sauce. Among the desserts you
might find chocolate pots, tiramisu or baked bananas with
butterscotch sauce. *Seats 35. D only 5.30-10. Closed Sun,*
Nov-Easter. Access, Visa.

Kenmare	Park Hotel Kenmare 87%	£264
Tel 064 41200 Fax 064 41402		**HR**
Kenmare Co Kerry		Map 2 A6

In late Victorian times the gentry travelled from various parts
of the country by train, stopping at Kenmare, and the hotel was

See over

built in 1897 by the Great Southern and Western Railway
Company for passengers to stay overnight, before continuing their
journey the next day. The company sold the hotel in the late 70s,
and since then, under the direction of Francis Brennan, it has
enjoyed an enviable reputation – indeed, it was our UK Hotel
of the Year in 1988 and Francis is our Ireland Host of the Year for
1994. Set in eleven acres of unspoilt gardens on the shores
of Kenmare Bay, and yet only a short walk from town, the hotel
is particularly renowned for its fine antiques, stained-glass
windows, marvellous paintings, attention to detail (an expert
Dutch gilder spends the entire off-season painstakingly restoring
every crevice in the ornate plasterwork and cornices), comfortable
and elegant day rooms, and beautiful flower arrangements. On a
cold day one can relax in front of a crackling log fire, or in
summer and autumn take a stroll in the grounds and admire the
changing colours. Bedroom refurbishment ensures that guests can
sleep both soundly and in supreme comfort – the nine suites and
most of the rooms are very spacious indeed with wonderful views,
and offer every conceivable luxury, from bathrobes, slippers and
exquisite toiletries in the marble bathrooms to fresh fruit, mineral
water and books. Quality bed linen, good furniture, fine fabrics
and excellent towels, backed up by superb housekeeping, complete
the picture. Breakfast is a quite wonderful experience, including
a 'healthy' alternative prepared in accordance with the
recommendations of the world's heart associations. Special
'programmes' for Christmas and New Year – ask for their
brochure. Children up to 10 may share their parents' room at no
charge. Banqueting for 30, conference facilities for 50. No dogs.
Rooms *50. Garden, croquet, tennis, golf (18), games room.*
Closed mid Nov-22 Dec, 4 Jan-Easter. Access, Visa.

Restaurant ★   £90

The Park's warm welcome and special magic continue right from
the ever-burning fire in the hall through to the beautifully
appointed, yet surprisingly relaxed, high-ceilinged dining room
with its wonderful views. Formal touches such as antiques are
amusingly offset by quirks of personal taste – no designer co-
ordinations here. Enjoy an aperitif in the bar, where the door
opens to give a view of the mountains beyond, framed by palm
trees stirring in the wind. If you're lucky enough to sit at a
window table the view broadens to include the upper reaches
of the estuary and hotel lawn. Both daily-changing tables d'hote
(3-course at lunch, 4-course at dinner) and carte are available, the
former offering a choice of three dishes at each stage, the latter
tempting with dishes described in refreshingly plain English on a
menu that uses a watercolour of Kenmare's rich scenery as a
backdrop. Chef Brian Cleere works with obvious confidence and
verve in his recently revamped kitchen, often presenting
breathtakingly beautiful dishes, and also understanding when to let
the natural flavours and textures speak for themselves. Typically,
a table d'hote lunch doesn't stint on the involved nature of dishes,
starting with cassoulet of snails, Parma ham and oyster mushrooms
with a thyme sauce, followed by poached fillet of turbot with
a ravioli of lobster and prawns with a tomato and herb bouillon;
strawberry sablé with a blackcurrant coulis and amaretto sauce
to finish. The carte might offer home-made fettuccine with
Atlantic oysters, ribbons of wild smoked salmon, leek sauce and

caviar, terrine of guinea fowl and pigeon with a truffle vinaigrette, seafood (including lobster) from Kenmare Bay, pan-fried fillet of beef with a chartreuse of oxtail, onion confit and a red wine glaze and half a dozen or so tempting desserts. A selection of Irish cheeses is served with home-made walnut bread and a glass of port – a very civilised way to end an enjoyable meal in a delightful setting. Service under Jim McCarthy mirrors the balance shown in the kitchen – superbly professional complemented by the right amount of friendliness. The exceptional wine list offers several French classics of different vintages, as well as a comprehensive Californian section of over 30 bins; the Australian, Italian and Spanish sections present perhaps the best value. *Seats 80. Private Room 30. L 1-1.45 D 7-8.45. Set L £18 Set D £36.*

Kenmare   The Purple Heather

Tel 064 41016	**P**
Henry Street Kenmare Co Kerry	Map 2 A6

One of those delightful Kerry establishments which begins as a bar near the door and goes on to declare its real interest in food with tables and chairs properly set up for comfortable eating towards the back, the Purple Heather began serving good, simple food long before it was fashionable in these parts, in 1975. Gutsy home-made soups served with home-made, crusty brown bread (£1.60), wild smoked salmon with salad (£6.75), home-made chicken liver terrine with Cumberland sauce (£3.75), omelettes (from £4) and a wide range of sandwiches (from £1.30) – regular, open and toasted – are typical savoury offerings, followed by irresistible desserts like wholemeal apple crumble or hazelnut meringue. *Bar Food noon-6pm. Closed Sun. No credit cards.*

Kenmare   Sheen Falls Lodge   87%   £230

Tel 064 41600 Fax 064 41386	**H R**
Kenmare Co Kerry	Map 2 A6

There are several remarkable aspects of this hotel, not the least being that only a small part – the original 17th-century house – is not new, though you wouldn't know it from looking at the rest of the buildings. So cleverly has it been designed, and so beautifully does it blend into its surroundings – on one side the cascading waters from the Sheen River, on the other woodland and gardens overlooking Kenmare Bay – that it's really not apparent that the hotel has only been open for three years. On the site of a country estate dating back to the 1600s, including a long stretch of the river (private salmon fishing arranged), there are over 300 acres of grounds featuring lawns, semi-tropical gardens and tranquil woodland walks. Inside, the spacious foyer features marbled columns and a welcoming fire; there's also a mahogany-panelled library with deep green leather sofas, relaxing lounges, and a snooker room with arguably the finest views you'll ever cue in! Really spacious bedrooms, featuring natural wood and fine fabrics, include a self-contained apartment and eight suites (one suitable for disabled guests); all have equally spectacular views and feature amenities such as three telephones, personal safe, remote-control satellite TV and video recorder, iron and trouser press, mineral water and a bowl of fresh fruit daily. Naturally, there's a nightly turn-down service, and in the marble bathrooms with

See over

his and hers washbasins you'll find bathrobes, slippers, hairdryer, excellent toiletries and decent-sized towels. The state-of-the-art William Petty Conference Centre, named after the original landowner, can accommodate up to 160 delegates and lies in the basement, almost undetected and unnoticed by other guests, alongside the superbly equipped leisure facilities. *Rooms 40. Garden, croquet, gymnasium, sauna, spa bath, steam room, solarium, tennis, riding, bicycles, clay-pigeon shooting, coarse & game fishing, games room, boutique, helipad. Closed Jan–mid Mar.* AMERICAN EXPRESS *Access, Diners, Visa.*

La Cascade Restaurant ★ £90

Chef Fergus Moore's sophisticated menus are as attractive as the glorious views of the falls, which are floodlit at night. Both a daily, four-course table d'hote dinner and an extravagant à la carte are offered and should please even the most discerning diner. Typical starters might include coriander-scented lasagne of prawns with buttered juices, oven-roasted quail on a tatin of glazed apple, and slivers of fresh lobster with a concassé of tomato and red onion and a sea urchin rouille; main courses continue the involved theme with dishes like lightly wood-smoked fillet of beef on a fumet of Hermitage and shallots, fillets of black sole with sesame prawns and a red wine butter sauce, plus a vegetarian choice of agnolotti of wild mushrooms on a bed of steamed couscous finished with white butter and chervil. Local wild Atlantic salmon is cured and smoked on the premises, served with a sour cream and fresh herb dressing to start or (fresh) chargrilled and served with a purée of new potatoes with saffron and truffle oil dressing. Finish, perhaps, with chocolate marjolane, baked kumquat and orange pekoe tart with a mascarpone cream or compote of cherries with a brulée of sweet rice. Irish farmhouse cheeses are served with Parmesan biscuits. Excellent service is led by Joseph McColgan. Weekday food is waitress-served in the lounge from 11am–11pm (oysters, open sandwiches, fish casserole, stir-fried chicken, tasting plate of desserts), and afternoon tea (£8.50) from 3-5pm. The impressive wine list is notable for its good selection of half bottles; yes, it's quite expensive, but not too outrageous for a hotel of this class. Visit the marvellous cellars, which are also used for private parties, tastings and after-dinner imbibing! *Seats 120. Parties 8. Private Room 24. L Sun only 1-2 D 7.30-9.30. Set Sun L £17.50 Set D £35.*

Kilcolgan	Moran's Oyster Cottage	
Tel 091 96113 Fax 091 96503		**P**
The Weir Kilcolgan Co Galway		Map 2 B4

Willie Moran, champion oyster-opener, is the sixth generation of Morans to run this immaculate thatched cottage pub, whose bar looks out on to the pier. Gigas oysters (£7.50 a dozen) are available all year round, others from September to April. Alternatives include crab and smoked salmon (platters or sandwiches), mussels, seafood chowder, seafood cocktail and egg mayonnaise. All dishes are served with home-made brown bread. *Open 10am–midnight (Sun 12-2 & 4-11). Bar Food served all day. Garden, outdoor eating.* AMERICAN EXPRESS *Access, Visa.*

Kilcolgan   Places of Interest

Dunguaire Castle   Kinvara Tel 091 37108
Thoor Ballylee   by Gort. W B Yeats' home. Tel 091 31436

Kilcoran   Kilcoran Lodge   58%   £68

Tel 052 41288 Fax 052 41994	**H**
Kilcoran Cahir Co Tipperary	Map 2 C5

On the N8, 5 miles from the town of Cahir in the Cork direction. Set in 20 acres of grounds, this former hunting lodge overlooking the Suir Valley is run by Waveney Inns, Ireland. Conference/ banqueting facilities for 300/220. *Rooms 23. Indoor swimming pool, keep-fit equipment, sauna, spa bath, solarium, riding, coarse & game fishing.* AMERICAN EXPRESS® *Access, Diners, Visa.*

Kilkenny   Caisléan Ui Cuain

Tel 056 65406	**P**
2 High Street Kilkenny Co Kilkenny	Map 2 C5

Eccentric, perhaps, but popular nonetheless, this tall, narrow pub on three floors is situated on a prominent corner in the city centre and is striking, both inside and out. The interior is a mix of simple modern and traditional, with lots of aged wood and a good scattering of original posters. It has a relaxed, friendly and comfortable atmosphere and attracts a youngish, cosmopolitan crowd; writers, artists and musicians tend to congregate here due to the bar's reputation for lively discussion in Irish and for their live music. Officially, all year round, Monday night is traditional Irish music night but, in practice, an impromptu session can take off without warning at any time, to the great delight of all. Food varies according to seasonal demand and, in addition to conventional bar fare (soup £1.20, starters £2.75, main courses £3.95, desserts £1.50) there's now an à la carte restaurant at the top of the pub. *Bar Meals 10-8 (Sun 12.30-2 in summer only). Children allowed in bar to eat. No credit cards.*

Kilkenny   Kilkenny Kitchen

Tel 056 22118 Fax 056 65905	**R**
Kilkenny Design Centre Castle Yard Kilkenny Co Kilkenny	Map 2 C5

Situated in the Design Centre, a collection of craft shops and studios in the beautifully built outbuildings opposite the Castle, the Kilkenny Kitchen offers good home cooking on the premises and, in the shape of crusty home-made breads and delicious cakes (also to take away). Both hot and cold meals are much admired for their variety and general wholesomeness – all the more enjoyable when taken in such pleasant surroundings: overlooking the yard, the Kitchen occupies part of several floors right up to the open-beamed eaves and is sympathetically decorated with attractive oil cloths and a little vase of fresh flowers on the pine tables, kitchen-style chairs, cord carpet and simple white-washed stone walls all complementing the character of the old buildings. Typical dishes on the daily menu are salmon terrine, vegetarian quiche, chicken Wellington and braised steak. Among the desserts (all home-made) are Irish whiskey gateau and apple Bakewell tart. Afternoon tea with a slice of cherry flapjack or a finger of buttery

See over

shortbread is delicious. *Seats 170. Light meals 9-5 L 12-4 (Sun 10-5). Closed Good Friday, Christmas, Sun Jan-April.* AMERICAN EXPRESS *Access, Diners, Visa.*

Kilkenny	Lacken House	£60
Tel 056 61085 Fax 056 62435		**RR**
Dublin Road Kilkenny Co Kilkenny		Map 2 C5

One of Kilkenny's leading restaurants (and guesthouses) is run by highly respected chef Eugene McSweeney and his wife Breda; they have built up their reputation over the last ten years. Situated on the edge of the town in a Victorian house with a pleasant, well-proportioned drawing room/bar, the basement restaurant has rather small tables, but the quality of the food is more than adequate compensation. Eugene's dinner menu is in a progressive Irish mode and changes frequently, offering a well-balanced choice based on the classics but with concesssion to current trends; typical dishes might include fanned melon and orange with lemon grass syrup, Clonakilty black pudding with onion marmalade and wholegrain mustard sauce, braised duckling with mandarin sauce or poached salmon and hake in dill cream; Lacken House 'dessert plate' to finish. The choice is small, but only the freshest of local produce is used, much of it organic, particularly the vegetables. A varied Irish farmhouse cheese plate includes local specialities, notably Blue Abbey and Groghan goat's cheese. Bar snacks are available all day. *Seats 35. D only 7-10.30. Closed Sun & Mon except for residents, 1 week Christmas. Set D £22.* AMERICAN EXPRESS *Access, Diners, Visa.*

Rooms   £55

Eight bedrooms, all with shower or bath, provide simple accommodation; children up to 4 stay free in parents' room; children under 12, sharing parents' room, £10 B&B. Breakfast is excellent and is served either in the dining room or via room service. *Garden.*

Kilkenny	Langton's	
Tel 056 65133 Fax 056 63693		**P**
69 John Street Kilkenny Co Kilkenny		Map 2 C5

One of the best-known (and most praised) pubs in the country, run by Edward Langton since 1978 when he took over from his father. Edward has made a point of adding an extension or opening up a new area every year, so the huge premises are now a series of bars, each with its own individual style but all furnished to the highest standards in durable materials. Open fires with attractive basket grates are generously distributed through the various seating areas, all equally comfortable but with different attractions – one low-ceilinged area has a clubby atmosphere with buttoned leather wing chairs and banquette seating, while the next features an atrium, with walls of hanging plants and a genteel 'afternoon hotel tea' sort of atmosphere. Well-trained staff in black-and-white uniforms are helpful and efficient and bar menus offer food appropriate to the time of day – lunchtime sees a long list of sensibly-priced dishes (from chicken, honey and almond salad or fresh soup to smoked cod with egg and caper sauce, oyster-cut bacon and cabbage), through to a greater choice of dishes (like egg and Kilkenny ham mayonnaise, brunch, mussels farci, chicken curry and a daily special) in the afternoon and evening. Leave room for the likes of hot banana sponge pudding served with a brandy and coconut sauce (£1.25). Both fixed-price (£13.50 & £17.50) and à la carte menus are offered in the restaurant. Dancing Tue & Sat eves. *Bar Food & Restaurant Meals L 12-3, bar snacks 3-7, D 6 till late. Children allowed in bar to eat, children's menu. Garden.* AMERICAN EXPRESS® *Access, Diners, Visa.*

Kilkenny	Newpark Hotel	58%	£94

Tel 056 22122 Fax 056 61111	H
Castlecomer Road Kilkenny Co Kilkenny	Map 2 C5

The leisure centre and the banqueting/conference facilities supplement acceptable overnight accommodation at a 60s hotel on the N77. All-day snack service in the lobby. Plans for 1994 include 24 new family-size bedrooms. *Rooms 60. Indoor swimming pool, children's pool, keep-fit equipment, sauna, spa bath, steam room, solarium, tennis.* AMERICAN EXPRESS® *Access, Diners, Visa.*

Kilkenny	Shem's

Tel 056 21543	P
61 John Street Kilkenny Co Kilkenny	Map 2 C5

Pleasantly unfussy, clean-lined premises run along the lines of the simple old country pubs by Shem and Julie Lawlor. Lots of wood and, in winter, generosity with the heating, make this a warm and welcoming place and its relative simplicity and small size will please those who find larger premises somewhat overpowering. Julie looks after the cooking herself and takes pride in preparing simple food well – home-made daily soups (seafood chowder, Chinese chicken, Irish potato, all 95p), main courses (all £3.95) such as poached smoked haddock with parsley sauce, daily pasta dishes, Hungarian beef goulash, plus the likes of bread-and-butter pudding, grape pavlova and gateau Diane to finish (all puddings £1.25). Sandwiches (open, closed, toasted) also on an all-day bar snack menu. Children's menu of favourites (3 courses £3.50). *Bar Food L 12-3, bar snacks 3-6. Children allowed in bar to eat, children's menu. Access, Visa.*

Kilkenny	Tynan's Bridge House Bar

Tel 056 61828	P
Bridge House 2 Johns Bridge Kilkenny Co Kilkenny	Map 2 C5

One of the most genuine and interesting of Kilkenny's old pubs, Tynan's has had the same landlord for over 50 years – Michael Tynan, and his father was here before him. The spotless little bar features a marble counter, lots of mahogany and a charming tapestry on a wall. No children after 7pm. *No credit cards.*

Kilkenny	Places of Interest

Tourist Information   Tel 056 21755
Dunmore Cave   Tel 056 67726
Gowran Park Racecourse   Tel 056 26110
Irish National Design Centre   Tel 056 22118
Jerpoint Abbey   Tel 056 24623
Kilkenny Castle   Tel 056 21450
Rothe House   Parliament Street Tel 056 22893

Killaloe   Goosers

Tel 061 376792	P
Killaloe Ballina Co Tipperary	**Map 2 B4**

This delightful pub, in a quiet situation just across the road from
the lake, has built up a formidable reputation for its double act
of good food and characterful ambience. Settle into your choice
of several intimate bar areas, each with its own fireplace and
simply but comfortably furnished with country furniture and
a finely-judged selection of decorative rustic bric-a-brac, and enjoy
anything from a quick snack to a 3-course meal from the
blackboard menu. Seafood is the star among the bar food,
including oysters, mussels and scallops. Sandwiches and salads
provide satisfying snacks, and larger appetites will be allayed
by bacon and cabbage, Irish stew or a steak. *Bar Food 10.30-
10.30. Children's menu and portions available. Access, Visa.*

Killarney   Aghadoe Heights Hotel   70%   £136

Tel 064 31766 Fax 064 31345	HR
Aghadoe Killarney Co Kerry	**Map 2 A5**

Low-rise concrete and glass hotel of 1960s' origin refurbished
in varying styles but to a generally high standard in public areas
and the views over Lake Killarney and the mountains beyond are
wonderful, especially from the elegantly appointed dining room.
Leisure facilities, although conspicuous from the road, do not
intrude. Bedrooms and bathrooms are neat, although not large.
Conference/banqueting facilities for 130/100. Sister hotel
to *Fredrick's* in Maidenhead, England. *Rooms 60. Garden, indoor
swimming pool, gymnasium, sauna, spa bath, steam room, solarium,
beauty salon, tennis, fishing, boutique, helipad.* *Access,
Diners, Visa.*

Fredrick's Restaurant   ↑   £100

In this luxuriously appointed first-floor dining room with
dramatic (probably unrivalled) views over the Lakes of Killarney,
chef Robin Suter is running a very fine kitchen with dinner
menus changing daily and lunch menus every week. The style
is formal, imaginative, distinctly French and based on superb
quality produce – everything positively zings with freshness and
portions are unexpectedly generous. Try, perhaps, avocado with
fresh crab and grapefruit (colourful, light and beautifully
presented with a generous amount of white crabmeat) or cassolette
of Kerry seafood and linguini (an excellent mixture of shellfish –
fresh prawns, crab claws, mussels – white fish and salmon with
home-made pasta in an outstandingly flavoursome light creamy
sauce). An exceptional selection of freshly baked breads, handed
separately, will undoubtedly prove irresistible. Typical main
courses on the lunch menu might include tournedos of cod with
tomato and thyme sauce (the cod is wrapped in streaky bacon,
making a very substantial dish) or succulent grilled lamb cutlets
maitre d'hotel prettily presented with a small salad and cherry
tomato garnish. An imaginative vegetable selection might
typically include new potatoes, pommes almondines, braised
fennel, batons of carrot, very light crisp onion rings and crisply
cooked broccoli. Fritters are a favourite dessert, mixed fruit
perhaps, very light and crisp, followed by fragrant cafetière coffee

and delicious home-made petits fours. An interesting wine list
includes some selected for exceptional value, from £13-£19.50,
a collection of 'Wild Geese' wines from Irish connected families,
and a good selection of half bottles. **Seats 84. Parties 24.**
Private Room 70. L 12.15-2 D 7-9.30. Set L £17.50 D £29.50.

Killarney   Cahernane Hotel   66%   £110
Tel 064 31895   Fax 064 34340   **HR**

Muckross Road Killarney Co Kerry   Map 2 A5

Killarney's lakes and mountains create a majestic backdrop for
a fine hotel that was once the residence of the Earls of Pembroke.
Inside, Conor O'Connell and his staff create a warm, friendly
atmosphere, and standards of service, comfort and housekeeping
are high. There is a choice between traditional master bedrooms
in the main house and simpler but spacious and well-appointed
rooms in a sympathetic modern wing. Children under 12 may
stay free in parents' room. **Rooms 52.** *Garden, hairdressing, tennis,
pitch & putt, game fishing, boutique. Closed 31 Oct-1 Apr.*
AMERICAN EXPRESS *Access, Diners, Visa.*

The Herbert Room Restaurant   £65

In the smartly refurbished Herbert Room Eddie Hayes offers
a choice of menus for dinner – four courses plus coffee and petits
fours on the table d'hote, or a wide-ranging à la carte. The former
tends to be more traditional, with dishes such as mussels
provençale, beef consommé, paupiettes of Dover sole with prawn
tails and entrecote steak with mushrooms. Other choices – paillard
of salmon with lemon aïoli, fettucine with crabmeat sauce – move
into the slightly more adventurous realms of the carte, where you
could find snails cooked in port, served on black pasta with a sauce
of gorgonzola, cream and wild mushrooms, or a vegetarian
Buddhist stew. On this menu, too, are classics like sole véronique
and steak Diane. Light lunches are served in the lounge.
Something for everyone on the well-rounded wine list, though
a bottle of mineral water will set you back £4 and champagne
£40! **Seats 90. Parties 30. Private Room 14.** *D 7-9.30. Set D £24.*

When telephoning establishments in the Republic from *outside*
the Republic, dial 010-353 then the number we print without
initial zero: e.g. Cliffords in Cork is 010-353 21 275333.

Killarney   Dingles Restaurant   £45
Tel 064 31079   **R**

40 New Street Killarney Co Kerry   Map 2 A5

Genuine hospitality and congenial surroundings are the keynotes
at Gerry and Marion Cunningham's relaxed restaurant and it is
obviously a favourite rendezvous for locals who appreciate Gerry's
easy welcome as much as Marion's excellent uncomplicated food,
which is based on the best ingredients and delivered with
admirable simplicity. Open fires, ecclesiastical furniture and old
plates on the walls create a characterful ambience in which
to enjoy anything from a home-made burger with freshly cut
chips cooked in olive oil to a 4-course dinner. **Seats 45.** *Meals
12-10pm. Closed Sun, 20 Dec-1 Mar.* AMERICAN EXPRESS *Access,
Diners, Visa.*

Killarney   Hotel Europe   72%   £96

Tel 064 31900   Fax 064 32118   **H**

Killorglin Road Fossa Killarney Co Kerry   Map 2 A5

A large modern hotel next to Killarney Golf and Fishing Club,
catering equally well for private guests and conference delegates
(up to 500 theatre style). The mountain and lake views are quite
a feature, and most of the spacious bedrooms have balconies
to make the most of the setting. Day rooms include a lounge with
a pine ceiling copied from an English castle. There's an excellent
health and fitness centre. *Rooms 205. Garden, indoor swimming
pool, gymnasium, solarium, sauna, spa bath, beauty salon, hair salon,
fishing, tennis, riding, games room, snooker room, news kiosk, shop,
boutique, helipad. Closed Nov-Mar.* AMERICAN EXPRESS *Access,
Diners, Visa.*

Changes in data sometimes occur in establishments
after the Guide goes to press. Prices should be taken
as indications rather than firm quotes.

Killarney   Foley's Townhouse   £60

Tel 064 31217   Fax 064 34683   **R R**

23 High Street Killarney Co Kerry   Map 2 A5

A Killarney landmark since the late 40s, Foley's is another
example of the winning Kerry format – a front-of-house bar
which gradually develops into a fully-fledged restaurant further
back – in this case a cosy bar with an open fire, furnished
to encourage lingering, backed by rather business-like rows
of tables indicating clearly the level of turnover which might
be expected in high season. With Denis and Carol Harnett here
since 1967, the well-established feel of Foley's is reassuringly
disregarding of fashion and, although emanating from modern,
well-equipped and scrupulously clean kitchens, Carol Harnett's
menus reflect this in style and content, in dishes like soup of the
day (mushroom, perhaps – a thick country purée), sole on the
bone and scallops in potato-piped shells, both served surprisingly
with roast potato and mixed side salads reminiscent of the 60s.
Families are made welcome with good facilities for tots and their
parents. *Seats 95. Private Room 25. L (bar food) 12.30-3 D 5-11.
Closed mid-Jan to mid-Feb & 22-27 Dec. Private Room 25.*
AMERICAN EXPRESS *Access, Visa.*

Rooms   £70

Foley's Townhouse is the culmination of Carol Harnett's long-held
ambition to provide top-class accommodation at the restaurant –
twelve rooms are individually decorated to a high standard and
much thought has gone into planning each room to maximise use
of space and comfort, including double-glazing to reduce
traffic/late-night noise; special care was taken with the bathrooms,
which are all exceptionally well appointed with unusual colour
schemes, quality tubs and washbasins, special tiles and all the
touches more usually found in leading hotels. Guests use a separate
entrance and public areas include a residents' lounge and a private
dining room. Banqueting/conference facilities for up to 95/25.
No dogs.

Killarney   Gaby's Seafood Restaurant   £60

Tel 064 32519   Fax 064 32747   **R**

27 High Street Killarney Co Kerry   **Map 2 A5**

Although only in the present purpose-built premises since 1992,
chef Geert Maes has been indispensable to the Killarney dining
scene since 1976. The new restaurant is larger and has a bar area
near the door, with a little garden at the back. Within, the space
is cleverly broken into several levels, creating an unexpectedly
initimate atmosphere that is enhanced by plants and good lighting.
Whether for an informal lunch (home-made soups, open
sandwiches, seafood platter) or a leisurely dinner (cassolette
of prawns and monkfish, grilled lobster), this is a place where
respect for fresh local produce can be depended upon – seafood
is the speciality, but it is reassuringly dependent on availability.
A most fairly priced wine list offers an outstanding worldwide
selection and, unusually for a seafood restaurant (though it does
serve steaks and lamb), includes a super repertoire of red wines
as well. *Seats 65. L 12.30-2.30 D 6-10. Closed all Sun & L Mon,
3 weeks Feb.* AMERICAN EXPRESS *Access, Diners, Visa.*

Killarney   Great Southern   69%   £129

Tel 064 31262   Fax 064 31642   **H**

Killarney Co Kerry   **Map 2 A5**

Situated close to the town centre (3 minutes' walk), this former
railway hotel is a substantial building set in 36 acres of gardens
that curve around the main building and bedroom extensions.
The entrance hall is impressive, with Ionic columns, chandeliers
and a large seating area. Bedrooms vary considerably in size and
style; many have been recently refurbished (as have the main
public areas). Leisure facilities are good and the hotel offers
a variety of function facilities, taking conferences of up to 1000
theatre-style and banquets up to 650. The Punch Bowl cocktail
bar overlooks the hotel gardens. *Rooms 183. Garden, indoor
swimming pool, splash pool, sauna, spa bath, gymnasium, tennis,
hairdressing, baby-sitting. Closed 6 weeks Jan/Feb.* AMERICAN EXPRESS
Access, Diners, Visa.

Killarney   Kathleen's Country House   £55

Tel 064 32810   Fax 064 32340   **A**

Tralee Road Killarney Co Kerry   **Map 2 A5**

Just a mile from the centre of Killarney, this family-run
establishment is peacefully set in well-maintained gardens and
equally well-known for the warmth of Kathleen O'Regan-
Sheppard's welcome and her scrupulous attention to detail. Public
areas are spacious and individually decorated bedrooms with
views exceptionally well appointed, all with fully-tiled bath and
shower en suite, direct-dial phone, trouser press, tea/coffee
facilities, individually controlled central heating, radio alarm
clock, orthopaedic beds, TV and hairdryer. Good breakfasts are
cooked to order and served in an attractive dining room
overlooking the garden and unspoilt countryside. All rooms non-
smoking. No children under 10. No dogs. *Rooms 17. Garden,
croquet. Closed Dec-Feb. Visa.*

Killarney   The Killarney Park Hotel   73%   £110

Tel 064 35555   Fax 064 35266   **H**

Kenmare Place Killarney Co Kerry   **Map 2 A5**

This newish hotel with classical lines enjoys a central setting
in attractive gardens set with mature trees. First impressions are
carried through to the smart foyer, which is spacious, with fires,
plenty of comfortable seating and, in common with most of the
other public areas, notably the bar, a pleasingly bold colour
scheme with fabrics mixed to good effect. The restaurant is more
restrained and has a cosy area especially appropriate for winter
dining. Although not individually furnished, bedrooms are
planned in groups to have variety in shape and size as well
as colour schemes; all are spacious, several very large and
especially suitable for families, and marbled bathrooms are well
appointed. Banqueting/conference facilities for 160/150. The
leisure centre "Club at the Park" opens out on to its own furnished
patio. No dogs. ***Rooms** 55. Garden, indoor swimming pool, children's
pool, gymnasium, keep-fit equipment.* AMERICAN EXPRESS *Access,
Diners, Visa.*

Killarney   Killarney Towers Hotel   57%   £90

Tel 064 31038   Fax 064 31755   **H**

College Square Killarney Co Kerry   **Map 2 A5**

Very centrally located, this new hotel has quite spacious, identical,
but comfortably furnished bedrooms with tea-making facilities,
multi-channel TV and neat en-suite bathrooms. 55 more rooms
have been opened in the last year. Children under 3 share parents'
room free; 3- to 12-year-olds half price. Two bars include
a residents' lounge and the lively Scruffy's pub. Lock-up car park.
***Rooms** 157. Access, Visa.*

Killarney   Randles Court Hotel   £120

Tel 064 35333   Fax 064 35206   **H**

Muckross Road Killarney Co Kerry   **Map 2 A5**

Well-situated – it is convenient to Muckross House and Killarney
National Park but is also within walking distance of the town centre
– this attractive Edwardian house underwent extensive
refurbishment before opening as an owner-run hotel in 1992.
Period features including fireplaces and stained glass windows
have been retained however and comfortably furnished public
areas include a small bar, spacious drawing room with log fire,
murals and antiques and an elegant restaurant opening on to
a sheltered patio. Bedrooms have direct-dial telephones, satellite
television, radio, hairdryer and well-appointed bathrooms;
children under 5 may stay free in their parents' room. Banqueting
for up to 130. ***Rooms** 37. Patio, golf, riding, fishing, shooting.
Closed Jan & Feb.* AMERICAN EXPRESS *Access, Visa.*

Killarney   The Strawberry Tree   £77

Tel & Fax 064 32688   **R**

24 Plunkett Street Killarney Co Kerry   **Map 2 A5**

Owner-chef Evan Doyle and restaurant manager Denis Heffernan
have been running this first-floor restaurant to growing acclaim
since 1983 and now, as the first Irish restaurant to make

an absolute commitment to using wild, free-range and organic produce in 1993, a new standard has been set. The ambience is comfortably cottagey but sophisticated, with open stone and whitewashed walls, open fires and low ceilings with the elegantly appointed tables and thoughtfully written menus which give a hint of serious goings-on in the kitchen. Wild salmon is home-smoked over oak and apple wood, producing a pale, unusually subtle smoke, real (that is, organic) vegetable soups come with wonderful warm breads (several made daily – a worthy recipient of the Irish Brown Bread of the Year Award) and corned beef and cabbage is served unusually as a starter – and, more unusually still, they can tell you exactly where the beef came from. A sorbet might be made of gorse and wild mint, a duet of wild foods could be pan-fried breast of wood-pigeon with home-made rabbit sausages. Desserts include a good bread-and-butter pudding and home-made ices, such as lemon balm and honey. Fragrant coffees or herbal teas come with irresistible petits fours. The excellent house wine selection is made democratically each year by friends and regulars. Early Bird menus (6.30-8pm) are especially good value. *Seats 30. Parties 14. L by arrangement D 6.30-10.30. Set Early Bird menu (6.30-8) £14.95. Closed Jan/Feb.* AMERICAN EXPRESS *Access, Diners, Visa.*

Killarney   Torc Great Southern   63%   £91

Tel 064 31611 Fax 064 31824	**H**
Park Road Killarney Co Kerry	**Map 2 A5**

Modern, low-rise hotel half a mile from the town centre on the main Cork road. Well-run, with views of the Kerry mountains, it makes a good base for a holiday in the area. 20 bedrooms were refurbished last year and a new bar was added. *Rooms 96. Garden, indoor swimming pool, sauna, tennis. Closed Oct-end Mar.* AMERICAN EXPRESS *Access, Diners, Visa.*

> Our inspectors **never** book in the name of Egon Ronay's Guides. They disclose their identity only if they are considering an establishment for inclusion in the next edition of the Guide.

Killarney   Yer Man's Pub

Tel & Fax 064 32688	**P**
24 Plunkett Street Killarney Co Kerry	**Map 2 A5**

Underneath *The Strawberry Tree* restaurant and in common ownership, a characterful, old-fashioned pub is to be found. The modern accoutrements nowadays essential to a well-run bar have been skilfully disguised, while the comforts of yesteryear are much in evidence – the long narrow bar has two open turf fires, each with its own collection of mismatched but comfortable seating, including an old leather-upholstered car seat and the top half of an Edwardian armchair, easily set on a box. Plenty of shelf-height hooks for outerwear and a small back bar with original black range add to the appeal. Wholesome soups, sandwiches, salads, pies and seafood (oysters, smoked salmon, garlic mussels) from *The Strawberry Tree* kitchen are offered on a short bar menu. *Open 11-1am (in winter to 11 Mon-Fri).* **Bar Food** *12-6 (in winter to 3, no food Sun). Access, Diners, Visa.*

Killarney   Places of Interest

Tourist Information Tel 064 31633
Killarney National Park Tel 064 31947
Ross Castle Tel 064 32402
Crag Cave Castle Island Tel 066 41244

Killiney   Court Hotel   68%   £97

Tel 01 285 1622 Fax 01 285 2085	**H**
Killiney Bay Killiney Co Dublin	Map 2 D4

Half an hour from the city centre by car or DART railway, this
extended Victorian mansion looks over landscaped gardens
to Killiney Bay. The most recent additions include a new cocktail
bar and conservatory and the reception area has also been enlarged
and modernised. Bedrooms, most with sea views, are spacious and
pleasantly decorated with darkwood furniture and co-ordinated
fabrics; under-12s stay free in parents' room. An international
conference centre has facilities for up to 300. No dogs. *Rooms 86.*
Garden. AMERICAN EXPRESS *Access, Diners, Visa.*

Killiney   Fitzpatrick's Castle   68%   £147

Tel 01 285 1533 Fax 01 285 0207	**H**
Killiney Co Dublin	Map 2 D4

Dating back to 1741 and converted by the present owners
in 1974, this imposing castle hotel is half an hour's drive from
Dublin city centre and, despite its size and style, has a surprisingly
lived-in atmosphere. Extensive facilities include two large lounges,
two restaurants, a basement disco and a conference suite for up to
550 delegates. Roomy bedrooms, including some mini-suites, have
darkwood furniture and draped curtains. Children under 12 may
stay free in parents' room. *Rooms 85. Garden, indoor swimming
pool, gymnasium, squash, sauna, steam room, hair & beauty salon,
tennis.* AMERICAN EXPRESS *Access, Diners, Visa.*

Killiney   Place of Interest

Ayesha Castle Tel 01 285 2323

Killorglin   Nick's Restaurant   £65

Tel 066 61219 Fax 066 61233	**R**
Lower Bridge Street Killorglin Co Kerry	Map 2 A5

Nick and Anne Foley's popular seafood restaurant always has
a good buzz and Nick's cooking, which relies entirely on daily
catches for its seafood and local suppliers for lamb, beef and
organically grown vegetables, is mainly traditional French. From
a wide seafood selection, boosted by daily specials, could come
oysters, lobster, plaice, sole and salmon, plus filled grillets of brill,
turbot and John Dory with lemon butter sauce. Elsewhere on the
menu you might find asparagus with hollandaise, ballotine of duck
with cherry relish, chicken Cordon Bleu, pork or lamb cutlets and
various steaks. A really splendid wine list – note the extensive
selection from the Loire particularly, but also Alsace and
Burgundy. Even though Nick's is predominantly a seafood
restaurant, red wine drinkers will not be disappointed, nor
supporters of the New World. *Seats 80. Parties 50.*
Private Room 35. D only 6-10. Closed Nov-Easter, Mon & Tues.
AMERICAN EXPRESS *Access, Diners, Visa.*

ppp

Kilmoon — The Snail Box

Tel 01 354277 — **P**

Kilmoon Ashbourne Co Meath — Map 1 C3

Four miles north of Ashbourne on the N2, this pleasant local has a pool table bang in the middle of the friendly public bar and a comfortable lounge in rustic style, both with open fireplaces. But its curious name and the story of its origins are unique, going back to the early 1800s when the site was common land and a hedge schoolmaster settled there for a while. Taking exception to this intrusion, the local landlord took him to court to get him evicted – but the justice of the day ruled that 'the snail and his box can settle where he chooses'. *Open 4-11.30 (Fri & Sat from 1, Sun 12.30-2.30 & 4-11). No credit cards.*

Kinnegad — The Cottage

Tel 044 75284 — **R**

Kinnegad Co Westmeath — Map 1 C3

Baking is a speciality at this neat, homely cottage restaurant, so afternoon tea is a good time to drop in for scones, cakes and preserves. Sandwiches, salads and omelettes are popular orders for light meals, while at the luxury end of the menu are fresh and smoked salmon. *Seats 30. Parties 14. Private Room 26. L 12-3 D 6-8. Closed D Sat, all Sun, 10 days Christmas. No credit cards.*

Kinsale — Actons Hotel   60%   £100

Tel 021 772135   Fax 021 772231 — **H**

Pier Road Kinsale Co Cork — Map 2 B6

Overlooking the harbour, this attractive quayside hotel was created from several substantial period houses. Conference/banqueting facilities for up to 300. Children up to 14 stay free in parents' room. Forte Heritage. *Rooms 57. Indoor swimming pool, gymnasium, sauna, solarium.* *Access, Diners, Visa.*

Kinsale — Blue Haven Hotel   £84

Tel 021 772209   Fax 021 774268 — **HR**

3 Pearse Street Kinsale Co Cork — Map 2 B6

Serious fishermen and trenchermen alike should head for the small, cosy, blue-and-white Blue Haven hotel near the quay, where not only is there a 36' ocean-going angling boat for hire, but also good food and comfortable accommodation after a hard day's sport. Bedrooms vary from quite small to reasonably large (three have three beds), but all are neat with smart white furniture and pictures by local artists. Only one has a bath; the rest have showers or share a bathroom. The bar serves a wide choice of imaginative food – from a choice of soups to sandwiches and good seafood – and is very attractive, with wood panelling, natural stone and a log fire, and has many snug corners opening on to a cane-furnished conservatory which, in turn, leads on to a patio. The entrance has been upgraded and a new wine shop/delicatessen opened just off the lobby. Cots, high-chairs and baby-sitting can all be arranged on request. No dogs. *Rooms 10. Bar & conservatory (10.30am-9.30pm), teas & light snacks (3-5pm), sea fishing. Closed 25 Dec.* Access, Diners, Visa.

See over

Restaurant £60

The diner is left with no doubt as to the specialities of the
characterful restaurant, which has a strong maritime theme and
overlooks an attractive courtyard garden. Chef Stanley Matthews
kicks off with starters of seafood chowder, wild smoked salmon
or baked Rossmore oysters glazed with hollandaise, followed
by Oriental seafood Kashmiri, grilled Dover sole on the bone
or scallops on a skewer with bacon and mushrooms. Seafood
is balanced by dishes like sautéed herbed goat's cheese or Jack
Barry's lamb's kidneys, smoked chicken salad, Mitchelstown
venison or prime fillet steaks. Good local farmhouse cheeses,
including Carrigaline. A well-rounded wine list offers very fair
prices with little over £20. *Seats 45. Parties 18. D only 7-10.30.
Closed 25 Dec.*

Kinsale The Bulman Bar

Tel 021 772131	**P**
Summer Cove Kinsale Co Cork	Map 2 B6

About a mile along the harbour in the Charles Fort direction, this
traditional little waterside bar enjoys a tremendous setting looking
over the harbour towards Kinsale. The bar is sometimes quiet and
cosy, at other times very busy, and the large car park is liable
to turn into "the biggest lounge bar in Ireland". The food side
of the business is being developed, with seafood to the fore. *Open
10.30am-11pm (11.30 in summer), Sun 12.30-2 & 4-11pm.
No credit cards.*

Kinsale Chez Jean-Marc ↑ £55

Tel 021 774625 Fax 021 774680	**R**
Lower O'Connell Street Kinsale Co Cork	Map 2 B6

A cheerful yellow outside, beamed and country-cosy within, this
is a warm, welcoming place offering excellent food and efficient
service. Jean-Marc Tsai's cooking is traditional French with
Oriental accents. From the classic repertoire come French onion
soup, garlicky baked mussels, duck à la bigarade and roast pheasant
with shallots and brandy sauce and *pommes darphin*. Striking
a more exotic note are salad Mikado, Thai stir-fry and roast
monkfish steak on a bed of scallops and creamed tagliatelle
flavoured with a hint of curry. Desserts are simple and delicious.
The wine list includes a good choice of house bottles. *Seats 55.
L (Sun only, low season) 12.30-3 D 6.45-10.30 (winter 7-10).
Closed D Sun, all Mon (winter), 3 days Christmas, weekdays Feb.*

AMERICAN EXPRESS *Access, Diners, Visa.*

Kinsale The Dock Bar

Tel 021 772522	**P**
Castle Park Kinsale Co Cork	Map 2 B6

Well situated between the small marina at Castle Park and one
of the few south-facing sandy beaches in the area (a few hundred
yards across the peninsula), this traditional black and white pub
looks over towards Kinsale and, although the town is very near,
it feels like a world apart. The patio, where tables have a choice

of sun or leafy shade, has a slightly Continental atmosphere and
the interior is comfortable in the modern Irish idiom – quarry
tiles, varnished tables, upholstered benches and photographs
of some of landlord Michael Vance's winning rides to remind him
of his years in the saddle. Smoked salmon and fresh crabmeat are
the specialities on a short bar menu which also includes a range
of sandwiches (closed or open, toasted or plain), apple tart and
scones. *Open 12-12, Sun 12.30-2 & 4-11. Outdoor eating area.
No credit cards.*

Kinsale	Man Friday	£55
Tel 021 772260		**R**
Scilly Kinsale Co Cork		Map 2 B6

A popular and convivial restaurant housed in a series of little
rooms high above the harbour. Seafood is the natural speciality,
with oysters cold or poached, crab au gratin, sweet and sour
scampi, black sole (grilled or Colbert) and monkfish with a prawn
sauce among the wide choice. That choice extends outside the
fishy realms to the likes of Robinson Crusoe's warm salad (mixed
leaves, croutons and bacon), deep-fried Brie with a plum and port
sauce, Swiss-style veal escalope and roast rack of lamb with
rosemary and a red wine sauce. Strawberry crème brulée,
chocolate terrine, grape pudding or home-made ice creams round
things off. Consistency is a keynote here, and it's owner-chef
Philip Horgan (in charge since 1978) who maintains it. *Seats 80.
Private Room 35. L by arrangement only (groups) D 7-10.
Closed Sun (Nov-Mar), 24-26 Dec.* AMERICAN EXPRESS *Access, Visa.*

Kinsale	Max's Wine Bar	£40
Tel 021 772443		**R**
Main Street Kinsale Co Cork		Map 2 B6

Wendy Tisdall is coming up for 20 years at her charming little
restaurant, where highly varnished tabletops reflect fresh flowers
and plants and menus are always light and tempting. Duck liver
paté with plum sauce, half a dozen oysters or spinach pasta with
fresh salmon could start a meal, or there are some speciality salads
– Caesar, baked goat's cheese, crudités with a garlic or curry dip.
Next might come the day's fish catch, poached chicken,
beefburgers or rack of lamb, bread-and-butter pudding,
lemon pancakes or chocolate rum mousse to finish in style. The
early bird menu offers particularly good value for money.
*No smoking in the conservatory (10 seats). Seats 40. Parties 12.
L 1-3 D 7-10.30. Closed Nov-Feb. Set D £12. Access, Visa.*

Kinsale	The Old Bank House	£52
Tel 021 774075 Fax 021 774296		**A**
Pearse Street Kinsale Co Cork		Map 2 B6

A Georgian building of some character, formerly a branch of the
Munster and Leinster Bank. Individually furnished bedrooms are
spacious, elegant and comfortable, with good antiques and well-
appointed bathrooms. Public areas, including breakfast room and
sitting room, are non-smoking. Babies are accommodated, but 2-9
year olds are not encouraged. *Rooms 9. Closed 3 days Christmas.*
AMERICAN EXPRESS *Access, Visa.*

Kinsale   Old Presbytery   £36

Tel 021 772027   **RR**

Cork Street Kinsale Co Cork   Map 2 B6

Victorian antiques, many of rural interest, are a feature of Ken and
Cathleen Buggy's peaceful, comfortable home. The old kitchen has
been turned into a small restaurant, where Ken produces short,
daily-changing menus with old-fashioned unusual soups,
Continental salads and freshly caught fish among the specialities.
Restaurant only open to residents. *Seats 14. D only 7.30-8.30.
Closed Sun, 1 week Christmas. Set D £18. No credit cards.*

Rooms   £38

The six bedrooms are decorated in traditional style, with big beds
and Irish linen, and there's a comfortable sitting room with
an open fire. Breakfast is a splendid spread, with a choice of 52
items including freshly baked bread, home-made preserves and
yoghurts, apricots and figs in cider, pickled herrings and cheese.
"Children and dogs are not turned away if at the door, but are not
really encouraged."

Kinsale   Scilly House   65%   £80

Tel 021 772413   Fax 021 774629   **A**

Scilly Kinsale Co Cork   Map 2 B6

An old house of great charm and character overlooking the
harbour and Kinsale Bay. The style is American country, with old
pine furniture, antiques, traditional American quilts, floral prints
and folk art. Public rooms include a bar/library with grand piano,
a cosy sitting room and a dining room with views over the
garden down to the sea. There are views, too, from most of the
individually appointed bedrooms (two non-smoking). *Rooms 7.
Closed Dec-Feb.* AMERICAN EXPRESS *Access, Visa.*

Kinsale   1601

Tel 021 772529   **P**

Pearse Street Kinsale Co Cork   Map 2 B6

Named after the year of the battle of Kinsale, details of which
form an interesting and decorative presentation in the front
lounge, this centrally located pub has earned a reputation for good
bar food and is popular with locals and visitors alike. Service can
be a little slow at busy times, but their well-priced, freshly home-
made food is worth waiting for; the menu changes daily. There's
always a choice of chowder (£2.75) and another soup of the day
(£1.50) and a short, well-balanced menu offers starters/light main
courses such as a warm salad of goat's cheese (£4.25), several local
seafood dishes, traditional Irish fare like boiled bacon and cabbage
with parsley sauce and Irish stew (both £4.25) and the house
special, '1601 Battle Burger' (£4.50), a home-made burger served
with chips, salad and a choice of piquant dipping sauces such
as chili, ketchup and chutney. The rear of the Lounge Bar is the
Art Gallery restaurant, where food is served all day when it's busy.
*Bar Food 12.30-3, 6-9 (4-6 Sun). Children allowed in the bar to eat.
Access, Visa.*

Kinsale   The Spaniard Inn

Tel 021 772436	**P**
Scilly Kinsale Co Cork	**Map 2 B6**

High above the harbour near the *Man Friday* restaurant, the
Spaniard dispenses good cheer, good food and good music. Mary
O'Toole's bar food is plain and simple, running from salads, soups
and sandwiches to old favourites like Irish stew or bacon and
cabbage. Lunch can be taken on the terrace when the sun shines.
Music sessions include light jazz, contemporary folk and Irish
traditional (Wed). The inn comprises several low-beamed rooms
with stone floors, country furniture and assorted items of local
interest – notably a 35lb salmon caught in 1912 at Little Island,
Ardfinnan. *Open 10.30am-11.30pm Mon-Sat (to 11 in winter, Sun
12-2.30 & 4-11).* **Bar Food** *12.30-3 May-Sept, snacks only
in evenings and all day Sun. Terrace, outdoor eating. No credit cards.*

Kinsale   Place of Interest

Charles Fort   Tel 021 772263

Laragh   Mitchell's of Laragh

	£25
Tel & Fax 0404 45302	**R**
The Old Schoolhouse Laragh Co Wicklow	**Map 2 D4**

Jerry and Margaret Mitchell's lovingly restored old cut-granite
schoolhouse, with leaded window panes, open fires and country
pine furniture, provides adults with a tranquil haven from the
crowds which nearby Glendalough tends to attract – and very
good home cooking to boot. Menus, changed with the seasons,
might include sautéed lambs' kidneys, piquant with whiskey and
orange, or crisp hot button mushrooms on toast, fragrant in lemon
and garlic, followed by tender, juicy roast lamb with home-made
mint jelly, perhaps, or a real old-fashioned steak and kidney pie,
or salmon in filo, with a dill mayonnaise. "All types of food are
served all day to our visitors from all around the world", says
Margaret, so one can eat quiche for breakfast or a fry-up for
dinner if it takes one's fancy. Margaret's home baking is a great
strength and, not surprisingly perhaps, afternoon tea (£3.50) is a
speciality. Accommodation is offered in three neat en-suite twin
rooms with pleasant rural outlook. Two more rooms and a guest
sitting room are due for completion by summer '94. No dogs.
*Seats 30. Private Room 50. Meals 9am-10pm (Sun 9pm). Set Sun
L £10 Set D £15. Closed 2 days at Christmas.* AMERICAN EXPRESS
Access, Visa

Leighlinbridge   The Lord Bagenal Inn

	£45
Tel 0503 21668	**R**
Leighlinbridge Co Carlow	**Map 2 C4**

Food, wine and hospitality are all dispensed in good measure
at this renowned old inn just off the main M9 Waterford-Carlow
road. The style of cooking is always evolving, and more modern
dishes are joining old favourites like the oysters and mussels, the
crabs and the scallops, the home-made patés, the steaks and the fine
fresh fish. The whole family is made very welcome and there's
a special children's menu. Also a new tourist menu and plenty
of vegetarian dishes. Farmhouse cheeses. There are surprisingly few

See over

half bottles on an otherwise enterprising and comprehensive wine list that provides helpful notes and is fairly priced. *Seats 90. Parties 25. Private Room 40. L 12.30-2.30 D 6-10.30 (bar food 12.30-10.30). Closed 25 Dec, Good Friday. Set L £9.50 Set D £11.50/£17.50. Access, Diners, Visa.*

Leighlinbridge   Place of Interest

Altamont   by Tullow Tel 0503 59128

Letterfrack   Rosleague Manor   72%   £90

Tel 095 41101 Fax 095 41168	**HR**
Letterfrack Connemara Co Galway	Map 1 A3

Owned and managed by the welcoming Foyle family, the Georgian manor stands in 30 acres of gardens overlooking Ballinakill Bay. Character and comfort are in generous supply, the former including carefully chosen antiques and paintings, the latter assisted by central heating and peat fires. Bedrooms are nearly all of a very good size (with separate seating areas or mini-suites) and all have good bathrooms. There are two drawing rooms and a conservatory bar. *Rooms 20. Garden, sauna, tennis, billiards, fishing. Closed Nov-Easter.* AMERICAN EXPRESS *Access, Visa.*

Restaurant

Nigel Rush's four-course dinner menus are served at round antique tables under chandeliers in a delightfully civilised room. Local produce (some of it home-grown) is put to excellent use in dishes that range from fresh prawn mayonnaise, duck liver paté and marinated mushrooms in red wine, honey and herbs among the starters to potato and walnut soup as a second course, then grilled wild salmon with scallion butter, guinea fowl with brandy and raisins, and medallions of pork in cider sauce. Home-made ice creams feature among the sweets. Teas and coffees are served in the drawing rooms. No smoking in the dining room. *Seats 60. Parties 8. Private Room 10. L 1-2.30 D 8-9.30 (Sun to 9). Set D from £23.*

Letterfrack   Place of Interest

Kylemore Abbey   Connemara Tel 095 41146

Limerick   Castletroy Park Hotel   74%   £140

Tel 061 335566 Fax 061 331117	**HR**
Dublin Road Limerick Co Limerick	Map 2 B5

Located on the Dublin road on the outskirts of town, this well-designed red-brick hotel meets every business need. The new university concert hall and foundation building, just three minutes' walk away, will greatly enhance Limerick's growing reputation as a major conference centre, and with its own state-of-the-art conference and leisure facilities the hotel is ideally situated to benefit. A welcoming atmosphere warms the wood-floored entrance hall and conservatory, while the Merry Pedlar 'pub', which also serves bistro-style food, offers traditional and authentic Irish hospitality and a decent pint. Bedrooms are large with plenty of writing space, good lighting and up-to-date features – satellite TV, fax and computer points, two phones, minibar and trouser press; bathrooms are on the small side. Executive rooms offer

more extras including king-size bed, bathrobe and turn-down
service plus several other complimentary items. Whether your
needs require facilities for a conference (up to 450) or a private
boardroom, the hotel can cater for both and also provides a fully-
equipped business centre. Note the amenities available in the
superbly equipped leisure centre. Good buffet breakfast served
in the restaurant. No dogs. *Rooms 107. Garden, terrace, indoor
swimming pool, children's splash pool, gymnasium, keep-fit equipment,
solarium, sauna, spa bath, steam room, beauty salon, hair salon, tennis,
leisure centre. Closed 24 & 25 Dec.* AMERICAN EXPRESS *Access,
Diners, Visa.*

McLaughlin's Restaurant £65

Widely regarded as one of the leading restaurants in the area,
McLaughlin's tries hard to be cosy, with candle light and shelves
of old books to soften the surroundings – although the atmosphere
is still inclined to be impersonal, with a rather businesslike
approach by staff ('Smoking or non-smoking, madam?'),
a reminder that the restaurant is located in a large hotel. On the
four-course dinner menu Pat O'Sullivan, head chef since late 1992,
presents reliable *cuisine moderne* starting, perhaps, with a tasty
amuse-bouche such as a miniature barbecued kebab, followed
by country-style terrine with Cumberland sauce or a millefeuille
of wild mushrooms in a red wine sauce, then a choice of soups
or citrus sorbet. Main-course choices tend to lean towards fish or,
perhaps, a roast rack of lamb with a duxelles of mushrooms.
Rather jumpy service is characterised by persistent over-use of a
jumbo peppermill. Informal lunch and evening meals are available
from an international bar menu at the hotel's Merry Pedlar 'pub'.
*Seats 70. Parties 30. L 12.30-2 D 7-9.30. Set L £14.50 Set D £22.
Closed L Sat, D Sun.*

Limerick	Greenhills Hotel	62%	£111
Tel 061 453033 Fax 061 453307			H
Ennis Road Limerick Co Limerick			Map 2 B5

Continual improvement is the aim at this family-run hotel and,
although older rooms (due for refurbishment this year) seem quite
dated they have a pleasant outlook over garden or tennis court and
are all well equipped, with telephone, tea/coffee-making facilities,
trouser press and television. Newer rooms are larger and more
comfortable, with well-finished, fully-tiled bathrooms. Public
areas include a leisure centre, spacious lobby, a pleasant bar and
a brasserie/grill bar which is temporarily replacing the main
restaurant, damaged by fire in December '93; at the time of going
to press, renovations were at the planning stage and it was hoped
to re-open the restaurant in time for the main '94 season. Under-
12s may stay free in parents' room. No dogs. *Rooms 60. Garden,
indoor swimming pool, children's pool, gymnasium, sauna, steam room,
solarium, beauty salon, tennis. Closed 25 Dec.* AMERICAN EXPRESS *Access,
Diners, Visa.*

Limerick	Jackson's Turrett		£36
Tel 061 326186 Fax 061 326262			A
Clancy Strand Limerick Co Limerick			Map 2 B5

Right in the centre of Limerick, on the river between Thomond
and Sarsfield bridges, this lovely old house offers a haven of peace *See over*

and relaxation to the individualistic traveller. Although there are
no phones in the homely, interestingly decorated rooms, all are en-
suite and direct-dial phone, fax and secretarial help are available.
But the attraction of this place is its unlikeliness – hearing the rush
of the river from your bed, or the fascination of the old, new and
utterly timeless views from the drawing room, which is the
original Turrett Room; history, location and family comforts
explain much of its charm, but the effects of a breakfast of organic
produce such as wild smoked salmon and scrambled free-range
eggs or local farmhouse cheeses should not be underestimated.
No dogs. *Rooms 4. Garden. Closed January.* AMERICAN EXPRESS®
Access, Visa.

Limerick	Jurys Hotel	68%	£116
Tel 061 327777 Fax 061 326400			**H**
Ennis Road Limerick Co Limerick			**Map 2 B5**

Centrally situated just across the bridge from Limerick's main
shopping and business area, Jurys prides itself on hospitality and
service as well as convenience. A good impression is created in the
spacious lobby area and carried through the public areas, including
the pleasant Limericks Bar (which features the history of the
famous rhyming duel), two restaurants and extensive leisure
facilities, while a continuous programme of refurbishment has
ensured that standards are maintained. Service is a priority,
friendly staff provide 24 hour room service. Newer bedrooms are
larger and more stylishly decorated with smarter bathrooms but,
although slightly dated, older rooms are kept in good repair and
are equally well equipped (including trouser press and multi-
channel TV; tea/coffee-making facilities available on request).
*Rooms 100. Garden, indoor swimming pool, children's splash pool,
gymnasium, sauna, steam room, sun bed, tennis, coffee shop.
Closed 25 & 26 Dec.* AMERICAN EXPRESS® *Access, Diners, Visa.*

Limerick	Restaurant de La Fontaine		£60
Tel 061 414461 Fax 061 411337			**R**
12 Upper Gerald Griffin Street Limerick Co Limerick			**Map 2 B5**

Appropriately named after the great writer of fables, Alain Bras'
first-floor restaurant has an other-worldliness which strikes the
first-time visitor immediately on climbing wide carpeted stairs –
distinctly reminiscent of the approach to 1950s' picture houses – to
the reception area. Once inside, it could be provincial France,
a feeling strongly reinforced by chef Bernard Brousse's evocative
cuisine grand'mère in dishes such as venison terrine, accompanied
by delicious little Puy lentils, and excellent robust country main
courses like rabbit with cabbage. An exceptional French wine list
(for other countries you must ask), with house champagne almost
a bargain at only £20. *Seats 40. L Fri only 12.30-2.30 D 7-10.
Set L £10 Set D £20. Closed Bank Holidays & Christmas.*
AMERICAN EXPRESS® *Access, Diners, Visa.*

Limerick	Limerick Inn Hotel	68%	£115
Tel 061 326666 Fax 061 326281			**H**
Ennis Road Limerick Co Limerick			**Map 2 B5**

The helipad in front of this low-rise modern hotel attracts
considerable attention from passing traffic and there is usually a bit

of a buzz around the large, airy reception area and public rooms.
Good-sized rooms at the back of the hotel have a pleasant outlook
over countryside, have well-designed bathrooms and are equipped
to a high standard, including trouser press complete with iron and
ironing board in addition to hairdryer, phone, tea/coffee-making
facilities and multi-channel TV while superior rooms and suites
also have mini-bars. Conference and business facilities for
up to 600 delegates include secretarial services. Good health and
leisure facilities; resident hair stylist and beautician. *Rooms 153.*
Garden, indoor swimming pool, gymnasium, sauna, solarium, whirlpool
bath, tennis, putting, snooker, coffee shop (7.30am -11pm).
Closed 25 Dec. AMERICAN EXPRESS *Access, Diners, Visa.*

Limerick	Two Mile Inn Hotel	63%	£78
Tel 061 326255 Fax 061 453783			H
Ennis Road Limerick Co Limerick			Map 2 B5

Actually just three miles from the centre of Limerick, this striking
modern hotel features an enormous lobby with a large seating
area, rather like an airport lounge, but the hotel as a whole
is imaginatively laid out and other areas are surprisingly intimate.
Bedrooms are attractively arranged around garden areas which
afford a feeling of quietness and privacy and are furnished with
deck chairs and sunshades in summer. No dogs. *Rooms 125.*
Garden, shop. Closed 24-26 Dec. AMERICAN EXPRESS *Access, Diners, Visa.*

Limerick	Places of Interest

Tourist Information   Tel 061 317522
City Gallery of Art   Upper Mallow Street Tel 061 310663
City Museum   John Square Tel 061 417826
King John's Castle   Tel 061 411201
St John's Cathedral   Tel 061 414624
St Mary's Cathedral   Tel 061 310293
Limerick Racecourse   Tel 061 29377
Cratloe Woods House   Cratloe Tel 061 327028 *5 miles*
Lough Gur Interpretative Centre   Lough Gur Tel 061 85186 *6 miles*

Maddoxtown	Blanchville House	£50
Tel 056 27197		A
Dunbell Maddoxtown Co Kilkenny		Map 2 C5

Easily recognised by the folly in its grounds, this elegant Georgian
house is on a working farm and, while conveniently close to the
crafts and culture of Kilkenny city, has all the advantages of peace
and restfulness associated with the country – and similarly Tim
and Monica Phelan aim to provide guests with 20th-century
comfort to balance 19th-century style. The house has a lovely, airy
atmosphere, with matching, well-proportioned dining and
drawing rooms on either side of the hall and pleasant, comfortably
furnished bedrooms (most en-suite, two with private bathrooms)
overlooking lovely countryside. Dinner is available to residents
by arrangement and, like the next morning's excellent breakfast,
is taken at the communal mahogany dining table. *Rooms 6.*
Garden. Closed 1 Nov-1 Mar. Access, Visa.

Malahide   Bon Appétit   £80
`Tel 01 845 0314`   **R**

9 St James Terrace Malahide Co Dublin   Map 1 D3

An elegant Georgian terrace house, overlooking the estuary, has
been the setting for both the home and business of Catherine and
Patsy McGuirk since 1989. Aperitifs are served in the ground-
floor drawing room/bar, notable for its pleasing local
watercolours, while the cosy restaurant, decorated in warm tones
of red and dark green, is in the basement. Chef Patsy serves
classical French food based on top-quality fresh ingredients (Dingle
Bay scallops, Carlingford lobster, Kilmore crab, east coast mussels),
with a handful of daily specials added for variety. Thus, snails
in garlic butter and fillets of sole Walewska sit happily alongside
crispy duckling with potato, herb and Grand Marnier stuffing and
*gigot de lapin braisée à l'essence de Cabernet Sauvignon et filet roti aux
herbes et moutard.* The super wine list has many fine French classics,
most of which are accompanied by tasting notes (of varying
help!); the best value is outside these, with lots of good drinking
under £20. *Seats 55. Private Room 24. L 12.30-2 D 7-11.
Closed L Sat, all Sun, Bank Holidays, 1 week Christmas. Set L £10
Set D £20.* Access, Diners, Visa.

Malahide   Eastern Tandoori   £40
`Tel 01 845 4154/5`   **R**

1 New Street Malahide Co Dublin   Map 1 D3

Although it's on the first floor, overlooking the new Malahide
marina development, the atmosphere at this out-of-town branch
of the well-known city centre restaurant is distinctly other-
worldly, with an all-Indian staff, authentic furnishings and sound
effects. Choose from four set menus at varying prices, or from the
à la carte: between them they offer a wide, well-balanced choice
of dishes ranging from gently aromatic to fiery hot, suiting the
novice without offending old hands. Old favourites are there
in mild onion bhajee, served with a small salad, various tandoori
dishes – chicken tikka, mackerel, even quail and crab claws – and
several jalfrezi dishes such as beef, lamb or chicken, hot with chili,
fresh ginger and coriander. Chef's recommendations are more
interesting, some desserts garnished with the classic silver leaf, and
side dishes like tarka dal (lentils with fresh coriander) and aloo
jeera (dry potatoes with cumin seed) are good. Wine is pricy, but
Cobra Indian beer suits the food better anyway. *Seats 64.
Parties 20. D only 6-11.30. Set D from £10.95. Closed 25 Dec, Good
Friday.* Access, Diners, Visa.

Malahide   Grand Hotel   66%   £90
`Tel 01 845 0000   Fax 01 845 0987`   **H**

Malahide Co Dublin   Map 1 D3

Polished double doors in the splendid cream-painted frontage lead
into a pillared entrance hall resplendent with fine crystal
chandeliers, marble fireplace, comfortable, well-spaced settees and
winged armchairs. At the rear of the ground floor is Matt Ryan's
bar, a split-level room decorated in a distinctive 20s' Mackintosh
style, while to the left of the entrance is the Griffin bar, open
evenings only and due for refurbishment. Fifty rooms were

recently refurbished along with a further six in the old wing (30 more were due for completion as we went to press). 14 older-style rooms will be left until the end of next season. These rooms are very modest, some with candlewick bedspreads and rather uninviting bathrooms. The newer bedrooms contrast markedly in having smart pickled pine furniture and a host of amenities as well as being double-glazed and possessing bright, well-equipped bathrooms. **Rooms** *100. Garden. Closed 25 & 26 Dec.* AMERICAN EXPRESS *Access, Diners, Visa.*

Malahide   Roches Bistro   £55

| Tel 01 845 2777   Fax 01 324147 | **R** |

12 New Street Malahide Co Dublin   **Map 1 D3**

Family-run by sisters Orla Roche and Niamh Boylan, this is probably nearest to a French local restaurant to be found in Co Dublin. Set in Malahide's attractive main street, it's a small, intimate place with cheerful blue and white check linen and an open fire in winter. The wide-ranging set menus change daily and show a strong bias towards French country cooking and lots of seafood dishes – all cooked in an open kitchen, watched by guests taking an aperitif or coffee at the dividing bar. Go for specialities like crab soufflé à la crème or seafood pancakes or try an unusual combination like monkfish with fresh mint. Meat-lovers will find strip loin steak with pink and green peppercorns thick, tender and piquant. Apple and frangipane tart is a speciality and there's a good selection of farmhouse cheeses, then as much freshly brewed coffee as you like. The short French wine list is mostly under £20. **Seats** *35. Parties 30. Private Room 36. L 12-2.30 D 6-10.30. Closed L Mon Jan-Jun, D Mon & Tue, all Sun, Bank Holidays, 2 weeks Jan. Set L £10.95 Set D £18.95.* AMERICAN EXPRESS *Access, Diners, Visa.*

Malahide   Place of Interest

Malahide Castle   Tel 01 845 2655

Mallow   Longueville House   72%   £110

| Tel 022 47156   Fax 022 47459 | **H R** |

Mallow Co Cork   **Map 2 B5**

Three miles west of Mallow on the N72 Killarney Road, this handsome Georgian house built in 1720 has been run as a hotel since 1969 by the O'Callaghan family, descendants of the original occupants. While grandly proportioned, the gracious house has an easy informality which makes it seem natural to be surrounded by gilt-framed mirrors, family portraits and impressive fireplaces with log fires burning. Bedrooms are stylishly furnished with antiques, good fabrics and thoughtfully equipped modern bathrooms. Breakfast offers a fine choice, both hot and cold, including home-made bread. No dogs. **Rooms** *16. Garden, game & coarse fishing, games room, snooker. Closed 20 Dec-mid March.* AMERICAN EXPRESS *Access, Diners, Visa.*

Presidents' Restaurant   ↑   £65

William O'Callaghan's creative, imaginative cooking is surveyed by previous Presidents of Ireland, who look down from the walls of an elegant, lofty room. Produce from their private fishing on the Blackwater and his father's farm and gardens supplies most

See over

of his needs in the kitchen. Specialities on the short, well-chosen menus (fixed-price or à la carte) include home-smoked salmon timbale, ravioli of Castletownbere prawns and noisettes of Longueville lamb filled with tarragon mousse. Garden vegetables, served in little bouquets, are what they claim to be and have great depth of flavour. Desserts often come from the garden too, as in summer fruit soup. A highly unusual and very tempting alternative is caramelised pear on a slice of brioche with beer ice cream. The surprise menu (£32) is available from 7-9 and only to an entire party. Irish farmhouse cheeses are excellent and home-made chocolates and petits fours come with the coffee. *Seats 45. Parties 15. Private Room 20. L 12.30-2 D 7-9. Set L £15 Set D £26/£32.*

Mallow   Places of Interest

Annes Grove Gardens	Castletownroche	Tel 022 26145
Mallow Racecourse	Mount Ruby	Tel 022 21565

Maynooth	Moyglare Manor	75%	£120
Tel 01 628 6351 Fax 01 628 5405			**HR**
Moyglare Maynooth Co Kildare			Map 2 C4

Traffic-wise, Maynooth can be something of a bottleneck, but Moyglare itself is a couple of miles down the road past the church. A long tree-lined avenue leads to the fine Georgian house, which has a lovely garden and overlooks peaceful parkland and mountains beyond. Owned by Norah Devlin and managed by Shay Curran, the hotel is stuffed full of antiques, objets d'art, paintings and all manner of lamps. The public rooms are a veritable Aladdin's Cave of memorabilia and comfortable furnishings – a tranquil doze in front of the marble fireplace in the lounge is to be recommended. Period-style bedrooms, several with four-posters or half-testers, are individually furnished, but if you want a TV to interrupt or spoil your surroundings you must ask – they are available on request. A ground-floor garden suite is particularly grand. Bathrooms have been modernised and provide generously-sized towels and decent toiletries. Look out for the freshly-baked scones and bread which accompany excellent cafetière coffee at breakfast. No children under 12. No dogs. *Rooms 17. Garden, tennis. Closed 3 days Christmas.* AMERICAN EXPRESS, *Access, Diners, Visa.*

Restaurant   £75

The setting is romantic, with candles or Victorian lamps on the tables, and the menu features many fish dishes. Try a seafood terrine with champagne sauce, crab claws in garlic butter or poached fillets of brill served with a perfect hollandaise sauce. Hormone-free sirloin steak comes grilled with a green peppercorn sauce, while pork is done the traditional way – with a potato and herb stuffing and apple sauce. Lunch menus offer less choice. There's a good cheeseboard and a choice of sweets (white chocolate terrine perhaps), followed by either tea or coffee accompanied by home-made petits fours. Sample the home-made bread, and if you like your wine list classic there are many fine bottles from which to choose – eighteen vintages of Chateau d'Yquem alone! – though half bottles are thin in the cellar. No smoking. *Seats 80. Private Room 50. L 12.30-2.15 (Sun 12-2.30) D 7-9. Closed L Sat. Set L £11.95 Set D £21*

Maynooth   Place of Interest

Castletown House   Celbridge Tel 01 628 8252

Midleton   Place of Interest

Jameson Heritage Centre   Tel 021 613594

Monkstown	Mr Hung's	£64
Tel 01 2843982		**R**
5a The Crescent Monkstown Co Dublin		**Map 4 D1**

Standard Western-style Cantonese cooking is popular with locals
at this comfortable, well-appointed and friendly restaurant.
Typical offerings include starters like spare ribs, pancake roll
or stuffed crab claws; chicken, beef and seafood dishes, sizzling
or otherwise, can be good main courses. *Seats 80. L 12.30-2.30
D 6-12.30. Closed L Mon-Thu, Good Friday, 25 & 26 Dec.
Set D from £16.* AMERICAN EXPRESS *Access, Diners, Visa.*

Moone	Moone High Cross Inn	
Tel 0507 24112		**P**
Bolton Hill Moone Co Kildare		**Map 2 C4**

The Clynch family are the most welcoming of hosts, and their
rambling 18th-century pub is up among the front-runners in the
hospitality and home cooking stakes. As befits our Food Pub
of the Year, morning coffee, lunch, afternoon tea and evening
meals are all available, and the menus are based on the best
of ingredients, simply cooked and generously served. The lounge
service menu (lunch every day) announces that Jacob sheep roam
freely around the inn – at their peril, perhaps, because they also
appear inside as roasts; other favourites on the various menus
include brown bread sandwiches with home-cooked meats or local
Cheddar, vegetable soup, traditional bacon and cabbage, Irish stew
and the grandmother of apple pies. Steaks feature on the evening
à la carte; Sunday lunch is a particularly popular occasion. There
is a proper dining room, but many visitors opt for a seat by the
fire in the back bar, or a spot in the new beer garden. *Bar Meals
12-3, 7-9. Children allowed in bar to eat. Garden, outdoor eating. Visa.*

Mountrath	Roundwood House	58%	£64
Tel 0502 32120 Fax 0502 32711			**AR**
Mountrath Co Laois			**Map 2 C4**

Secluded in mature woods of lime, beech and chestnut, this
Palladian villa from the early Georgian period offers something
special to the visitor with a sense of history and, perhaps, a sense
of humour: do not expect 'every modern convenience' and you
will not be disappointed. Instead, enjoy staying in an unspoilt,
characterful old house with shutters on the windows of the old-
fashioned bedrooms instead of curtains and hot water bottles laid
out ready in your bathroom. Book-lovers will enjoy getting
between the covers of the vast library. Children, who will love
the animals and their young in the back garden, are free in parents'
room under 3; tea at 6.30. Tariff reductions for stays of two nights
or more. No dogs. *Rooms 6. Garden, croquet.* *Access,
Diners, Visa.*

See over

Restaurant   £60

Rosemarie Kennan's food suits the house perfectly – good
interesting cooking without unnecessary frills – and Frank
is a good host. The menu changes daily, offering four courses,
with a choice only at dessert stage. Sunday lunch is especially good
value. *Seats 26. Parties 16. L Sun only at 1.30 D at 8.30.
Set Sun L £11 Set D £19.*

Mountrath   Place of Interest

Damer House   Roscrea Heritage Centre Tel 0505 21850 *16 miles*

Moycullen   Cloonnabinnia House Hotel   61%   £55
Tel 091 85555   Fax 091 85640   **H**
Ross Lake Moycullen Co Galway   Map 2 B4

Situated in landscaped gardens overlooking Ross Lake, this
unpretentious 1960s' hotel owes its charm to the warmth and
genuine hospitality of the Kavanagh family. The atmospheric bar,
popular with locals and guests alike, is often the scene for much
talk of fishing. Public areas generally are a homely mixture of old
and new, with comfort and a relaxed atmosphere the keynotes.
Modest bedrooms are all en suite, with lovely views; function
rooms (conferences 300/banquets 240) are downstairs, well away
from residents and with a separate entrance. Four rooms are
designated non-smoking. Children under 12 stay free in parents'
room. Several self-catering cottages are also available. *Rooms 14.
Garden, fishing, hunting, shooting. Closed Nov-Mar. Access, Visa.*

Moycullen   Drimcong House Restaurant   ★   £60
Tel 091 85115   **R**
Moycullen Co Galway   Map 2 B4

A mile west of Moycullen on the main Galway/Clifden road is the
lakeland home of much-feted restaurateurs Gerry (worthy winner
of our Ireland 1994 Chef of the Year Award) and Marie Galvin,
who have been running their fine restaurant here since 1984.
Enjoy a drink in the relaxing, book-filled bar before settling down
at a polished oak table for dinner. Gerry's inventive, imaginative
cooking puts a modern accent on classical skills and both 5-course
table d'hote and à la carte menus change regularly to utilise the
best produce available. There's also a separate, interesting
vegetarian menu (5-course £16.50). Local seafood, Connemara
lamb, free-range poultry and game in season all feature regularly
in dishes such as a seafood stir-fry, roast rack of mutton with red
wine gravy, grilled chicken breast with pesto and lemon aïoli,
or confit of duck with plum purée. There's also usually a choice
of soups, perhaps Chinese broth or mussel soup. Desserts are wide-
ranging and there's an excellent Irish farmhouse cheeseboard.
Children who can eat the three-course special children's menu
(£9.50) are made especially welcome; no high-chairs for real
youngsters, though. The wine list is short, carefully chosen, and
features at least a dozen or so bottles under £15 (as well as around
eight or so half bottles); claret drinkers are given the opportunity
to stretch their budgets. *Seats 50. Private Room 32. D only 7-10.30.
Closed Sun, Mon, Bank Hols, Jan & Feb. Set D £15.95/£18.95.*
 Access, Diners, Visa.

Moydow   The Vintage

Tel 043 22122

P

Moydow Co Longford

Map 1 C3

Former cookery teacher Regina Houlihan has developed The
Vintage bar into quite a catering enterprise, looking after both
local functions and serving dinner three nights a week (plus
Sunday lunch). Officially they don't serve bar food but, as there's
always something going on in the kitchen, their natural hospitality
gets the better of them. Your request for a bite to eat is likely
to be met with a typcially Irish response: "We don't do bar food,
but I'll go and see what there is. What sort of thing do you feel
like?" – it's that kind of a place (and there's an open fire while
you wait). The four-course Sunday lunch menu (£8.95) may
be a seafood platter followed by home-made soup, then roast rib
of beef, and a pudding to follow. The evening dinner menu
(£13.95) offers a reasonable choice, possibly including tagliatelle
alfredo, stuffed quail with chicken mousseline, fillet of brill
Japanese-style and pan-fried chicken with wild mushroom sauce.
A la carte dishes are also available. ***Restaurant Meals*** *1-3 (Sun
only), 7-10.30 (Thur-Sun only). Garden, outdoor eating.*
AMERICAN EXPRESS *Access, Visa.*

Mullingar   Crookedwood House

£55

Tel 044 72165   Fax 044 72166

R

Crookedwood Mullingar Co Meath

Map 1 C3

Noel and Julie Kenny have plans to add accommodation to the
excellent restaurant at their 200-year-old former rectory
overlooking Lough Derravaragh. Noel's menus change with the
seasons and feature the best of local produce. From a winter
selection come grilled breast of wood pigeon on rösti with onion
marmalade, cream of parsnip and nutmeg soup, roulade of sole and
smoked salmon, and a duet of pheasant and venison with a wild
mushroom and juniper berry sauce. Good simple desserts, Irish
farmhouse cheeses. *Seats 35. Parties 14. Private Room 35. L (Sun
only) 12.30-2 D 7-10. Closed D Sun & Mon, Bank Holidays,
2 weeks Nov. Set L £12 Set D £17.* AMERICAN EXPRESS *Access,
Diners, Visa.*

Mullingar   Place of Interest

Tullynally Castle and Gardens   Castlepollard Tel 044 61159 *16 miles*

Naas   Fletcher's

Tel 045 97328

P

Commercial House Naas Co Kildare

Map 2 C4

A characterful pub that's well worth a visit just for the interest
of being there. It's a very old-fashioned place, a long, narrow hall,
broken up into sections in the traditional way with a mahogany
divider complete with stained-glass panels. Having escaped the
scourge of modernisation, Fletcher's remains somewhat austere and
masculine: the plain wooden floor and very long mahogany bar
with its full complement of built-in drawers and shelves behind
is softened by the occasional aspidistra in an old cachepot and

See over

a collection of magnificent meat plates displayed high on the end wall. Masculine – and adult, too: they prefer no children in the bar. *No credit cards.*

Naas   The Manor Inn

Tel 045 97471

Main Street Naas Co Kildare   Map 2 C4

The Manor Inn offers warmth, hospitality and good food in refreshingly 'undesigned' surroundings. Local interest is reflected in pictures and mementos connected with horses and the army base at the nearby Curragh, car racing at Mondello (note the clock in a racing helmet) and a clutter of notices giving due warning of upcoming local events. The menu offers a wide variety of familiar pub fare, from sandwiches, salads and omelettes to pasta, burgers, pies, grills, steaks and four choices 'from the smoke house'. *Bar Food 12-11 (Sun 12.30-2.30 & 5-10.30).* *Children allowed in bar to eat, children's menu.*

Navan   Ardboyne Hotel   60%   £75

Tel 046 23119   Fax 046 22355   **HR**

Dublin Road Navan Co Meath   Map 1 C3

A friendly, well-run modern hotel standing in its own grounds on the outskirts of town. Bedrooms, all with compact tiled bathrooms, are simple and practical, with fitted furniture and good desk/dressing table space. There's a bright, comfortable lounge and a warm, convivial bar. All-day snacks are available in the bar/foyer area. Children are more than welcome, and under-12s can stay free in their parents' room. *Rooms 27. Garden, disco (Fri & Sat). Closed 24-27 Dec.* *Access, Diners, Visa.*

Terrace Restaurant   £55

Simple, straightforward dishes are available on several menus, including à la carte, tourist, luncheon, table d'hote and early bird. 'Chef Recommends' on the carte include prawns provençale, wiener schnitzel, shish kebab and sirloin steak. Sweets from the buffet. *Seats 150. Private Room 50. L 12.30-2.30 D 5.30-10 (Sun till 9). Set L from £10.50 Set D £11.95/£16.95.*

Navan   Places of Interest

Hill of Tara   Tel 046 25903
Navan Racecourse   Tel 046 21350
Butterstream Garden   Trim Tel 046 36017

New Quay   Linnane's Bar

Tel 065 78120

New Quay Burrin Co Clare   Map 2 B4

This unassuming country pub has sliding doors at the back, which open virtually on to the rocks in summer and bring the magnificent seascape beyond right inside. In winter, it is inward-looking, as visitors (who may have had difficulty finding it if, as sometimes happens, gales have blown down local road signs) cluster round the peat fire. It has rightly attracted attention for the quality of its seafood: in addition to luxury lobster there's plenty of good but less expensive fare at Linnane's, with the best choice in summer: a steaming bowl of chowder, perhaps, served with brown bread; scallops New Quay, cooked in a wine sauce and served in a gratin dish, layered with rice to mop up the aromatic juices; or a huge crab salad, the plate burgeoning with the white meat of at least a pair of crabs. Simply delicious. **Bar Food** *12-9 Apr-Oct (daily in summer, weekends only in low season), 5-9 Nov-Mar. Children's portions. No credit cards.*

> See the 'Listing in County Order' section (highlighted by colour pages) at the back of the Guide for instant comparison of establishments in a particular area.

Newbawn	Cedar Lodge	62%	£75
Tel 051 28386 Fax 051 28222			**H**
Carrigbyrne Newbawn Co Wexford			Map 2 C5

14 miles from Wexford on the main Rosslare-Waterford road, this family-run hotel stands in lush countryside beneath the slopes of Carrigbyrne Forest. Redbrick walls, wooden ceilings and open fires create a warm and welcoming atmosphere in the public rooms and paintings and frescos by local artists provide interesting focal points. Bedrooms are practical and neatly appointed. Conference/function suite for up to 100 (banquets 70) in adjoining low-rise wings. *Rooms 18. Garden. Closed 25 & 26 Dec, Jan. Access, Visa.*

Newbawn	Place of Interest
John F Kennedy Arboretum Tel 051 88171	

Newbay	Newbay Country House	£60
Tel 053 42779 Fax 053 46318		**A**
Newbay nr Wexford Co Wexford		Map 2 D5

A comfortable family-run country house dating from 1822 but incorporating earlier outbuildings. The outside impression is a touch stern, but the real atmosphere is very warm and relaxed. Day rooms are of imposing proportions, with interesting antiques, amply sized country furniture and displays of dried flowers arranged by Mientje (Min) Drum. Bedrooms are spacious, comfortable and individually furnished with four-poster beds but without TVs or phones. Paul Drum's food (for residents only), offers no choice and is served at one large table. The house is situated 2 miles from Wexford and not far from the ferry port of Rosslare. No dogs. *Rooms 6. Garden. Closed mid Nov-mid Mar except for groups or by prior appointment. Access, Diners, Visa.*

Newbridge	Hotel Keadeen	68%	£80
Tel 045 31666 Fax 045 34402			**H**
Ballymany Newbridge Co Kildare			Map 2 C4

Leave the M7 at exit 10 and head back towards Newbridge to find 'the inn on the Curragh', a well-kept hotel in a garden setting near the famous racetrack. Conferences and functions are big business, but private guests are well catered for in good-sized bedrooms furnished in a variety of styles. No dogs. *Rooms 37. Garden. Closed 25-27 Dec.* AMERICAN EXPRESS *Access, Diners, Visa.*

Newbridge   Places of Interest

Punchestown Racecourse   Naas Tel 045 97704
Naas Racecourse   Tel 045 97391
Japanese Gardens   Tully Tel 045 21251 *5 miles*
Irish National Stud   Tully Tel 045 21617 *5 miles*
Emo Court and Gardens   Emo Tel 0502 26110 *10 miles*

Newmarket-on-Fergus   Clare Inn Hotel   64%   £99

Tel 061 368161 Fax 061 368622	H
Dromoland Newmarket-on-Fergus Co Clare	Map 2 B4

Outstanding leisure facilities are provided at the modern, low-rise
Clare Hotel, which stands in the middle of Dromoland's 18-hole
golf course (£14 green fee). The leisure centre (free to guests;
children under 16 must be accompanied, no children after 7pm)
includes a fully-equipped gymnasium, and deep-sea fishing can
be arranged from the hotel's catamaran, the *Liscannor Star*. The
Castlefergus Bar, with weekend entertainment, is a good place
to unwind, and there are residents' lounges, two restaurants and
a children's playroom. Bedrooms are of a decent size, most of them
suitable for family occupation. Children up to 5 are
accommodated free, while under-12s are charged £10, which
includes B&B and high tea. Conference facilities for up to 400.
Nine miles from Shannon Airport on the main Limerick/Galway
road. **Rooms** *121. Garden, indoor swimming pool, gymnasium, sauna,
steam room, spa bath, sun bed, solarium, tennis, pitch & putt, crazy
golf, croquet, lawn bowling, outdoor draughts, games room, coffee shop
(2.30-10pm).* AMERICAN EXPRESS *Access, Diners, Visa.*

Newmarket-on-Fergus   Dromoland Castle   79%   £252

Tel 061 368144 Fax 061 363355	HR
Newmarket-on-Fergus Co Clare	Map 2 B4

The castle's history can be traced back to the 16th century when
the estate belonged to the O'Brien clan, direct descendants of Brian
Boru, High King of Ireland; hence the name of the magnificent
and newly built conference venue, comprising a great hall, gallery,
boardrooms and business centre catering for up to 450 delegates.
Close to Shannon airport, the hotel is set among 370 acres
of woods and parkland (a stroll through the walled garden is also
a must) that include a championship golf course, the eighth green
of which is overlooked by the library bar. If the outside
is imposing, the public rooms inside are surprisingly intimate and
relaxed, with roaring log fires, elegant and comfortable seating,
many period antiques and a huge collection of family portraits, not
to mention the fine fabrics, glittering chandeliers, intricate
plasterwork and high ceilings. There is a variety of bedrooms,
some necessitating long walks down corridors; many of the rooms
have recently been refurbished and the best are extremely spacious
with lovely views of either the lake or the grounds. Each
is beautifully appointed with high-quality fabrics, excellent bed
linen and impressive furniture, and all the usual extras that you
would expect from a hotel of this class: flowers, fresh fruit and
mineral water on arrival, together with bathrobes, slippers,
toiletries and decent towels in the good bathrooms (some of which
are on the small side). Standards of service, under the direction
of General Manager Mark Nolan, are high and housekeeping

is exemplary (a nightly turn-down of beds can be expected,
of course). Children up to 12 stay free in their parents' rooms.
No dogs. Sister hotel to *Ashford Castle*, Cong (see entry).
Rooms 73. *Garden, golf, riding, fishing, clay-pigeon shooting, shooting,
archery, tennis, snooker, bicycles.* AMERICAN EXPRESS *Access, Diners, Visa.*

The Earl of Thomond Room ↑® £115

The elegance of the castle is perhaps best illustrated by the
grandness of the dining rooms: high ceilings, chandeliers and
splendid drapes matched by fine china, gleaming crystal and linen
cloths. In the evenings you'll be further seduced by a traditional
Irish harpist and maybe even a fiddler, together with the dishes
of long-serving executive head chef Jean-Baptiste Molinari.
He presents a variety of menus: a four-course table d'hote, say pan-
fried scallops 'niçoise' style, beef consommé, supreme of chicken
roasted with a confit of shallots in a thyme-scented jus and a choice
of dessert; a £45 6-course Taste of Ireland (also written in Gaelic)
featuring such dishes as rabbit paté, plaited fillet of sole braised
with cider and cabbage and hot brown bread soufflé; or à la carte
– home-made lamb ravioli with a creamy sauce of herbs and meat
juices, braised fillet of turbot with a champagne sauce and Beluga
caviar, ending with a dark chocolate gateau filled with a compote
of banana or apple and Calvados pie (prepared by chef-patissière
Elma Campion). Much work goes into the composition of the
menus, reflected by the high standard of execution, and it's a real
pleasure to encounter such professional, courteous and
knowledgeable staff. The good-quality bread, coffee and petits
fours complete the satisfaction one will experience here. Prices
on the the good wine list are not modest – you will have to hunt
carefully for bargains! *Seats 90. Parties 10. Private Rooms 24 & 60.
L 12.30-2 D 7.30-10. Set L £18 Set D £33.*

Newport	Newport House	67%	£120
Tel 098 41222	Fax 098 41613		**HR**
Newport Co Mayo			Map 1 A3

A creeper-clad Georgian house stands in large gardens adjoining
the town and overlooking the Newport river and quay –
an unusual location for one of the most attractive and hospitable
country houses in Ireland, run by Kieran and Thelma Thompson.
Fishing is the major attraction, with salmon and sea trout fishing
on the river and nearby loughs. Golf, riding and pony trekking
are also available locally, but the appeal of the house itself with its
beautiful central hall and sweeping staircase (now clad in a hand-
woven McMurray carpet from Connemara) and gracious drawing
room is enough to draw guests without sporting interests.
Bedrooms, like the rest of the house, are furnished in style with
antiques and fine paintings and bathrooms which can be eccentric
but work well; most of the rooms are in the main house, a few
in the courtyard. The day's catch is weighed and displayed in the
hall and a cosy fisherman's bar provides the perfect venue for
a reconstruction of the day's sport. *Rooms* 20. *Garden, sea & game
fishing, snooker. Closed 7 Oct-18 Mar.* AMERICAN EXPRESS *Access,
Diners, Visa.*

Restaurant £70

A high-ceilinged dining room overlooking the gardens and
decorated in restrained period style provides an elegant setting for

See over

John Gavin's confident cooking, based on the best of local produce, much of it coming from the organically-worked walled kitchen garden. Salmon, home-smoked by Owen Mullins who has been at Newport since 1946, makes a perfect starter on a 6-course dinner menu, followed by soup (cream of vegetable or carrot and coriander) and, perhaps, pan-fried quail with mousseline of chicken and a tarragon sauce or pan-fried salmon with lemon and chive cream sauce. Oysters (either *au naturel* or baked Rockefeller) are usually offered as an additional course. Vegetables and salads are as fresh as it is possible to be and there's a choice of farmhouse cheese or a fine dessert menu (Baileys soufflé with chocolate sauce, rhubarb tartlet with fruit coulis and vanilla sauce) to finish. Though Italian wines are sandwiched between Jura and Provence, the predominantly French wine list is otherwise clearly laid out and easy to use; however, there are no tasting notes, not much from the New World and nothing from California. No smoking in the dining room. **Seats** *39. Parties 16. Private Room 35. D only 7.30-9.30. Set D £28.*

Oughterard   Connemara Gateway Hotel   65%   £105
Tel 091 82328   Fax 091 82332   **H**
Oughterard Co Galway   Map 1 B3

Originally a 1960s' motel, systematically improved over the years and now concealing some characterful public areas, especially the foyer with its old pine boarding and the bar, where a surprisingly rural atmosphere has been created through choice of furnishings and agricultural memorabilia. Open turf fires are welcoming and an abundance of fresh and dried flower arrangements brings colour and adds interest throughout, as does the work of local artists and sculptors. Bedrooms are variable, the best having co-ordinated floral schemes, tweedy bedcovers and well-finished bathrooms. Good children's facilities: children's meal 6.30pm, videos at 7.30pm. Golf available nearby. Conference/banqueting for 100/150. No dogs. **Rooms** *64. Garden, indoor swimming pool, sauna, solarium, snooker, tennis, children's playground. Closed Jan (usually). Access, Visa.*

Oughterard   Currarevagh House   65%   £89
Tel 091 82313   Fax 091 82731   **AR**
Oughterard Co Galway   Map 1 B3

Harry and June Hodgson, fifth generation and here for nearly 30 years, practise the art of old-fashioned hospitality in their Victorian manor house set in parkland, woods and gardens by Lough Corrib. Day rooms are homely and traditional, and the drawing room is the perfect setting for afternoon tea. Bedrooms are peaceful, with no phones or TV. The hotel has sporting rights over 5000 acres and fishing facilities that include boats and ghillies. **Rooms** *15. Garden, tennis, fishing, mooring, swimming, hotel boats. Closed Nov-Mar. No credit cards.*

Restaurant   £50

A succulent meat dish is the centrepiece of no-choice five-course dinners prepared by June Hodgson from the pick of local produce. That dish might be haunch of venison with brandy and apple sauce, rack of lamb with honey and Guinness or roast beef with Yorkshire pudding. Preceding it could be duck liver paté and

poached salmon, or cold consommé indienne and smoked salmon
en choux, with a dessert, Irish cheeses and coffee to complete
a really satisfying meal. No smoking. Snack lunches. *Seats 28.
D only at 8. Set D £18.*

Oughterard	Sweeny's Oughterard House	59%	£98*
Tel 091 82207 Fax 091 82161			**H**
Oughterard Co Galway			Map 1 B3

A 200-year-old house with a sympathetic modern extension, just
over the road from the Owenriff River (salmon fishing) and
protected by trees and gardens. Owned and run by the Higgins
family for 80 years, it has cosy, cottagey public rooms furnished
with antiques. Bedrooms, where under-12s may stay free with
their parents, vary considerably in size and appointments. ★Half-
board terms. *Rooms 21. Garden. Closed 4 weeks Dec/Jan.*
AMERICAN EXPRESS® *Access, Diners, Visa.*

Oughterard	Place of Interest
Aughnanure Castle Tel 091 82214	

Oysterhaven	The Oystercatcher	£65
Tel 021 770822		**R**
Oysterhaven Co Cork		Map 2 B6

Bill and Sylvia Patterson, both originally from Scotland, run
a most attractive, cottagey restaurant known for its charming
atmosphere and consistently excellent food. Oysters naturally
make appearances on the dinner menu – simmered in garlic butter
with almonds, in sausages on a saffron sauce and in angels
on horseback. Wild mushrooms in a brioche is another speciality
dish, and you might also find gateau of foie gras with apples,
scallops on a julienne of vegetables, pig's trotter stuffed with veal
sweetbreads and Madeira-sauced chateaubriand. Fine fresh cheeses,
and a selection of savoury alternatives to "the sweet things in life".
There's a good all-round wine list with plenty of excellent
drinking under £20; note that big name champagnes and fizz
come at the end of the list, rather than with the house champagnes
at the front – odd! *Seats 30. Parties 20. Private Room 20. L by
arrangement for parties of 7 or more D 7.30-9.30 (bookings only
in winter). Closed for a month early each year – phone for details.
Set D £21.95. Access, Visa.*

Parknasilla	Great Southern	72%	£156
Tel 064 45122 Fax 064 45323			**H**
Parknasilla Sneem Co Kerry			Map 2 A6

Overlooking Kenmare Bay (on which the hotel's own *Parknasilla
Princess* offers pleasure cruises) and set in 200 acres of sub-tropical
parkland, this late-Victorian building blends well with its exotic
surroundings. An air of tranquillity is immediately conveyed by a
sense of space, antiques and fresh flowers in the foyer and the tone
of restful luxury is continued through all the public areas
to elegantly decorated bedrooms. Good indoor leisure facilities are
matched by a wide range of outdoor attractions, including a series
of scenic walks through the estate. Banqueting for 70. No dogs.
Rooms 83. Garden, indoor & outdoor swimming pool, outdoor

See over

Canadian hot-tub, sauna, spa bath, steam room, tennis, golf (9), riding, games room, snooker, sea-fishing, water sports, bicycles, clay-pigeon shooting. Closed Jan-Mar. AMERICAN EXPRESS *Access, Diners, Visa.*

Parknasilla   Place of Interest

Derrynane National Historic Park   Caherdaniel Tel 066 75113

Portsalon   Rita's

Tel 074 59107   **P**

The Pier Portsalon Letterkenny Co Donegal   **Map 1 C1**

"Nothing's changed here in 100 years" says Rita Smyth, landlady of this multi-purpose establishment by the beach. The grocery bar serves as a general store for locals and holiday-makers, and there are two other bars – harbourside at the front and a cosy back bar with an open fire. Self-contained flats are let in summer, with meals and baby-sitting available. *Open 10.30am-11pm, Sun 12.30-2 & 4-11. No credit cards.*

We endeavour to be as up-to-date as possible, but inevitably some changes to key personnel may occur at restaurants and hotels after the Guide goes to press.

Rathmullan   Rathmullan House   62%   £121

Tel 074 58188   Fax 074 58200   **HR**

Rathmullan nr Letterkenny Co Donegal   **Map 1 C1**

For more than 30 years Bob and Robin Wheeler have run their extended Georgian mansion, which stands in lovely tranquil gardens running down to the shore of Lough Swilly. Open fires warm the antique-furnished day rooms, which include a period drawing room, library and cellar bar. Not the least of the distinctive features here is the unique pool complex with Egyptian Baths. Accommodation ranges from well-appointed master suites to family rooms and budget rooms without bathrooms. Outstanding breakfasts. *Rooms 23. Garden, indoor swimming pool, steam room, tennis. Closed Nov-mid Mar.* AMERICAN EXPRESS *Access, Diners, Visa.*

The Pavilion   £60

Liam McCormick's famous tented Pavilion restaurant makes a delightful setting for one of the best hors d'oeuvre buffet displays in the country (a speciality on Sundays) although the temptation is to try too many things from a selection of fishy starters including eels, smoked salmon and various terrines (both sliced to order), lots of salads and vegetarian options. Main-course choices also take vegetarians seriously and are understandably strong on seafood; good soups, interesting sauces and accompaniments. Desserts usually include carrageen pudding, which also appears with a choice of fruits on the breakfast buffet, and coffee is served with petits fours in the drawing room. Booking essential for both lunch and dinner. *Seats 60. Parties 20. Private Room 20. L (Sun only) 1-1.45. D 7.30-8.45. Set Sun L £12 Set D £22. Closed Nov-mid Mar.*

Rathmullan   Places of Interest

Glebe House and Gallery   Church Hill Letterkenny Tel 074 37071
Glenveagh National Park   Tel 074 37088

Rathnew	Hunter's Hotel	60%	£80
Tel 0404 40106 Fax 0404 40338			**H R**
Newrath Bridge Rathnew Co Wicklow			Map 2 D4

The Gelletlie family and their forebears have been running this delightfully old-fashioned coaching inn since 1820, so it is not surprising that it should encompass a mixture of styles, including some interesting antiques. The current owner, Maureen Gelletlie, adds just the right element of eccentricity to the very real charm of the place. Rooms vary considerably; co-ordinated schemes are not to be expected, but all rooms were being upgraded to include en-suite facilities as we went to press. More important is the meticulously maintained garden leading down to a river at the back, with its wonderful herbaceous borders – the perfect place for their famous afternoon tea, an aperitif or coffee after a meal. Inclement weather is also anticipated, with a welcoming open fire in the cosy bar. Friendly, informal service is excellent. *Rooms* 17. *Garden. Closed 25-28 Dec.* AMERICAN EXPRESS *Access, Diners, Visa.*

Restaurant   £55

Several steps back in time, the restaurant overlooks the garden and everything about it, including the service, is refreshingly old-fashioned. Long-standing chef John Sutton offers daily-changing 3- and 4-course set menus; try oak-smoked fresh trout fillets, roast Wicklow lamb with fresh herbs, vegetables from the garden and nursery puddings such as apple and blackberry tart or lemon meringue pie. Prices are fair on a cosmopolitan wine list. *Seats 54. Parties 14. L 1-2.30 (Sat & Sun to 3) D 7.30-9. Set L £13.50 Set D £19.50*

Rathnew	Tinakilly House	76%	£110
Tel 0404 69274 Fax 0404 67806			**H R**
Rathnew Wicklow Co Wicklow			Map 2 D4

A substantial Victorian mansion built in the 1870s for Captain Robert Halpin, Commander of the *Great Eastern*, which laid the first telegraph cable linking Europe and America. It's set in seven acres of gardens overlooking a bird sanctuary and sweeping down to the Irish Sea. The building has been extensively renovated both inside and out, with the addition of a period-style wing, and run as a hotel by William and Bee Power since 1983. Furnished to a high standard with antiques, good pictures and an interesting collection of Halpin memorabilia, the interior is a model of good taste with a deal of old world charm – a fine mix of Victorian style and modern comforts. Comfortably furnished period bedrooms vary; the best are large, with four-posters and lovely sea views; ground-floor rooms have direct access to the garden. Children are welcome, with cots, high-chairs and baby-sitting provided by arrangement. The new wing houses fifteen bedrooms, the restaurant and conference and banqueting facilities for up to 150. Friendly, professional service. Very good breakfasts; all-day   *See over*

snacks, including afternoon tea, served in the residents' lounge.
No dogs. **Rooms** 29. *Garden, tennis, putting green, croquet.*
 Access, Diners, Visa.

Restaurant £75

"Splendid fresh food in elegant Victorian surroundings" rings true
– the best of old and new combine in John Moloney's cooking.
His creative seasonal menus are based on the best of local produce,
especially seafood; fresh fruit and vegetables are grown on the
premises. For a light lunch, try a smoked salmon salad and cheeses
with some of Bee's renowned brown bread; alternatively, the set
lunch menu might offer duck liver parfait with Melba toast and
tomato chutney followed by poached salmon with Noilly Prat
and herbs from their own garden; a fresh fruit mousse on a
raspberry coulis to finish. The four-course table d'hote dinner
changes daily, offering the likes of grilled goat's cheese in a
poppyseed crust with salad, a freshly made soup (perhaps tomato
and orange or cream of leek and potato), pan-fried fillet of beef
with red wine and chanterelles, with blackcurrant parfait
in sponge biscuit and a selection of fruit sauces to finish. A French
and Irish (when available) cheeseboard is also offered. The wine
list covers a diverse range and there's a good selection of half
bottles. **Seats** 70. *Private Room 40. L 12.30-2 D 7.30-9 (Sun to 8).
Set L £16.50 Set D £27.50.*

Rathpeacon   Country Squire Inn

Tel 021 301812   **P**

Mallow Road Rathpeacon Co Cork   Map 2 B6

A couple of miles out of Cork on the N20 towards Mallow, Pat
McSweeney's immaculate roadside pub is very much geared up to
eating. The small bar has not only old 'sewing machine' tables but
also some of the original cast-iron 'Singer' stools, now comfortably
upholstered to match the banquette seating. Bar lunches are
a blackboard affair with the likes of vegetable soup (£1.20),
grilled garlic-stuffed mussels (£2.30), cheese-topped shepherd's pie
(£3.50) and cold ham with salad (£3.95); the evening offerings
on a written menus are a bit more extensive – sirloin steak with
garlic butter or pepper sauce (£11.75), lemon sole stuffed with
crab in a fresh prawn sauce (£10), half a roast chicken with ham
and stuffing (£6.75). The home-cooked food is generously
portioned, so bring a healthy appetite. In the evenings (only),
a cosy, 28-seat candle-lit restaurant offers similar fare with meals
from around £19 (priced according to one's choice of main
course). No children under 12. *Open 12-2.30 (not Sun) & 4.30-11.*
Bar Food *12.30-2.30 (not Sun) & 6.30-9.30 (to 10 Sun). No bar
food Bank Holidays.* **Restaurant** *6.30-10 Tues-Sat. Closed L Sun
& 1 week Jan. Access, Visa.*

Renvyle   Renvyle House   64%   £118

Tel 095 43511   Fax 095 43515   **H**

Renvyle Co Galway   Map 1 A3

Heading towards Clifden on the N59, Renvyle is signposted from
Recess. On the edge of the Atlantic, backed by farmland and with
its own private lake, the hotel offers a wealth of leisure pursuits.
Conference capacity of 120, banqueting for 150. Bedrooms vary
from attic rooms with dormer windows to family-size rooms

with balconies (they're family friendly, with a crèche in summer and other facilities). **Rooms** *64. Garden, outdoor swimming pool, tennis, golf (9), putting, bowling green, riding, fishing, snooker. Closed 1 Jan-mid Mar.* Access, Diners, Visa.

Riverstown　　Coopershill House　　69%　　£84

Tel 071 65108　Fax 071 65466　　**A R**

Coopershill Riverstown Co Sligo　　Map 1 B3

Standing at the centre of a 500-acre estate, this immaculate Georgian mansion has been home to seven generations of the O'Hara family since it was built in 1774 and now successfully combines the spaciousness and elegance of the past with modern amenities and the warmest of welcomes. The rooms retain their original regal dimensions and are furnished in period style with family portraits and antiques. Spacious bedrooms all have en-suite bathrooms and most have four-poster or canopy beds; no smoking in the bedrooms. Peace and tranquillity sum up the atmosphere: no TVs or radios, but books and personal touches like fresh flowers and mineral water. A splendid breakfast starts the day at this most hospitable of country hotels. No dogs in the house. **Rooms** *7. Garden, croquet, coarse and game fishing, games room, boating. Closed end Oct-mid Mar (except for house parties).* Access, Diners, Visa.

Restaurant　　　　　　　　　　　　　　　£50

Antique polished tables, silver candelabra and a log fire in the white marble fireplace provide a fitting setting for Lindy O'Hara's good home cooking. A no-choice 5-course menu might include cheese parcels, a traditional soup, stuffed pork with fresh apricot sauce, a good choice of farmhouse cheeses and, perhaps, lemon mousse. No smoking. **Seats** *14. D only 8 for 8.30. Set D £21.*

Rosses Point　　Austie's

Tel 071 77111　　**P**

Rosses Point Co Sligo　　Map 1 B2

Named after the previous owner, Austie Gillen, and close to the house where Yeats and his brother used to stay on summer holidays (now neglected and in disrepair), this 200-year-old pub overlooking Sligo Bay is a nautical place – not a 'theme' pub but one that has always been associated with a seafaring family and is crammed full of nautical paraphernalia which is both decorative and fascinating to anyone with an interest in maritime history. The simple bar menu is strong on local seafood – chowder, garlic mussels, open sandwiches or salads with crab, prawns and salmon. **Bar Food** *12-5.30 summer only. A la carte menu 6-9.30 all year. Pub closed until 4pm in winter. Waterside terrace.* Access, Visa.

Rosses Point　　The Moorings　　　　　£45

Tel 071 77112　　**R**

Rosses Point Co Sligo　　Map 1 B2

With an almost waterside location (there's a road between it and the sea), views over Sligo Bay and a cosy dining room with open beams and traditional furniture, The Moorings makes an attractive venue and, not surprisingly, Sunday lunch is a speciality. Local

See over

seafood predominates in old favourites – Galway Bay oysters
on ice, chowder, coquilles St Jacques, poached sea trout with
lobster and brandy sauce, monkfish in garlic butter. Popular food,
freshly cooked at reasonable price. *Seats 90. Parties 20.*
Private Room 45. L 12.30-2.30 (Sun) D 5.30-9.30. Set L £7.50.
Closed Mon low season, 1 week in winter, 24-28 Dec. AMERICAN EXPRESS
Access, Visa.

Rosslare	Great Southern	62%	£87
Tel 053 33233 Fax 053 33543			**H**
Rosslare Co Wexford			Map 2 D5

Its position overlooking Rosslare harbour makes this modern hotel
a useful stopover for ferry users and there's plenty to keep children
happy with a crèche, playground and their own restaurant. Public
rooms are light and spacious, with ample seating; many of the
simply-furnished bedrooms are suitable for family occupation.
Up to 150 conference delegates can be accommodated theatre-
style, 200 for a banquet. Ask for their helpful golfer's guide
to local courses. *Rooms 99. Garden, indoor swimming pool, keep-fit
equipment, tennis, sauna, steam room, snooker, hairdressing, children's
play area. Closed Jan-Mar.* AMERICAN EXPRESS *Access, Diners, Visa.*

Rosslare	Kelly's Strand Hotel	71%	£84
Tel 053 32114 Fax 053 32222			**H**
Rosslare Co Wexford			Map 2 D5

William J Kelly really started something in 1895 when
he established a tea room here. A century on, the place is out on its
own as a family resort hotel, with an almost endless list of ways
to keep guests as busy, as relaxed and as entertained as they choose.
Heading the facilities is the excellent Aqua leisure club (including
an outdoor Canadian hot tub), and there's also live entertainment
every night and plenty of diversion for children. Bright, fresh
bedrooms are in practical modern style. No dogs. *Rooms 99.*
*Garden, indoor swimming pools, gymnasium, squash, sauna, spa bath,
solarium, beauty & hair salon, indoor & outdoor tennis, badminton,
bicycles, games rooms, crazy golf, snooker, crèche, children's play area,
giant chess and draughts. Closed early Dec-late Feb.* AMERICAN EXPRESS
Access, Visa.

Rosslare	Places of Interest

Ferry Terminal Tourist Information   Tel 053 33622
Windsurfing Centre   Tel 053 32101

Rossnowlagh	Sand House Hotel	69%	£88
Tel 072 51777 Fax 072 52100			**H**
Rossnowlagh Co Donegal			Map 1 B2

Improvements continue at the crenellated Sand House hotel,
which sits right by a large sandy beach overlooking immense
Donegal Bay and the Atlantic Ocean. The Atlantic conservatory
lounge takes full advantage of views that are also enjoyed by many
of the bedrooms (those with the very best views attract a small
supplement). Mary and Brian Britton, together with their son and
staff, extend a warm welcome, reinforced by a fire in the
Victorian-style lobby. Bedrooms, immaculate like the rest of the
hotel, are individually decorated with expensive, stylish fabrics;

furniture varies from antiques to fairly modest fitted units, and
superior rooms have chaises longues. A delightful, peaceful hotel,
as the many regular guests will testify. Banqueting/conference
facilities for 60. Good golf and riding facilities nearby. *Rooms 40.
Garden, tennis, mini-golf, croquet, surfing, canoeing, board sailing, sea,
game & coarse fishing, games room, indoor children's play room,
helipad. Closed late Oct-Easter.* AMERICAN EXPRESS *Access, Diners, Visa.*

Rossnowlagh	Smugglers Creek Inn	£35
Tel 072 52366		**P**
Rossnowlagh Co Donegal		Map 1 B2

Perched high on the cliffs overlooking the wonderful golden
strand at Rossnowlagh, an imaginatively restored pub and
restaurant. Visitors have the endless fascination of watching the
powerful Atlantic rollers come in from afar to spend themselves
on the beach far below – and all this while sitting in considerable
comfort, with open fires and delicious bar food from which
to choose. A typical selection might include home-made soups
(always one with fish) served with lovely nutty brown bread,
garlic mussels, freshly made paté and hot toast, Irish farmhouse
cheeses, smoked salmon, or just tea with hot scones and home-
made jam. Across the corridor from the bar (and sharing the same
dramatic view), the stone-floored restaurant is furnished
in country style and, although the menu works the smugglers
theme to death, the same excellent kitchen is common to bar and
restaurant. So start, perhaps, with Donegal Bay oysters or a warm
salad that includes smoked bacon, blue cheese and croutons,
followed by a main course from a wide choice of seafood or,
perhaps, vegetarian tagliatelle or a stir-fry. Children are well
catered for and there's a selection of special coffees for their
parents. Accommodation is offered in five rooms, all en suite,
interestingly decorated and with sea views. Rooms vary
considerably and most are on the small side – one corner room,
with windows in two walls, is slightly larger than average and has
even better views. The inn's wide-ranging attractions earn it our
Award of Irish Pub of the Year. *Seats 50. Parties 10. Private
Room 30. L (Sun) 12.30-3 Bar snacks daily 1-6 D 6-9.30. Set Sun
L £8.75. Closed 24 & 25 Dec, Mon & Tue in winter. Access, Visa.*

Roundstone	O'Dowd's Seafood Bar and Restaurant	
Tel 095 35809		**P**
Roundstone Co Galway		Map 2 A4

A reassuringly unchanging traditional pub and seafood bar
overlooking the harbour. It's an oasis of calm where regular
summer visitors – notably Dublin lawyers and doctors, plus the
odd politician – return to recharge their batteries. The simple, old-
fashioned bar is a relaxing place to renew old friendships over
a pint and a bite from the reasonably-priced bar menu, which
includes a good range of seafood choices – chowder (a speciality),
Mannin Bay oysters, crab claws in garlic, stuffed mussels, crab
salad, smoked salmon pasta and an unusually named salmon
burger with spicy tomato sauce – plus old favourites like
shepherd's pie and sirloin steak for carnivores and vegetarian
specialities such as bean burgers. Salmon is smoked or cured for
gravlax locally; herbs and lettuce come from their own garden.

See over

Lobster, grilled oysters, game (mallard, quail, venison and
pheasant) and blackberry and apple pie are always popular in the
restaurant; a roast goose is a traditional offering on New Year's
Eve. *Bar Food 11-10 (Sun 12.30-2, 4-10). Restaurant Meals
12.30-3, 6-9.30 (Sun 12.30-2, 4-10). Restaurant closed mid Oct-
Christmas & 2nd week Jan-Easter.* AMERICAN EXPRESS *Access, Visa.*

Roundwood   Roundwood Inn   £60

Tel 01 281 8107   **R**

Roundwood Co Wicklow   **Map 2 D4**

Set amidst spectacular scenery in the highest village in the
Wicklow Hills, this 17th-century inn is furnished in traditional
style with wooden floors, darkwood furniture and huge log fires
throughout. Excellent bar food is available every day and includes,
typically, soup, sandwiches, fresh or smoked salmon, Galway Bay
oysters, chicken in the basket, goulash and Irish stew. The
restaurant menu leans towards bigger dishes like rack of Wicklow
lamb, roast wild Wicklow venison and other game in season.
German influences are evident in long-established specialities like
wiener schnitzel, triple liqueur parfait and a feather-light fresh
cream gateau which is not to be missed. A mainly European wine
list, strongest in France and Germany, starts at under £10 for the
house selection and ascends to 40 times that for a 1967 Pauillac.
*Seats 45. Parties 35. Private Room 32. L 1-2.30 D 7.30-9.30 (Sat
to 10). Closed D Sun, all Mon, 25 Dec, Good Friday. Set L £13.95.
Access, Visa.*

Schull   T J Newman's

Tel 028 28223   **P**

Main Street Schull Co Cork   **Map 2 A6**

On the corner of the main street and the road that leads down
to the quay, this characterful little bar makes up in charm
and warmth what it lacks in cubic capacity. That capacity
is supplemented on summer evenings by the pavement.
*Open 10.30am-11pm (to 11.30 in summer), Sun 12.30-2, 4-11.
No credit cards.*

Scotshouse   Hilton Park   62%   £111

Tel 047 56007   Fax 047 56033   **A**

Scotshouse nr Clones Co Monaghan   **Map 1 C3**

Magnificent woodlands and gardens make a lovely, peaceful
setting for 18th-century Hilton Park. The mansion has been in the
Madden family for over 250 years and Johnny and Lucy are the
eighth generation to live here. They run it very much as a family
home which takes in guests, and it's full of interest, with
heirlooms, family portraits and four-poster beds. Large bedrooms,
some with dressing rooms and characterful bathrooms, afford
wonderful views. Lucy cooks an excellent no-choice five-course
dinner in traditional country house style, with most of the raw
materials produced in their own grounds or locally. The estate
covers 600 acres, including three lakes where swimming, boating
and fishing keep visitors occupied. A fine breakfast starts the day,
served in the bright, charming Green Room. Enter the estate
by the main entrance on the Clones-Scotshouse road and look out
for a black gate with silver falcons. Children not encouraged.

No dogs. **Rooms** 5. *Garden, golf (9), shooting, coarse & game fishing, boating. Closed Oct-Easter except for parties by arrangement. Access, Visa.*

Scotshouse   Place of Interest

Castle Leslie   Glasloughby Monaghan Tel 047 88109

Shanagarry   Ballymaloe House   66%   £120

Tel 021 652531   Fax 021 652021   **AR**

Shanagarry Co Cork   **Map 2 C6**

Part of an old castle that became a farmhouse, modernised through the centuries, but with the 14th-century keep remaining in its original form. The hotel is situated in the middle of a 400-acre farm, both owned and run by Ivan and Myrtle Allen, recipients of our International Hospitality Award, and part of a group of family enterprises that includes a cookery school, craft shop and the *Crawford Gallery Café* in Cork (see entry). Two miles from the coast, near the small fishing village of Ballycotton, the main house provides the day rooms, a large drawing room with an open fire and a TV room, complete with video recorder. Throughout, there's an interesting collection of modern Irish paintings with works by Jack B Yeats in the dining room. Thirteen bedrooms in the main building are traditionally furnished, and a further five modern, garden rooms open on to a lawn. Another eleven rooms, more cottagey in character, surround the old coachyard, with some on ground level suitable for wheelchairs. Teenagers especially will appreciate the self-contained 16th-century Gatehouse which has its own small entrance hall and a twin-bedded room with its bathroom up a steep wooden staircase. Ballymaloe is a warm and comfortable family home, especially welcoming to children of all ages (high tea is served at 5.30pm), who can rely on the Allen (grand)children to relay the latest news from the farm or share the sandpit and pool. For the delightful breakfasts, all the ingredients are local or home-made, with even the oatmeal used for porridge ground in an old stone mill down the road. **Rooms** 30. *Garden, outdoor swimming pool, tennis, golf (9), children's outdoor play area. Closed 24-26 Dec. Access, Visa.*

Restaurant   ★   £80

Perhaps more than anyone else in the country, Myrtle Allen has nurtured, encouraged and cajoled chefs from her kitchen to spread their wings further afield after first achieving high standards here. Wherever you go in Ireland, you're likely to come across an individual who at some time has cooked alongside this doyenne of Irish chefs. There are several smallish interconnecting dining rooms, any of which can be used privately, all furnished with antiques, and a conservatory with a black-and-white tiled floor, Lloyd Loom furniture and lots of greenery. With the bread home-baked, the fish caught locally (sometimes the menu is deliberately late to see what the fishing boats have brought in), and the salads and vegetables picked that day, you can certainly rely on the ingredients being fresh and wholesome – indeed, much produce comes from their own farm. With Irish and French as the main influences, the cooking is simple, enhancing the quality of the raw materials. Typically, nightly-changing menus might feature

See over

Ballycotton fish soup, hot dressed crab, brill *en papillote* with fresh herbs, a selection of patés, hot buttered lobster, fillet of sole with spinach butter sauce, roast stuffed loin of Shanagarry pork with apple sauce and red cabbage, or roast chicken with *pipérade*. Try some Irish cheeses before the dessert (perhaps an apricot tart or praline gateau) and linger awhile over some excellent cafetière coffee. Ivan Allen has built up a fine wine cellar over many years with some exceptional vintage Bordeaux and an increasing awareness of quality New World wines. *Seats 90.*
Private Room 30. L 12.30-2 (Sun buffet at 1) D 7-9.30 (Sun buffet at 7.30). Set D £30.

Shannon   Great Southern   64%   £110

Tel 061 471122   Fax 061 471982   **H**

Shannon Airport Shannon Co Clare   Map 2 B4

Situated directly opposite the main terminal building, a modern airport hotel, totally refurbished three years ago. Soundproofed bedrooms include 11 Executive rooms and three suites. Fourteen rooms designated non-smoking. Conference facilities for up to 170, banqueting for 140. *Rooms 115. Garden, coffee shop.* *Closed 25 & 26 Dec.* AMERICAN EXPRESS *Access, Diners, Visa.*

Shannon   Oakwood Arms Hotel   63%   £88

Tel 061 361500   Fax 061 361414   **H**

Shannon Co Clare   Map 2 B4

A family-owned, redbrick hotel (opened in 1991) that creates a good first impression with its neatly laid-out flower beds. If the mock-Tudor style of the hotel is somewhat surprising in this setting, its aviation theme is less so: the lounge bar and function room both honour the memory of the pioneer female pilot Sophie Pearse, who came from the area, and the restaurant is named after Howard Hughes's famous flying boat, *The Spruce Goose*. Public areas are quite spacious and comfortably furnished and, although not individually decorated, bedrooms have all the necessary comforts and are double-glazed. *Rooms 45. Patio.* *Closed 24 & 25 Dec.* AMERICAN EXPRESS *Access, Diners, Visa.*

Shannon   Place of Interest

Airport Tourist Information   Tel 061 61664/61565

Skerries   Red Bank Restaurant   £60

Tel 01 849 1005   Fax 01 849 1598   **R**

7 Church Street Skerries Co Dublin   Map 1 D3

Terry McCoy – wit, wag, owner and chef – creates imaginative, generous dishes based on local seafood in his well-known north Dublin restaurant located in a converted bank. Have a drink and read the menu in the comfortable reception area, then settle down to specialities such as baked crab 'Loughshinney' (blended with dry sherry and served in its own shell), whole Dublin Bay prawns cooked in fish stock and served with garlic butter or black sole 'Red Bank' (stuffed with mussels and prawns). There's always a choice of soups (try the cockle and mussel consommé or smoked haddock and leek) on the carte, alongside the long list of fish dishes. To complete the picture, loin of pork, rack of lamb, breast of duck and steaks make regular appearances with interesting sauces. Tempting desserts, including a very good baked chocolate cheesecake, are served from the trolley and there's a farmhouse cheeseboard. Three-course Sunday lunches and table d'hote both offer a good choice. Menus change with the seasons and favour organic produce whenever available. There's something for everyone on the fairly priced wine list, which has useful notes to complement menu items; good drinking under £20. Not really suitable for children under 8. Smoking is permitted in the dining room, but the 'ban smoking in restaurants completely' campaign has an eager proponent in Mr McCoy. *Seats 45. Parties 14. Private Room 10. L (Sun only) 12.30-2.15 D 7-10. Closed D Sun, all Mon, 4 days Christmas, 2 weeks Nov. Set L £13 Set D £17.95/£21.* AMERICAN EXPRESS *Access, Diners, Visa.*

Skerries   Place of Interest

Ardgillan Castle   Balbriggan Tel 01 849 2212

Skryne   O'Connell's

Tel 046 25122	**P**
Skryne nr Tara Co Meath	Map 1 C3

The old castle on top of the hill is your marker for this delightfully unspoilt old country pub, whose main attraction is a good pint pulled by charming landlady Mary O'Connell (she has held the reins for 10 years, but the pub has been in her husband's family for three generations). The two simple bars contain friendly locals, records of sporting endeavours and a history of the nearby monastery. The pub was up for sale as we went to press. *Open usual pub hours. No credit cards.*

Sligo   Hargadon's

Tel 071 70933	**P**
O'Connell Street Sligo Co Sligo	Map 1 B2

Hargadon's is one of the great legendary pubs of Ireland: bought by a British MP in 1868, it passed into the hands of the Hargadon family in 1908 and has been maintained by them, unspoilt, ever since. When they decided to venture into providing food (served from 10.30-6, to 7 in summer) it was soup and sandwiches bought in from talented local (Ballymaloe-trained) caterers; now they offer a full bar food service. Dinner is served in a room at the back where it will not interfere with the real business of running a bar. Otherwise it is as it was – the snugs, the pot-belly stove, the wooden benches and the shelves which used to hold groceries. Children allowed in the bar during the daytime only. Go and enjoy. Beer garden. *No credit cards.*

Sligo   McGettigan's (An Cruíscín Lán/ Cruskeen Lawn)

Tel 071 62857	**P**
Connolly Street Sligo Co Sligo	Map 1 B2

The McGettigan family's comfortable, unselfconscious pub is well supported by locals and visitors alike. It reputation is based on serving good, plain food at a very fair price; the emphasis throughout is on old-fashioned courtesy and service rather than on quaintness of decor or tradition. Expect simply presented, middle-of-the-road food in generous portions, with value for

See over

money firmly in mind. Good-value lunches offer the likes of Irish
stew and roast stuffed chicken and bacon; bar snacks, including
children's favourites, are served all day every day. Leave room for
sherry trifle and custard or home-made apple tart and cream (both
£1.20). Accommodation is also offered in 11 modest rooms (B&B
£27 for two). *Bar Meals 12.30-2.30 (except Sat & Sun). Children
allowed in bar to eat, children's menu, cot & high-chair provided. Pub
closed in winter months 3-5pm. No credit cards.*

Sligo	Sligo Park	58%	£95
Tel 071 60291 Fax 071 69556			H
Pearse Road Sligo Co Sligo			Map 1 B2

Standing in parkland one mile from Sligo on the Dublin road, this
modern hotel caters for private guests and also for business/
function groups from 10 to 450. Bedrooms offer the basic range
of accessories, and there's a well-appointed leisure centre. Children
under six stay free in their parents' room. *Rooms 89. Indoor
swimming pool, gymnasium, sauna, spa bath, steam room, solarium,
snooker, tennis, coffee shop (10am-7pm).* AMERICAN EXPRESS *Access,
Diners, Visa.*

Sligo	Truffles Restaurant	£22
Tel 071 44226		R
The Mall Sligo Co Sligo		Map 1 B2

Bernadette O'Shea's 'new age pizza' restaurant is unusual, to say the
least: a delightfully wacky dining room with amusing trompe
l'oeil decorations and a peat fire setting the tone. Thoroughly
original treatments for the humble pizza (served in 8" and 10"
sizes) include a variety of eclectic ingredients – the Californian
Classic will include sun-dried tomatoes and roasted garlic, the
Mexicano, spicy sausage and fresh hot chili peppers and so on, but
the best of all is the Irish Cheese Board, a surprisingly light taste
experience adding melting goat's cheese, Cashel blue, smoked Brie,
cream cheese, cottage cheese, Irish mozzarella and fresh herbs to a
crisp base and fresh tomato sauce. A more worthy winner of our
Cheese Dish of the Year Award you couldn't wish to find. Home-
made soups, garlic bread, filled stromboli bread, wonderful main
course salads – including Italian, Roquefort and Greek – based
on locally grown organic produce, and a choice of fresh pastas
(made with free-range eggs) are other attractions. It's a small,
eccentric place ("service charge not included, but anticipated"),
now deservedly popular, so book ahead. The wine bar upstairs
is open from 7pm (Sun 5-10pm). *Seats 38. Parties 10. D only
5-10.30 (Sun to 10). Closed Mon, 3 days Christmas, 4 days Easter.*

Sligo	Places of Interest

Tourist Information Tel 071 61201
Parkes Castle Tel 071 64149
Sligo Racecourse Cleveragh Tel 071 62484/60094

Spiddal	Boluisce Seafood Bar	£45
Tel 091 83286 Fax 091 83285		R
Spiddal Connemara Co Galway		Map 2 B4

Kevin and Monica MacGabhaun have kept more or less to the
formula operated so successfully by the Glanville family for 20

years. Seafood is of course the star of the show in both the first-floor restaurant and the downstairs bar: seafood chowder, mussels in cream sauce, oysters natural or baked, Atlantic black sole, Galway Bay salmon, lobster thermidor. Also good steaks and stir-fries in the bar; children's portions. *Seats 60. Parties 10. Meals 12-10 (Sun 12.30-10). Closed 24-26 Dec.* AMERICAN EXPRESS *Access, Visa.*

Spiddal	Bridge House Hotel	£65

Tel 091 83118 **H**

Spiddal Connemara Co Galway — Map 2 B4

All the bedrooms at Esther Feeney's spruce little hotel on Galway Bay are now en suite, and all have colour TVs. The neat pine-clad bar has French windows opening on to the garden and the Stirrup Room is open all day for food. No children under 2. No dogs. *Rooms 14. Garden. Closed Christmas-mid Feb.* AMERICAN EXPRESS *Access, Visa.*

Stillorgan	China-Sichaun Restaurant	£50

Tel 01 288 4817   Fax 01 288 0882 **R**

4 Lower Kilmacud Road Stillorgan Co Dublin — Map 4 C1

The China Sichuan Food Authority sponsors this smart, civilised restaurant five miles south of Dublin city centre, and many of the dishes are hot with spices and chili. Among these (denoted on the menu by an asterisk) are orange-flavoured sliced cold beef, fried prawns in garlic sauce and fried lamb shreds in aromatic sauce. Wines include Great Wall white and red from China. *Seats 50. Parties 20. L 12.30-2.30 (Sun & Bank Holidays 1-2.30) D 6-11. Closed 25-27 Dec. Set L from £6 Set D £16.50.* AMERICAN EXPRESS *Access, Visa.*

Stillorgan	The Mill House	

Tel 01 288 8672   Fax 01 283 6353 **P**

Lower Kilmacud Road Stillorgan Co Dublin — Map 4 C1

The Mill House is hard to miss with its coat of bright pink and shiny gold paintwork. Inside, once past the rather off-putting porch/hall area, the interior is surprisingly calm and peaceful, broken up into a number of small semi-snug areas with plenty of gas coal-effect fires. The large, irregular mahogany bar is pleasingly solid and there's a lot of dark wood in the traditional style, successfully offset by plenty of mirrors, pictures and plants in old china cachepots. Traditional lunchtime pub grub includes basket snacks (£2.95) and the likes of lasagne (£3.95), burger, curry, chicken Kiev (£4.95) and fried fillet of plaice. *Bar Food 12-2.30, 5-8. Patio.* AMERICAN EXPRESS *Access, Diners, Visa.*

Stillorgan	The Stillorgan Orchard	

Tel 01 288 8470   Fax 01 943803 **P**

Stillorgan Co Dublin — Map 4 C1

Despite its slightly incongruous situation close to a large suburban shopping centre, the Orchard's main claim to fame is 'the largest thatched roof in Ireland'. Inside, there's a surprisingly genuine country cottage atmosphere with low ceilings, small windows, lots of tapestry style and chintzy seating in snugs and alcoves and all the traditional clutter of brass, copper and old plates on the walls.

See over

Bar food is not adventurous, but everything is fresh and wholesome. Standard, short printed menus for lunch and evening bar food are augmented by daily specials including a roast, a traditional dish such as baked Limerick ham with parsley sauce (£5.25), steak (£7.15), some kind of chicken (braised breast £5.15) and a fish of the day, plaice perhaps, or sometimes something more unusual such as grilled sea trout with caper butter (£5.05). **Bar Food** *12.30-3, 5-8. Children allowed to eat in bar until 4pm (Sun to 7pm). Garden.* ~~AMERICAN EXPRESS~~ *Access, Diners, Visa.*

Straffan	Kildare Hotel	87%	£245
Tel 01 6273333 Fax 01 6273312			**HR**
Straffan Co Kildare			Map 2 C4

Already affectionately known as the K Club (attached to the hotel is the country club which is centred around the golf course designed by Arnold Palmer), the hotel is best reached from Dublin (17 miles) via the N7, taking a right at Kill to Straffan. Reputedly, previous owners of the original (*Straffan*) house were dogged by bad luck, but those myths have now been discarded with the creation of this magnificent complex, surrounded by beautifully landscaped gardens (ask for the garden walk leaflet), with the River Liffey running through the grounds. The new buildings blend in tastefully with the old house (indeed it's hard to see the 'join') and inside there's much opulence, highlighted by sumptuous furnishings, fine period antiques and an outstanding collection of paintings, including several by Jack B Yeats, who has a room devoted to his works. Each of the spacious bedrooms has been individually designed – note the different *trompe l'oeil* designs, also apparent in the bar – and no two of the marble bathrooms (luxury toiletries, bathrobes, slippers and huge towels) are the same. All rooms are lavishly and handsomely furnished; on arrival, guests are treated to a bowl of fruit, hand-made chocolates and mineral water; satellite TV, video recorder, mini-bar and personal safe are standard amenites, along with handily-placed telephones. Such luxury, of course, requires levels of service, housekeeping and maintenance to match, a task that General Manager Ray Carroll and his motivated team of staff achieve admirably. There are two meeting rooms in the main house, one an imposing boardroom, and up to 600 can be accommodated in the indoor tennis arena, part of the sports centre, which is easily transformed to suit the occasion. Also available, adjoining the hotel, are self-contained, two-bedroomed courtyard apartments and a three-bedroomed lodge. **Rooms** *45. Garden, indoor swimming pool, gymnasium, squash, sauna, solarium, hair & beauty salon, golf (18), tennis, snooker, bicycles, coarse and game fishing, clay-pigeon shooting.* ~~AMERICAN EXPRESS~~ *Access, Diners, Visa.*

The Byerley Turk   £100

The restaurant's name, perhaps unfamiliar to those who do not follow horse-racing sport, comes from one of the three Arab stallions in the male line of every thoroughbred horse in the world; its impressively draped tall windows, marble columns and rich decor in tones of deep terracotta, cream and green harmonise perfectly with the style of the original house. The room is cleverly shaped to create semi-private areas and make the most of window

tables, laid with crested china, monogrammed white linen,
gleaming modern crystal and silver. Chef Michel Flamme's
leanings towards classical French cuisine are tempered
by traditional Irish influences – in, for example, layers of crubeens
and ox tongue with a cream of spinach with a confit of onions and
mustard sauce – and, with his kitchen garden now in full
production, by local and home-grown seasonal produce, as in
warm asparagus salad with garden leaves in a walnut dressing
or supreme of chicken with a stew of broad beans scented with
garlic and basil. An additional Seasonal Fayre Menu offers
sophisticated dishes and the 3-course table d'hote dinner menu
might include roast monkfish accompanied by a cream of lobster
sprinkled with mussels, followed by roast spring lamb with
a vegetable parcel and finishing, perhaps, with a plate of caramel
desserts or a selection of Irish and French cheeses. The modest (but
not modestly priced) wine list would benefit from a clearer layout
and some notes. The Legend Restaurant in the golf club offers
a buffet lunch (£14.95) in summer and table d'hote in winter; à la
carte in the evenings. *Seats 80. Parties 30. Private Room 50. L Sun
only 12.30-2 D 7-10. Set Sun L £17.95 Set D £35.*

Straffan   Places of Interest

Steam Museum   Tel 01 627 3155
Castletown House   Celbridge Tel 01 628 8252
Irish National Stud   Tully Tel 045 21617 *15 miles*
Japanese Gardens   Tully Tel 045 21251 *15 miles*

Swords   Le Chateau   £55
Tel 01 8406533	**R**
River Mall Main Street Swords Dublin Co Dublin	**Map 1 D3**

In a shopping mall near Dublin airport, John Dowd's cooking
easily outclasses the surroundings. The menu is mainly French
with a few more original offerings – such as pasta Tara, a well-
balanced dish of home-made pasta with garlic, cream, bacon and
baby mushrooms – added for good measure. Lunch is especially
good value. No children after 8.30pm. *Seats 60. Parties 20.
L 12.15-2.30 D 7-11. Closed Mon in winter, Bank Holidays, 1 week
Christmas/New Year. Set L £10.50 Set D £19.75.* AMERICAN EXPRESS
Access, Diners, Visa.

Swords   Forte Travelodge   £42
Tel 01 840 9233	**H**
N1 Dublin/Belfast Road Swords Bypass nr Dublin Co Dublin	**Map 1 D3**

On the southbound carriageway of the Swords bypass at Swords
roundabout, 1½ miles north of Dublin airport, 16 miles north
of Dublin city centre. The room rate of £32 (without breakfast)
could include up to 3 adults, a child under 12 and a baby in a cot.
Rooms 40. AMERICAN EXPRESS *Access, Visa.*

Swords   The Old Schoolhouse   £50
Tel 01 840 4160 Fax 01 840 5060	**R**
Coolbanagher Swords Co Dublin	**Map 1 D3**

Set in a quiet backwater away from the main road, this old stone
building has been sympathetically restored and converted to make
a delightful restaurant. There are always daily specials on the   *See over*

blackboard, patés, soups and offal are good choices and fish from nearby harbours Skerries and Howth often features in dishes such as a meal-in-a-soup-bowl chowder or simple grilled black sole on the bone. Steaks of 6, 8 or 10 ounces are served with a choice of sauces. Country desserts like apple and blackberry crumble are hard to resist. *Seats 70. Parties 20. Private Room 20. L 12.30-2.30 D 6.30-10.30. Closed L Sat, all Sun, Bank Holidays, 3 days Christmas. Set L £10.95/£12.95 Set D £19.50.* AMERICAN EXPRESS *Access, Diners, Visa.*

Swords	Place of Interest

Newbridge House   Donabate Tel 01 843 6534 *4 miles*

JAMESON The Spirit of Ireland

Thomastown	Mount Juliet Hotel	84%	£195

Tel 056 24455   Fax 056 24522   **HR**

Mount Juliet Thomastown Co Kilkenny   Map 2 C5

The imposing 18th-century Mount Juliet House stands in 1500 acres of parkland and formal gardens through which flow the rivers Kings and Nore; a traditional stone bridge crosses the latter for access to the hotel. Its exquisite interior is no less striking: public rooms feature wonderful moulded plasterwork and the Parlour boasts a colourful marble fireplace. The bedrooms and generously proportioned suites are individually styled, with soft floral fabrics, solid oak furniture and deep-cushioned sofas; most have fine Adam fireplaces. Bathrooms are equally luxurious, with many extras. Three Rose Garden suites are in Ballylinch House on the estate. Recreational facilities include the Iris Kellett equestrian centre, a magnificent Jack Nicklaus-designed golf course (home of the 1994 Irish Open) and golf academy, an impressive new leisure centre abutting the clubhouse and one of Ireland's oldest cricket clubs. Children under 12 stay free in their parents' room. Kennelling for dogs. Meeting rooms for up to 50, banqueting for 140. *Rooms 32. Garden, indoor swimming pool, health and beauty treatments, sauna, steam room, exercise room, tennis, game fishing, golf (18), archery, clay-pigeon shooting, riding, snooker, helipad.* AMERICAN EXPRESS *Access, Diners, Visa.*

Lady Helen Dining Room   £66

Although grand, this gracefully elegant, high-ceilinged room, softly decorated in pastel shades and with sweeping views over the grounds, is not forbidding and has a pleasant atmosphere. To match these beautiful surroundings, enthusiastic new chef Rory Morahan is developing his Celtic kitchen theme, with "fine dining" in the evening offering both four-course table d'hote and à la carte featuring grills. In the sporting centre, Hunter's Yard, the 64-seat *Loft* restaurant offers a very popular Sunday brunch (£14) and all-day (7am-9.30pm) menu during the week. The wine list is unambitious for an aspiring hotel such as this; only two modest clarets under £30, just one white burgundy that pre-dates the '90s vintages and few half bottles. *Seats 55. Parties 6. Private Room 40. L Sun only D 7-10.30. Set Sun L £16 Set D £33.*

Timoleague   Dillon's

| Tel 023 46390 | **P** |

Mill Street Timoleague Co Cork   Map 2 B6

That one can see in through the plant-filled clear shop window
immediately distinguishes Dillon's from the usual Irish town bar;
their description of themselves as a café-styled bar is very apt.
There's a conventional bar counter down one side of the single
room, a mixture of furniture that includes a few Lloyd Loom
chairs around eating-height tables and arty black-and-white photos
of the likes of James Dean and Billie Holliday on the walls. It's run
by two French sisters, Isabelle (Dillon) and Anne (Boulineau), who
originally procured all the food from nearby Lettercollum House
restaurant (which is no disadvantage) but are increasingly
substituting dishes of their own. Thus one gets beef bourguignon
(£5.50), free-range chicken cooked in white wine (£6.50) and
tarte tartin (£1.95) along with shepherd's pie (£2.90), lasagne
(£3.95) and cheesecake (£2.20). The same menu is available
throughout the opening hours. Good cafetière coffee and pots
of tea are served alongside the pints of stout. *Open (& **Bar Food**
served) Noon-11 (to 11.30 in summer). Closed Tues (except June-
Aug), Nov-mid March (except 3 weeks Christmas). No credit cards.*

Timoleague   Place of Interest

Timoleague Castle Gardens   Tel 023 46116

Tralee   Ballyseede Castle Hotel   60%   £85

| Tel 066 25799 Fax 066 25287 | **H** |

Tralee Co Kerry .   Map 2 A5

Just off the Killarney road, this 15th-century castle was once the
chief garrison of the Fitzgeralds, Earls of Desmond. Granite pillars
and wrought-iron gates stand at the entrance and impressive
public rooms include a lobby with Doric columns, two drawing
rooms with fine plasterwork and a dining room overlooking
ancient oaks. Bedrooms are spacious and comfortable; bathrooms
vary considerably. Conference/banqueting for 180/80. Golf,
fishing, riding and shooting available nearby. Children up to the
age of 10 stay free in their parents' room. No dogs. ***Rooms 15.***
Garden. Access, Diners, Visa.

Tralee   Places of Interest

Kerry The Kingdom   Tel 066 27777
Tralee Racecourse   Tel 066 26188
Listowel Racecourse   Tel 068 21144

Tuam   Cré na Cille   £50

| Tel 093 28232 | **R** |

High Street Tuam Co Galway   Map 1 B3

Venetian blinds, darkwood tables with place mats, simple cutlery
and paper napkins create quite a businesslike lunchtime
atmosphere that is enhanced by the crush of people coming
in from the street – perhaps more Toulouse than Tuam. Evenings
are more formal and the setting softer, but the common link
is chef Cathal Reynolds's confident use of local ingredients
in generously served food at remarkably keen prices. Typical

See over

dishes include hearty duck liver paté or pan-fried Irish Brie in a vermouth sauce followed by brill fillets in a saffron cream sauce or a vegetarian dish of the day. Good baked desserts, typically in classic tarts – frangipane, Bakewell – given a modern twist. *Seats 45. Private Room 30. L 12.30-2.30 D 6-10. Closed Sun, 24-27 Dec, Bank Holidays.* AMERICAN EXPRESS *Access, Diners, Visa.*

Tubbercurry   Killoran's Traditional Restaurant & Lounge

Tel 071 85679 Fax 071 85111	**P**

Main Street Tubbercurry Co Sligo   **Map 1 B2**

"The welcome doesn't die on the doormat" is the motto at Tommy and Anne Killoran's whale of a place; no-nonsense, reliably priced food and authentic entertainment are the draws. On Thursday nights from Jun-Sept its 60-seater bar/restaurant/ lounge (call it what you will) is crammed to the gunwales, with all and sundry tucking into boxty, potato cakes, crubeens and cali – a local name for hot potato, spring onion and melted butter, better known as champ – to help along the traditional music and Irish dancing. Visitors can even try their hand at butter-churning in the middle of it all. Organic vegetables, local goat's cheese (cheese plate £3) and home-made brown bread are regulars on the menu, alongside more everyday fare. In season, the salmon comes from the river right on the doorstep. There's nowhere else quite like it in Ireland – Killoran's is an original. Not elegant, not folksy, but definitely different. "Children are welcome at any time." *Open 9am-12pm, Sun 10am-10pm.* **Bar Food** *12.30-3, 7-9 (bar snacks only winter eves). Garden.* AMERICAN EXPRESS *Access, Diners, Visa.*

Waterford   Dwyer's Restaurant   £55

Tel 051 77478	**R**

8 Mary Street Waterford Co Waterford   **Map 2 C5**

In a backstreet near the bridge Martin Dwyer's comfortable, low-key converted barracks provides an undemonstrative background for his quietly confident cooking. A limited choice 3-course early evening menu is extremely good value, or there's a more flexible table d'hote with a wider choice, plus a good à la carte menu. The Dwyer style is original without being gimmicky, with careful attention to flavour and texture contrasts/combinations. Typical dishes on a winter evening included spiced carrot soup, lamb's kidneys with black pepper, monkfish with smoked salmon sauce, roast breast of pheasant mousseline with port wine sauce and medallions of fillet steak sauced with onion and thyme leaves. Desserts such as marquise of three chocolates, pear and almond tart or hot bananas and ginger with ice cream are equally irresistible. *Seats 30. Parties 10. D only 6-10 (early evening menu 6-7.30). Closed Sun, 1 week Christmas, Good Friday, 2 weeks July. Set D £13.* AMERICAN EXPRESS *Access, Diners, Visa.*

Waterford   Granville Hotel   69%   £79

Tel 051 55111 Fax 051 70307	**H**

1 Meagher Quay Waterford Co Waterford   **Map 2 C5**

On the quay by the River Suir, the Granville is kept in tip-top condition by owners Liam and Ann Cusack and their staff. The

style throughout the day rooms is traditional, and there are many
reminders of the hotel's history: the Thomas Francis Meagher bar
honours an early owner, the Bianconi restaurant salutes another
owner (the man who started Ireland's first formal transport
system) and the Parnell meeting room remembers where Charles
Stewart Parnell made many famous speeches. Stylishly decorated
bedrooms of various sizes all have good bathrooms. Children
under 12 stay free in parents' room. No dogs. *Rooms 74.*
Access, Diners, Visa.

Waterford   Jack Meade's

Tel 051 73187	**P**
Ballycanvan Little Halfway House Waterford Co Waterford	Map 2 C5

This delightful early 18th-century pub has been in the same family
for 150 years and has managed to retain its essential character and
charm remarkably well. The building, which is well kept and
cottagey, has not been altered or extended and they make the most
of its sun-trap position, with flower tubs at the door and climbing
plants up the walls contrasting with the cool, dark, low-ceilinged
interior with its two small traditional bars complete with pictures
and photographs of local interest and open fires for cold weather;
in summer there's traditional music in the open and a barbecue.
A museum of farm machinery and (across the bridge) an old
limekiln (for making fertiliser) and ice house (for preserving fish)
are among the things to look at. *No credit cards.*

Waterford   Jurys Hotel   61%   £106

Tel 051 32111 Fax 051 32863	**H**
Ferrybank Waterford Co Waterford	Map 2 C5

Large modern hotel dominating a hillside on the opposite side
of the River Suir to Waterford town. The spacious lobby/lounge
features a long white marble reception desk, a pair of fine
Waterford crystal chandeliers and a comfortable sitting area.
Of the five floors of bedrooms, all of which share the same fine
view over the city, only the top floor (which is very dated) has
yet to benefit from refurbishment with darkwood furniture,
matching floral curtains, polycotton duvets and smart new
bathrooms with white marble vanity units providing good shelf
space. Up to two children under 12 stay free in parents' room; 20
rooms have both a double and single bed. Activity club and video
room for children (Mon-Fri) during school summer holidays. 38
acres of garden. Banqueting for 600, conference facilities for 700.
*Rooms 98. Garden, indoor swimming pool, plunge pool, gymnasium,
solarium, sauna, spa bath, steam room, beauty salon, hair salon, tennis,
children's outdoor play area. Closed 25 & 26 Dec.*
Access, Diners, Visa.

Waterford   Prendiville's Restaurant & Guesthouse   £60

Tel 051 78851	**RR**
Cork Road Waterford Co Waterford	Map 2 C5

Peter and Paula Prendiville serve imaginative food at reasonable
prices and with professionalism at their converted gate lodge,
which is just out of the centre and a short drive from the crystal
factory. Paula plans her menus around the best of fresh local
ingredients, and her dishes show a deal of controlled creativity:

See over

escalopes of warm smoked salmon with chives, cucumber and
cream; deep-fried tempura-battered squid with an aïoli dip; roast
honey-glazed duck breast served with wine-poached pears; fillet
of lamb baked in a potato crust with a beer and onion gravy. Irish
farmhouse cheeses; tempting desserts. *Seats 50. Private Room 20.
L 12.30-2.15 D 6.30-10.30. Closed Sun, 24-26 Dec. Set L £10.95
Set D (till 8pm) £13.25.* AMERICAN EXPRESS *Access, Diners, Visa.*

Rooms   £44

Nine recently redecorated simply-furnished rooms are available,
seven with en-suite facilities and all with phones. Some have
crochet bedspreads and seven rooms have TVs. Children
up to 8 stay free in their parents' room.

Waterford	Tower Hotel	59%	£114
Tel 051 75801 Fax 051 70129			**H**
The Mall Waterford Co Waterford			Map 2 C5

Opposite, and taking its name from, an ancient Viking tower, the
hotel has recently been extended and refurbished. The now
spacious lobby copes well with tour groups and a large plush bar
overlooks the River Suir. Apart from a couple of singles,
bedrooms are of good size and similarly decorated and furnished
with plain walls and simple darkwood furniture whether in the
old or new part of the building. All have good easy chairs and
modern bathrooms. 24hr room service. Banqueting for 600,
conference facilities for 500. *Rooms 141. Indoor swimming pool,
children's splash pool, gymnasium, solarium, sauna, spa bath, steam
room. Closed 25 & 26 Dec.* AMERICAN EXPRESS *Access, Diners, Visa.*

Waterford	Waterford Castle	76%	£205
Tel 051 78203 Fax 051 79316			**HR**
The Island Ballinakill Waterford Co Waterford			Map 2 C5

From the town centre, head for Dunmore East and follow the
signs to the hotel, which is situated on its own island. A small
chain car ferry transports you across the water to the imposing
18th-century castle with a carved granite arch entrance and
studded oak doors. The great hall has a roped-off coat of arms
hand-woven into the carpet, a cavernous fireplace, again with the
Fitzgerald coat of arms on the chimney breast, old panelling, a fine
ribbon plaster ceiling and antique leather chairs, as well as many
portraits on the walls. The stylish drawing room has several
comfortable sofas and genuine antiques, which also feature in some
bedrooms, notably the suites. Others are a combination of the old
and the new, but nearly all command fine views of the
surrounding parkland and water. Bathrooms, offering good
toiletries and bathrobes but small and poor-quality towels, have
freestanding Victorian bath tubs with gold fittings (but
no protective shower curtains), painted washbasins and loos with
wooden seats and overhead cisterns and chains! First-rate breakfast
includes fresh orange juice and leaf tea. Two conference rooms can
accommodate up to 30. The indoor swimming pool is housed
separately, a few hundred yards from the hotel. Dogs in kennels
only. *Rooms 19. Garden, indoor swimming pool, tennis, golf (18),
bicycles.* AMERICAN EXPRESS *Access, Diners, Visa.*   See over

Restaurant   £80

Chef Paul McCluskey has been cooking here for several years, and
the spectacular dining-room setting – old oak panelling, plaster
ceiling, oil paintings and Regency-striped chairs – presents the
perfect backdrop for his sound cooking. Pity then about the
intrusive piped music that is inappropriate for a hotel of this
standing. Both lunch and dinner menus change daily, the latter
priced almost double, with only a soup or sorbet in addition.
A typical offering might consist of asparagus in puff pastry on a
butter sauce, cream of carrot and bacon soup, pan-fried fillets
of brill with tomato and chives, finishing with a chocolate cup
on a coffee bean sauce. Service is pleasant enough, the bread good
and the coffee strong. The wine list is safe without being
particularly outstanding. *Seats 60. Private Room 26. L 12.30-2
D 7-10 (Sun to 9). Set L £15.50 Set D £30.*

Waterford   Places of Interest

Tourist Information   Tel 051 75788
Waterford Cathedral   Tel 051 74757
Waterford Crystal Glass Factory   Kilbarry Tel 051 73311
Waterford Racecourse   Tramore Tel 051 81425

Waterville   The Huntsman

Tel 066 74124	**P**
Waterville Co Kerry	Map 2 A6

Owner-chef Raymond Hunt has been serving up specialities like
lobster (from the tank), Dublin Bay prawns and local salmon
in this well-established bar and restaurant since 1978 – and red
is the predominant colour in the decor too, so the cool blues and
greys of the sea and sky make a welcome contrast. The snack
menu offers a wide choice of sensibly priced dishes ranging from
a choice of soups, including fresh crab bisque with home-made
bread, through grilled or natural oysters, mussels marinière,
smoked Waterville salmon salad and deep-fried sole with French
fries to a popular selection including hamburgers, spaghetti
bolognese, omelettes and curries ... and Irish stew. There's also
a full restaurant menu. The wine list is serious, with France
particularly well represented, though the New World gets a look
in as well. Accommodation is available – B&B or half-board.
Bar Food 12-10. AMERICAN EXPRESS *Access, Visa.*

Waterville   The Smugglers Inn

Tel 066 74330 Fax 066 74422	**P**
Waterville Co Kerry	Map 2 A6

In a beachside location by Waterville championship golf course,
Harry Hunt and his wife Lucille took a 100-year-old farmhouse
and turned it into a warm and welcoming bar and restaurant with
accommodation. There's a strong emphasis on seafood, from
oysters and mussels marinière to smoked salmon mousse, cod
provençale, sautéed monkfish, poached scallops au gratin and black
sole grilled and served with garlic butter. A snack menu,
including sandwiches, is available all day. The bay was once
notorious for smuggling – wine, brandy, gold and silk inwards,
wool and poteen out! *L 12-3 D 6.30-9.30. Bar snacks 12-9.30.
Set L £12.95 Set D £20.* AMERICAN EXPRESS *Access, Diners, Visa.*

Wexford   White's Hotel   62%   £69

`Tel 053 22311   Fax 053 45000`   **H**

George Street Wexford Co Wexford   Map 2 D5

Recent developments at this historic hotel (whose look is now
largely modern) are centred mainly around the new fitness and
leisure centre. There's also a new night club (the Cairo Club) and
refurbishment work has been carried out in many areas. Bedrooms
are practical, with fitted units and neat, fully-tiled bathrooms.
Conference/banqueting facilities for up to 600/450. No dogs.
Rooms 82. Coffee shop (8am-9.30pm). AMERICAN EXPRESS *Access,
Diners, Visa.*

Wexford   Places of Interest

Tourist Information   Tel 053 23111
Westgate Heritage Centre   Tel 053 42611
Johnstown Castle Demesne and Agricultural Museum   Tel 053 42888
Irish National Heritage Park   Ferry Carrig Tel 053 41733
Wexford Racecourse   Tel 053 23102

Wicklow   Old Rectory   59%   £88

`Tel 0404 67048   Fax 0404 69181`   **AR**

Wicklow Co Wicklow   Map 2 D4

Since 1977 Paul and Linda Saunders have been welcoming hosts
at their delightful early-Victorian rectory on the edge of town,
near the famous Mount Usher gardens (2 miles away). It's
decorated with great individuality throughout; the cosy sitting
room has a white marble fireplace and traditional furnishings are
brought to life by some unusual collections, notably ex-fireman
Paul's display of helmets and related paraphernalia. Colourfully
decorated bedrooms are all en suite and have many homely extras
including fresh flowers. There's an outstanding choice at breakfast
(Irish, Scottish or Swiss menus). *Rooms 5. Garden.*
Closed Nov-Easter. AMERICAN EXPRESS *Access, Visa.*

Restaurant   £60

Linda Saunders presents a blend of Victorian and modern, French
and Irish in the Orangery dining room area. Most guests choose

the special gourmet menu, a no-choice meal which might typically comprise salmon trout quenelles, melon sorbet, pheasant en croute with ginger wine sauce and chocolate and Cointreau mousse in a little chocolate pot accompanied by candied oranges. A particularly unusual and imaginative feature is Wednesday's floral dinner menu containing such delights as gravad lax with chive flowers, hot marigold muffins and cheesecake with a garland of frosted pansy and lilac flowers. No smoking. *Seats 12 à la carte (20 for set menu). Parties 8. D only at 8. Set D £24.*

Wicklow   Places of Interest

Tourist Information   Tel 0404 69117
Mount Usher Gardens   Ashford Tel 0404 40116

Youghal Aherne's Seafood Restaurant	£60
Tel 024 92424 Fax 024 93633	**RR**
163 North Main Street Youghal Co Cork	Map 2 C6

The current owners are the third generation of the FitzGibbon family to run this renowned restaurant and bar on the N25. It would be hard to find a more appropriate Restaurant for Seafood Dish of the Year: local seafood is very much the star of the show, appearing famously in chowder, moules marinière, a hot potato and smoked salmon gratin and Youghal Bay lobster served thermidor or hot and buttered. If your budget doesn't stretch to lobster, try the pasta with smoked salmon and cream, grilled cod with herb butter or a trio of seafood with a shellfish sauce. The all-day bar menu offers snackier items as in open fishy sandwiches on home-made brown bread, salads and even a house pizza. Lovely desserts might include chocolate and orange bavarois, lemon cheesecake or sherry trifle. The wine list, perhaps surprisingly, has almost as many reds as whites. Prices are fair, with several bottles under £15. *Seats 60. Private Room 20. L 12.30-2.15 (Sun to 1.45 in bar) D 6.30-9.30 Bar food 11-10.30. Closed 5 days Christmas. Set L £13.50 Set D £23.* AMERICAN EXPRESS *Access, Diners, Visa.*

Rooms	£67

Aherne's ten stylish en-suite bedrooms are individually decorated to a very high standard and furnished with antiques.

Youghal   Places of Interest

Myrtle Grove   Tel 024 92274
Lismore Castle Gardens   Lismore Tel 058 54424 *17 miles*

JAMESON

IRISH WHISKEY

Northern Ireland

Aghadowey   Greenhill House

£40

H

Tel 0265 868241

24 Greenhill Road Aghadowey Coleraine Co Londonderry BT51 4EU

Map 1 C1

The Hegartys bought their pleasant Georgian farmhouse in 1980 because they wanted the land and, although graciously framed by mature trees and lovely countryside views, it is still very much the centre of a working farm. Elizabeth Hegarty greets arrivals at her guest house with an afternoon tea in the drawing room that includes such an array of home-made tea breads, cakes and biscuits that dinner plans may well waver. Rooms, including two large family rooms, are unostentatious but individually decorated with colour co-ordinated towels and linen; good planning makes them exceptionally comfortable and there are many thoughtful touches – fresh flowers, fruit basket, chocolate mints, tea/coffee-making facilities, hairdryer, bathrobe, proper clothes hangers, even a torch. A 5-course set dinner is available to residents (£24 for two) at 6.30pm, except on Sundays; no wines are provided. *Rooms 6. Garden. Closed Nov-Feb. Access, Visa.*

Annalong   Glassdrumman Lodge   69%

£95

HR

Tel 039 67 68451   Fax 039 67 67041

85 Mill Road Annalong Co Down BT34 4RH

Map 1 D2

Situated just off the A2 coast road, with lovely views over the sea or back into the Mournes, this former farmhouse now has luxurious bedrooms with fresh flowers, fruit, mineral water and exceptionally well-appointed bathrooms. Service is a high priority, including 24hr room service, overnight laundry and a secretarial service, and breakfast a speciality – you can even go and choose your own newly-laid egg if you like. Beaches, walking, climbing, and fishing available locally. No tariff reductions for children. *Rooms 10. Garden, tennis, riding. Access, Visa.*

Memories Restaurant

£60

In the French-style restaurant good use is made of organically grown vegetables and naturally reared beef and pork from the hotel farm and seafood from local ports. Individual wines by the glass are chosen to go with each course of the daily-changing menu (£14 per person extra). No smoking in the dining room. *Seats 40. Private Room 20. L by reservation only to residents. D at 8. Set D from £19.50.*

Ballycastle   House of McDonnell

P

Tel 02657 62975

21 Castle Street Ballycastle Co Antrim BT64 6AS

Map 1 D1

Unusually, even for a characterful old pub, McDonnell's is a listed building and as such no changes are allowed inside or out. Not that change is much on the cards anyway, as it has been in the family for 250 years and is clearly much loved – as visitors soon discover from the colourful chatelaine Eileen O'Neill, affectionately known as 'the Tipperary Tinker'. She enjoys nothing better than sharing the history of the once traditional grocery-bar with its long, narrow bar and mahogany bar. Alas, no food is now offered, but The Open Door, a good traditional Northern Ireland

bakery across the road, has hot snacks and a wide range of fresh
sandwiches to order. *Open 11.30-11 (Sun 12.30-2.30 & 7-10).*
No credit cards.

Ballymena	Galgorm Manor	71%	£95
Tel 0266 881001 Fax 0266 880080			**HR**
136 Fenaghy Road Ballymena Co Antrim BT42 1EA			Map 1 D1

Next to a natural weir on the River Maine, which runs through
the 85 acres of grounds, this Georgian manor has recently been
acquired by new owners, who have made a good job
of refurbishing the public areas with rich fabrics, warm colour
schemes and a scattering of antiques to create an unashamedly
luxurious atmosphere. The 'designer-rustic' Ghillies Bar
in a converted outbuilding offers a change of mood. As we went
to press work was just beginning to bring the bedrooms, which
are all in a new wing, up to the standard of the day rooms.
Bathrooms all have separate shower cubicles in addition to the tub.
There are also six self-catering cottages in the grounds. 24hr room
service. An equestrian centre to the rear of the house includes
a show-jumping course, eventing cross-country practice area,
specially constructed gallops and numerous rides through the
estate. Banqueting/conference facilities for 60. **Rooms** *23. Garden,
riding, game fishing.* AMERICAN EXPRESS *Access, Visa.*

Restaurant £68

A fine room with glittering chandeliers, elaborately draped
curtains and Arcadian murals depicting the four seasons. The
dinner menu – priced by the course (ie starter £4.50, main
£13.50) – offers starters such as confit of duck with wild
cranberries and rocket salad, papaya wrapped in smoked Parma
ham or venison terrine with the likes of roast pheasant with onion
and sage sauce, pan-fried halibut in a white wine and cream sauce
and rack of lamb with bubble and squeak garnish to follow; dishes
are competently cooked. Lunch brings a shorter, fixed-price menu.
Several good wines and growers on the concise wine list, though
few half bottles. **Seats** *73. Private Room 14. L 12-2.30 D 7-9.45
(Sun 6 to 9). Set L £8.50/£11.*

Belfast	Antica Roma		£62
Tel 0232 311121 Fax 0232 310787			**R**
67 Botanic Avenue Belfast Co Antrim			Map 1 D2

Impressive decor based on ancient Rome – mosaic floor, classical
murals, columns, distressed stucco – combines with more
sophisticated Italian cooking at this fashionable restaurant in the
university district. The evening à la carte includes the likes of wild
mushrooms with crushed chili peppers, garlic and olive oil
on toasted bread; gratinated oak-smoked crab claws in a light
bisque sauce; chicken liver salad with croutons, mushrooms and
pine nuts in a walnut oil dressing; fillet of salmon on a spinach and
sorrel purée with orange sauce and sliced scallops; saltimbocca and
duck *al limone*. Good puds include *mandorle alla barese* (rich
almond cake with layers of mocha and praline butter cream and
chocolate ganache) and *frutta candita* (fresh fruit deep fried in a
light batter and served hot with puréed fruit dips). No à la carte
at lunchtime but two good-value set menus each provide a choice
of four main dishes. Particularly good Italian section on the wine

See over

list with some recherché offerings. *Seats 160. Private Room 70.
L 12-3 D 6-11. Set L £8.95/£12.95. Closed L Sat & all Sun, 3 days
at Christmas & 31 Dec.* AMERICAN EXPRESS *Access, Visa.*

Belfast   Bengal Brasserie   £33

Tel 0232 640099   **R**

339 Ormeau Road Belfast Co Antrim BT7 3GL   Map 1 D2

About a mile south of the city centre, this recently refurbished
Indian restaurant is situated in a modern shopping arcade. Sound
Bengali cooking includes a list of daily blackboard specials such
as scampi masala, tandoori duck and Indian river fish as well
as a wide choice on the main menu with lamb and chicken dishes
jostling for space beside prawns, lobster, crayfish and 'European
dishes' (steaks with sauces, omelettes, chicken Kiev). Friendly,
helpful staff. *Seats 46. Private Room 50. L 12-1.45 D 5.30-11.15
(Sun to 10.15). Closed L Sun, 25 Dec, 1 Jan. Set meal £15.95.*
AMERICAN EXPRESS *Access, Diners, Visa.*

Belfast   Crown Liquor Salon

Tel 0232 325368   **P**

44 Great Victoria Street Belfast Co Antrim   Map 1 D2

Belfast's most famous and best-preserved bar, High Victorian and
wonderful in its exuberant opulence; some original stained-glass
windows were recently blown out and were awaiting replacement
as we went to press. The building belongs to the National Trust
and is run by the donors, Bass Taverns, who acquired it in 1979.
The Britannic Lounge, with an Edwardian feel, is fitted out with
original timbers from the *SS Britannic*, sister ship to the *Titanic*.
Open 11.30-11.30 Sun 12-2 & 7-10. No credit cards.

Belfast   Dukes Hotel   67%   £92

Tel 0232 236666   Fax 0232 237177   **H**

65 University Street Belfast Co Antrim BT7 1HL   Map 1 D2

A Victorian facade covers a bright modern hotel in a residential
area close to Queen's University and the Botanical Gardens. Black
leather and chrome feature in the foyer seating, and guests with
a thirst now have an additional bar (Champagne Bar) from which
to choose. There are function facilities for up to 140 and a health
club. Pastel decor and impressionist prints set the tone in the
bedrooms, all double-glazed and some designated non-smoking.
Children up to 16 stay free in parents' room. Much reduced
weekend rates. *Rooms 21. Keep-fit equipment, sauna.* AMERICAN EXPRESS
Access, Diners, Visa.

Belfast   Europa Hotel   £120

Tel 0232 327000   Fax 0232 327800   **H**

Great Victoria Street Belfast Co Antrim   Map 1 D2

Under new ownerships (Hastings Hotels) this well-known city-
centre high-riser was in the midst of a total refurbishment
programme as we went to press early in 1994. The first bedrooms
were due to come on stream in early February with all work to be
completed by the summer of 1994. No dogs. *Rooms 184.
Closed 25 Dec.* AMERICAN EXPRESS *Access, Diners, Visa.*

Belfast   Kelly's Cellars

Tel 0232 324835	**P**
30/32 Bank Street Belfast Co Antrim	Map 1 D2

A protected building, this characterful bar boasts the oldest cellars
in Ireland, dating back to 1720. Food is served in the upstairs bar
at lunchtime. Friday and Saturday bring live traditional Irish
music. *Open 11.30-11 (till 1am Thur-Sat). Closed Sun & some Bank
Holidays.* *Access, Diners, Visa.*

Belfast   Manor House Cantonese Cuisine   £40

Tel 0232 238755	**R**
43-47 Donegall Pass Belfast Co Antrim BT7 1DQ	Map 1 D2

The main menu at this family-run Cantonese restaurant runs
to more than 300 items, and there are others on the vegetarian and
Peking-style set menus (book 3 days ahead for the vegetarian party
menu). Sound cooking over the whole range, which adds fish
head and duck's web to all the familiar favourites. *Seats 80.
Private Room 50. Meals 12-12. Closed 25 & 26 Dec, 12 & 13 Jul.
Set L from £5.50 Set D from £13.50. Access, Diners, Visa.*

Belfast   Nick's Warehouse   £45

Tel 0232 439690 Fax 0232 230514	**R**
35-39 Hill Street Belfast Co Antrim BT1 2LB	Map 1 D2

A popular and lively "bar with wine and restaurant", whose
menus cover a fair range of tasty, straightforward dishes. From the
evening table d'hote (available on both floors) could come carrot
and coriander soup, pork and duck terrine, halibut beurre blanc
and lamb chops with a piquant port sauce. Similar à la carte
selection in the restaurant at lunchtime, plus informal lunchtime
menu and evening snack menu in the wine bar. *Seats 90.
Private Room 45. Wine bar open for drinks 11.30-11 L 12-3 D 6-9.
Closed D Mon, L Sat, all Sun, Bank Holidays. Set D £13.50/
£16.50. Access, Diners, Visa.*

Belfast   Plaza Hotel   64%   £82

Tel 0232 333555 Fax 0232 232999	**H**
15 Brunswick Street Belfast Co Antrim BT2 7GE	Map 1 D2

Ultra-modern city-centre business hotel with well-equipped
bedrooms, all with satellite TV, hairdryer and trouser press
as standard, and five conference suites (capacity 70 theatre-style,
100 restaurant-style). There are 14 rooms reserved for non-
smokers. Children up to 10 stay free in parents' room; four rooms
have extra beds. No dogs. *Rooms 83.* *Access,
Diners, Visa.*

Belfast   Roscoff   ★   £75

Tel 0232 331532	**R**
Lesley House Shaftesbury Square Belfast Co Antrim BT2 7DB	Map 1 D2

Bright, white, clean-cut 'designer' decor with a splash of colour
added by the waiters' waistcoats. Roscoff is at the same time the
best and the most chic restaurant in town. Informed by periods
in some of the best restaurants in England and a sojourn
in California, Paul Rankin returned to his native Northern Ireland

See over

with his own brand of thoroughly modern cooking: ballotine of salmon and lobster with sun-dried tomato mayonnaise; seared beef salad with celery, Parmesan and truffle oil; sweetbreads with fresh pasta, bacon and roast garlic; roast monkfish with a fennel brandade and a red wine sauce; spiced sesame fried hake with stir-fried cabbage and ginger. Vegetables include both potato skins and polenta with a basil pesto. Good-value set lunch. An excellent and inexpensive wine list features the New World prominently. *Seats 70. L 12.15-2.15 D 6.30-10.30. Set L £14.50 Set D £19. Closed L Sat, all Sun, 11 & 12 July, 24, 25 & 26 Dec, 1 Jan.* **AMERICAN EXPRESS** *Access, Diners, Visa.*

Belfast	Speranza	£38
Tel 0232 230213		**R**
16 Shaftesbury Square Belfast Co Antrim		Map 1 D2

Large, bustling pizzeria/restaurant on two floors with red check tablecloths and rustic chalet-style decor. The menu offers a range of huge crisp-based pizzas and about a dozen pasta dishes (all at around a fiver) plus a few chicken and other meat dishes between £6.95 and £10.95 (for the fillet steak). Attentive service from boys and girls smartly kitted out in bright red cummerbunds with matching bow ties. For children there are high-chairs and a special menu written on colouring mats (crayons supplied) that are entered each week into a prize draw for a toy. In the same ownership as *Antica Roma* and *Villa Italia* (qv). *Seats 170. D only 5-11.30. Closed Sun, 3 days at Christmas & 12 Jul. Access, Visa.*

Belfast	Stormont Hotel	69%	£115
Tel 0232 658621 Fax 0232 480240			**H**
587 Upper Newtownards Stormont Belfast Co Down BT4 3LP			Map 1 D2

Way out of town on the Newtownards Road, opposite Stormont Castle, this modern hotel is always busy and bustling, having various function rooms in addition to the Confex Centre with its 10 purpose-built trade and exhibition rooms. Public areas centre around a sunken lounge (sometimes used as a conference 'break-out' area) off which is a cosy cocktail bar. A mezzanine lounge has huge glass windows overlooking the castle grounds. The majority of bedrooms have been completely refurbished in recent times and are spacious, comfortable and practical with good, well-lit work space and modern easy chairs. Good bathrooms feature marble tiling. A few rooms are more dated and await refurbishment but are equally well equipped with satellite TV etc. Smart, helpful staff offer attentive lounge service and there's a 24hr room-service menu. Good breakfasts are served in the informal all-day brasserie. *Rooms 107.* **AMERICAN EXPRESS** *Access, Diners, Visa.*

Belfast	Strand Restaurant	£35
Tel 0232 682266		**R**
12 Stranmillis Road Belfast Co Antrim BT9 5AA		Map 1 D2

Anne Turkington's popular restaurant/wine bar has been refurbished with Charles Rennie Mackintosh inspiration, and the eating area has been opened out somewhat. Food is served throughout the day, and one-plate meals at a bargain £3.95 are

served from noon till 11pm Mon-Thur and noon till 7 Fri and Sat
(cod and chips, French onion flan, chili con carne, liver and bacon
hot pot). A la carte, the selection runs from soup, oyster fritters
and devilled kidneys to burgers, fillets of pink trout, pork
gorgonzola and aubergine parmigiana. *Seats 80. Parties 20.*
Private Room 25. L Sun 12-3 D Sun 5-10 Meals Mon-Sat 12-12.
Closed 25 & 26 Dec, 12 & 13 July. AMERICAN EXPRESS *Access,*
Diners, Visa.

Belfast	Villa Italia	£44
Tel 0232 328356		**R**
39 University Road Belfast Co Antrim BT7 1ND		Map 1 D2

Sister restaurant to *Speranza* (see above) but with a little less
emphasis on pizzas and more on pasta and other Italian dishes.
A shade more upmarket too, although still informal in style, with
quieter background music and less rustic decor. Service is equally
friendly and efficient. *Seats 110. D only 5-11.30 (Sat from 4, Sun*
to 10.30). Closed 25, 26 & 31 Dec, 12 July & Easter Sun.
AMERICAN EXPRESS *Access, Visa.*

Belfast	Welcome Restaurant	£40
Tel 0232 381359		**R**
22 Stranmillis Road Belfast Co Antrim BT9 5AA		Map 1 D2

The entrance is topped by a pagoda roof, and inside dragons,
screens and lanterns establish that this is indeed a Chinese
restaurant. The menu runs to over 100 items, mainly familiar,
popular dishes, and there are special menus for individuals and
small parties. *Seats 80. Parties 25. Private Room 30. L 12-2*
D 5-11.30 (Sun to 10.30). Closed L Sat & Sun, 24-26 Dec. Set meals
from £11. AMERICAN EXPRESS *Access, Diners, Visa.*

Belfast	Wellington Park	59%	£90
Tel 0232 381111 Fax 0232 665410			**H**
21 Malone Road Belfast Co Antrim BT9 6RU			Map 1 D2

Redesigned foyer, amalgamated bar and restaurant areas and
bedroom upgrades have kept the Wellington Park up to date. The
locality and a thriving conference business (capacity 150 theatre-
style) ensure a lively atmosphere, but one of the three bars is kept
exclusively for residents. Children up to 12 stay free in parents'
room. Residents have free use of Queens University's sports centre,
5 minutes from the hotel. No dogs. *Rooms 50.* AMERICAN EXPRESS
Access, Diners, Visa.

Belfast   Places of Interest

Tourist Information Tel 0232 246609
Mount Stewart House and Gardens (NT)   Greyabbey Tel 02477 88387
    17 miles
Ulster Museum and Botanic Gardens Tel 0232 381251
Belfast Zoo Tel 0232 776277 *5 miles North*
Malone House Art Gallery and Gardens Upper Malone Rd
    Tel 0232 681246
Dixon Park Upper Malone Rd Tel 0232 320202
Transport Museum Tel 0232 451519
Down Royal Racecourse Lisburn Tel 0846 621256 *6 miles*
    Theatres and Concert Halls
Grand Opera House Great Victoria St Tel 0232 241919   *See over*

Lyric Theatre Ridgeway St Tel 0232 381081
Ulster Hall Bedford St Tel 0232 323900
Group Theatre Bradford St Tel 0232 229685

Belfast International Airport   Novotel   62%   £75

| Tel 08494 22033   Fax 08494 23500 | **H** |

Belfast International Airport Co Antrim BT29 4AB   Map 1 D2

The only hotel actually at the international airport, which is about
17 miles to the north of the city centre. Opened in 1993, the hotel
offers practical standardised bedrooms, open-plan public areas and
conference facilities for up to 250 delegates (theatre-style),
banqueting for 180. For children there is a 'kids corner' with Lego
table and video by the informal restaurant and a small outdoor
play area in addition to the usual amenities. Children under 16
stay free in parents' room. 24hr room service. *Rooms 108.*
AMERICAN EXPRESS *Access, Diners, Visa.*

Any person using our name to obtain free hospitality is
a fraud. Proprietors, please inform the police and us.

Bushmills   Bushmills Inn   58%   £74

| Tel 02657 32339 | **H** |

25 Main Street Bushmills Co Antrim BT57 8QA   Map 1 C1

After the Giant's Causeway, the world's oldest distillery
at Bushmills is the biggest attraction in the area (and well worth
a visit; mid-week is most interesting); the Bushmills Inn also
attracts year-round local support. The exterior, including a neat
garden at the relocated (back) main entrance, creates a welcoming
impression that extends into the hall, with its open fire and
country antiques, and other public areas that encompass several
bars and a large dining room. Bedrooms are quite modest,
individually decorated and comfortably furnished; some family
rooms are remarkable for their ingenious use of space. A beamed
loft provides a splendid setting for private functions (up to 85
people) and the 'secret library' a unique venue for special occasions.
Rooms 11. Garden, fishing. Access, Visa.

Bushmills   Places of Interest

Giant's Causeway Tourist Information Tel 02657 31855/31582
Dunluce Castle
The Old Bushmills Distillery Tel 02657 31521

Carnlough   Londonderry Arms

| Tel 0574 885255 | **P** |

20 Harbour Road Carnlough Glens of Antrim Co Antrim BT44 0EU   Map 1 D1

In the same family for nearly half a century, this hotel and bar
makes a good stop at a most attractive little harbour on the famous
scenic coastal route and it's well known for 'good, plain food'. The
same snacks are available in both bars (hotel and public): soup
with home-baked wheaten bread, scones, open prawn sandwich,
paté, chef's lunchtime roast. *Open 11.30-11.30 (Sun 12-11). Bar
Food 10am-8pm (only sandwiches after 6). Garden.* AMERICAN EXPRESS
Access, Diners, Visa.

Carnlough   The Waterfall

No Telephone   **P**

High Street Carnlough Co Antrim   **Map 1 D1**

Not as old as it may first appear to be, the little public bar
is nevertheless full of charm, with red-tiled floor and low beamed
ceiling. Both the fireplace and bar are made of reclaimed
bricks from an old mill across the road and there's a clatter
of memorabilia hanging from the ceiling; the walls are used
to show off a collection of horse tackle and old posters. Behind,
there's a cosy lounge bar with stained-glass window (from the
owner's previous pub), decorative plates and another brick
fireplace, where bar meals are served. A welcoming place with
a lovely friendly atmosphere. *No credit cards.*

Carrickfergus   The Wind-Rose Wine Bar

Tel 09603 64192   Fax 09603 51164   **R**

The Marina Carrickfergus Co Antrim BT38 8BE   **Map 1 D2**

Overlooking the marina at Carrickfergus, a well-appointed formal
restaurant on the upper floor is approached by an exterior spiral
staircase and has clear views across Belfast Lough (booking
essential). The ground-floor wine bar below has a pubby
atmosphere with a strongly nautical theme and provides simple
bar food that includes freshly-made sandwiches (cheese and pickle
£1.50), toasted sandwiches (steak £3.25) and a variety of hot
snacks and main dishes (vegetarian spring roll £2.80, steak and
kidney pie £6). *Seats 85. Open 12-12. Bar Food L 12-2.30 snacks
2.30-5 D 5-9. Closed L Sat, D Sun & Mon, 25 & 26 Dec.
Access, Visa.*

Comber   La Mon House   59%   £85

Tel 0232 448631   Fax 0232 448026   **H**

The Mills 41 Gransha Road Comber Co Down BT23 5RF   **Map 1 D2**

Public areas in this low-rise modern hotel include a bar featuring
copper-topped tables, a small residents' lounge (which may be in
private use), carvery restaurant and a fun bar with disco (Fri).
Practical bedrooms have simple fitted furniture; nine large rooms
have balconies and there are eight small singles with shower only.
Families will enjoy the country health club and outdoor areas.
Banqueting facilities for 450, conference up to 1100 theatre-style.
Regular Saturday night dinner dances. In the countryside, 5 miles
from Belfast city centre. No dogs. *Rooms 38. Garden, indoor
swimming pool, gymnasium, sauna, solarium, whirlpool bath, putting.*
AMERICAN EXPRESS *Access, Visa.*

Comber   Places of Interest

Down Country Museum Downpatrick Tel 0396 615218
Mount Stewart Newtownards Tel 024774 387
Wildfowl and Wetlands Centre Castle Espie Tel 0242 874146 *3 miles*
Nendrum Monastery Mahee Island
Rowallane Garden Tel 0238 510131
Downpatrick Racecourse Downpatrick Tel 0396 612054
Newtownards Priory *3 miles*
Ballycopeland Windmill *8 miles*

See over

Northern Ireland Aquarium   Portaferry Tel 02477 28062
   26 miles
Grey Abbey *10 miles*

Crawfordsburn	Old Inn		£85
Tel 0247 853255 Fax 0247 852775			**H**
15 Main Street Crawfordsburn Co Down BT19 1JH			**Map 1 D2**

Located off the main Belfast to Bangor road, this 16th-century inn
is in a pretty village setting and is supposed to be the oldest
in continuous use in all Ireland. Its location is conveniently close
to Belfast and its City Airport. Oak beams, antiques and gas
lighting emphasise the natural character of the building,
an attractive venue for business people (conference facilities for
150, banqueting for 90) and private guests alike. Individually
decorated bedrooms vary in size and style, most have antiques,
some four-posters and a few have private sitting rooms; all are
non-smoking. Romantics and newly-weds should head for the
honeymoon cottage. Free private car parking for overnight guests.
No dogs. *Rooms 34. Garden. Closed 24-26 Dec.*
Access, Diners, Visa.

Cushendall	P J McCollam		
No Telephone			**P**
23 Mill Street Cushendall Co Antrim BT4 0RR			**Map 1 D1**

In the family for 300 years and under the current ownership
of Joe McCollam for the last 73 years, this magical place has a tiny
front bar complete with a patchwork of photographs of local
characters, many of them sheep farmers (and great fiddle players)
who come down from the glens at weekends. The range in the old
family kitchen behind the bar is lit on cold evenings and
a converted 'cottage' barn across the yard makes a perfect setting
for the famous traditional music sessions. Hospitable and full
of character. *Open 11.30-11 (Sun 7-10pm only).*
Closed Sunday lunchtime. No credit cards.

Dunadry	Dunadry Inn	64%	£105
Tel 0849 432474 Fax 0849 433389			**H**
2 Islandreagh Drive Dunadry Co Antrim BT41 2HA			**Map 1 D2**

Originally a paper mill founded early in the 18th century, later
a linen mill, now a well-known riverside hotel 15 minutes from
Belfast city centre and 10 from the airport. Best bedrooms are
on the ground floor, with access to the gardens. The Copper Bar

under the main staircase is a popular spot for a drink and the lunchtime buffet. Extensive conference facilities. Children up to 5 stay free in parents' room. No dogs. *Rooms 67. Garden, croquet, crazy golf, game fishing, bicycles, indoor swimming pool, keep-fit equipment, spa bath, sauna, steam room, solarium. Closed 24-27 Dec.* AMERICAN EXPRESS *Access, Diners, Visa.*

Dunadry   Place of Interest

Antrim Round Tower

Dunmurry   Forte Crest Belfast   67%   £98

Tel 0232 612101   Fax 0232 626546   **H**

300 Kingsway Dunmurry Co Antrim BT17 9ES   Map 1 D2

Business-oriented hotel a short drive from Belfast city centre and airport. Accommodation includes Lady Crest rooms, non-smoking rooms and rooms designated as family-size. Children up to 12 stay free in parents' room. 24hr room service. Conference/meeting facilities for up to 450. Free parking for 200 cars. *Rooms 82. Keep-fit equipment, squash.* AMERICAN EXPRESS *Access, Diners, Visa.*

Enniskillen   Blakes of the Hollow

Tel 0365 322143   **P**

6 Church Street Enniskillen Co Fermanagh BT74 3EJ   Map 1 C2

Named after the natural dip at the centre of the town where it is located, Blakes has been in the same family since 1929. Although its age and agelessness (it was restored in 1882) are the main attractions, body and soul can be kept together on the premises by the consumption of sandwiches and soup (the latter at lunchtime only). *Open 11.30-11 (Sun 7-10). Closed L Sun. No credit cards.*

Enniskillen   Places of Interest

Enniskillen Keep
Castle Coole   Tel 0365 322690
Florence Court   Tel 0365 348249 *8 miles*

Garvagh   MacDuff's Restaurant, Blackheath House   £50

Tel 0265 868433   **RR**

112 Killeague Road Garvagh nr Coleraine Co Londonderry BT51 4HH   Map 1 C1

A basement restaurant under a fine, immaculately kept Georgian house, MacDuff's is characterful, comfortable and convivial. There's a small separate reception area and it is run by staff who cope well under the busiest of circumstances. The generally relaxed atmosphere is carried through to a comforting ring of familiarity on Margaret Erwin's menu in starters like Stilton puffs with hot, sweet and sour sauce and twice-baked soufflé with summer salad – popular perennials kept on the menu by requests from regulars. Spicing is a feature, but traditional main courses like grilled wild local salmon with hollandaise are also given a further lift, as in a garnish of crispy dulse; local catches feature in a classic seafood symphony with halibut, fat prawns and mussels in a light wine sauce. Good desserts (see Dessert of the Year awards) might include hazelnut meringue with raspberries (including a generous 'wee dram' of Drambuie in the cream)

See over

or simple Jamaican banana, split and grilled with rum and sugar. No children under 12. No smoking. On the A29 four miles north of Garvagh. *Seats 36. Parties 10. Private Room 12. D only 7-9.30. Closed Sun & Mon. Closed 4/5 days at Christmas. Access, Visa.*

Rooms   £55

Accommodation is available in five large, comfortably furnished en-suite rooms with lovely views over the gardens and surrounding countryside.

Garvagh	Place of Interest

Leslie Hill Farm Park   by Ballymoney Tel 0265 666803

Helen's Bay	Deanes on the Square	↑	£58
Tel 0247 852841			**R**
7 Station Square Helen's Bay Co Down BT19 1TN			Map 1 D2

When the railways arrived in the 1860s the first Marquis of Dufferin and Ava built his own station – in Scottish baronial style. Still a functioning railway station, the building is now a novel restaurant and home to some exciting cooking by Michael Deane. Dishes like smoked salmon sausage with basil pesto, marinated duck with tandoori sausage and soya, and tender slices of venison on rösti potato surrounded by strips of pheasant and chicken in a mustard sauce are full of flavour and if you think whiting is a dull fish try Michael's creamed whiting with baby capers as a starter. Portions are generous and presentation attractive yet unfussy. No à la carte but a couple of fixed-price menus, both with choices, or try the multi-course tasting menu – most fun when you allow each dish to be a surprise when it arrives. From part of the restaurant you can see into the kitchen and some windows look out on to the platform. There is a small bar in the basement. *Seats 40. Sun L 12.30-2.30 (Tue-Sat by arrangement) D 7-10. Set L £15 Set D from £17.85. Closed D Sun & all Mon, 2 weeks Jan & 1 week July.*

Holywood	Bay Tree
Tel 0232 426414	**R**
Audley Court 118 High Street Holywood Co Down	Map 1 D2

Reached via an archway opposite the police station in the main street (one can also drive through to a small car park at the rear), the Bay Tree is part pottery shop, with the work of over 30 Irish potters on show, and part small coffee shop where Sue Farmer's delicious cooking is the big attraction. Throughout the day there are various cakes – carrot, chocolate (both 90p), fresh pineapple crunch, chocolate chantilly tart (both £1.50), tray bakes (50p) and their hot cinnamon scone speciality (65p). Lunchtime brings savoury items like egg, dill and tuna mousse (£3.50); vegetable moussaka (£3.60); ham open sandwich (£4); vegetable and chicken lasagne (£3.70) and home-made soup (£1.50). Open for dinner on the last Friday of each month but booking is essential, usually several months in advance. There are a couple of tables on a small patio. No smoking. *Seats 34. L 10-4.30 (D last Fri of month only 7.30-11, must book). Closed Sun, 3 days Christmas, 3 days Easter & 12 July. Access, Visa.*

Holywood   Culloden Hotel   72%   £140

Tel 0232 425223   Fax 0232 426777   **HR**

142 Bangor Road Craigavad Holywood Co Down BT18 0EX   Map 1 D2

Originally a palace of the bishops of Down, this splendid 19th-century building in Scottish Baronial style stands in 12 acres of gardens overlooking Belfast Lough. Antiques, stained glass, fine plasterwork and paintings grace the day rooms (though the Gothic Bar is in modern mode). Good-sized, well-furnished bedrooms are mostly in an extension. There are two restaurants, an inn in the grounds, various function suites and a well-appointed health and fitness club. No dogs. *Rooms 91. Garden, indoor swimming pool, keep-fit equipment, squash, sauna, spa bath, solarium, tennis, snooker. Closed 24-25 Dec.* AMERICAN EXPRESS® *Access, Diners, Visa.*

The Mitre Restaurant   £65

Comfortable and relaxing, with friendly, efficient service. The menu is quite extensive, ranging from traditional grills and classics such as scampi provençale or garlic snails to more contemporary creations like pan-fried monkfish with vegetable tagliatelle and a tomato/Pernod sauce. Separate vegetarian menu. There is also a grill bar in the complex, 'The Cultra Inn'. *Seats 150. Parties 20. Private Room 50. L 12.30-2.30 D 7-9.45 (Sun to 8.30). Closed L Sat. Set L & D £17.*

Holywood   Sullivans   £55

Tel 0232 421000   **R**

Sullivan Place Holywood Co Down BT18 9JF   Map 1 D2

Bright and cheerful with sunny yellow walls and colourfully upholstered chairs, Sullivans operates as a coffee shop during the day (Devon scones, pecan pie and lunchtime savouries like venison terrine, salmon and leek quiche and soup) before turning into a fully-fledged restaurant at night. After only a few months (see Newcomers of the Year awards) the accomplished cooking of young chef/patron Simon Shaw (formerly at *Roscoff* in Belfast) has already gained a loyal following such that booking is advisable at weekends. Dishes like a duck confit with sweet chilis, vegetable strudel, warm pigeon salad with lentil and leeks, monkfish with saffron vinaigrette and rack of lamb with green peppercorn cream come in portions substantial enough to satisfy local appetites. Desserts range from rice pudding with fruit compote to mango tart with lemon sorbet. There's a short à la carte in addition to the prix fixe. Unlicensed but there are a couple of wine merchants nearby. *Seats 40. L 10-4 D 6.30-10. Set D (Tue-Thur only) £14.95. Closed D Mon, all Sun & Bank Holidays. Access, Visa.*

Holywood   Place of Interest

Ulster Folk and Transport Museum   Cultra Tel 0232 428428

Larne   Magheramorne House   63%   £66

Tel 0574 279444   Fax 0574 260138   **H**

59 Shore Road Magheramorne Larne Co Antrim BT40 3HW   Map 1 D1

43 acres of woodland overlooking Larne Lough provide a fine setting for a late-Victorian house which offers fresh, bright

See over

bedrooms, banqueting/conference facilities for up to 180 and free parking for 150 cars. No dogs. *Rooms 22. Garden.* *Access, Diners, Visa.*

Larne Places of Interest

Ballylumford Dolmen Island Magee
Carrickfergus Castle *12 miles*

Londonderry	Beech Hill House Hotel	59%	£85
Tel 0504 49279 Fax 0504 45366			**HR**
32 Ardmore Road Londonderry Co Londonderry BT47 3QP			Map 1 C1

More hotel than country house, Beech Hill has rapidly become a favourite venue for local private functions, with banqueting and conference facilities for 80. Spacious, well-proportioned public areas include a lounge/bar comfortably furnished in somewhat clubby style. Bedrooms, all recently refurnished, vary considerably in size and comfort. Children under 10 may share their parents' room at no charge. Outdoor tennis court due for completion as we went to press. No dogs. *Rooms 17. Garden. Closed 25 & 26 Dec.* *Access, Visa.*

Ardmore Room Restaurant ↑ £50

In what was once the billiard room, the restaurant overlooks mature gardens and is the prettiest and most intimate room in the hotel – a fitting setting for the fine food for which head chef Noel McMeel has established a well-deserved reputation since the hotel opened in 1991. Classical dishes are handled with confidence and flair and the saucing is excellent. Start, perhaps, with a spot of role reversal in poached pear with a timbale of Cashel Blue cheese and raspberry vinaigrette, or a more traditional terrine of duck, flavoursome and chunky, served in a ring of delicious chopped port and apple jelly. Breads, including tea breads typical of the area, come warm from the oven and main dishes, such as pan-fried, marinated monkfish accompanied by a spaghetti of vegetables with a ginger and balsamic vinaigrette, have great verve. Good vegetable selection and pretty desserts. *Seats 40. Parties 20. Private Rooms 18 & 30. L 12-2.30 D 6-10. Set L £10.95 Set D £16.95.*

Londonderry	Everglades Hotel	59%	£78
Tel 0504 46722 Fax 0504 49200			**H**
Prehen Road Londonderry Co Londonderry BT47 2PA			Map 1 C1

South of the town on the banks of the River Foyle, this modern low-rise hotel is a popular venue for conferences and banqueting (350/250) besides providing bright, practical accommodation. Top of the bedroom range are two suites with jacuzzis and turbo showers. Children up to 12 stay free in parents' room. *Rooms 52. Garden. Closed 24 & 25 Dec.* *Access, Diners, Visa.*

Londonderry Places of Interest

Tourist Information Tel 0504 267284
Derry's Walls
St Columb's Cathedral off London St Tel 0504 262746
O'Doherty's Tower Magazine St Tel 0504 265238
Display Centre Butcher St Tel 0504 362016

Ulster-American Folk Park   Omagh Tel 0662 243292
Brachmore Stone Circus   nr Cookstown

Newcastle	Slieve Donard Hotel	63%	£99
Tel 03967 23681 Fax 03967 24830			**H**
Downs Road Newcastle Co Down BT33 OAG			Map 1 D2

Imposing red-brick Victorian railway hotel facing the Irish Sea (next to the Royal County Down Golf Club) with the Mountains of Mourne in the background, 'The Slieve' caters mainly to conferences in winter and holidaymakers, tour groups and weddings in the summer. A grand, galleried entrance hall sets the tone for public areas which include a large elegant lounge with conservatory extension (sometimes used for functions), cosy library sitting room and a bar named after Charlie Chaplin, who once stayed here. Bedrooms vary in shape and size but, apart from the third that are awaiting refurbishment, share the same blue and peach colour scheme, polycotton duvets and dark mahogany furniture. The only advertised room service is breakfast, and that not for conference delegates. Good leisure centre. Parking for 200 cars. *Rooms 110. Garden, indoor swimming pool, gymnasium, solarium, spa bath, steam room, beauty salon, tennis, shop.* ᴀᴍᴇʀɪᴄᴀɴᴇxᴘʀᴇss *Access, Diners, Visa.*

Newcastle   Places of Interest

Seaforde Gardens   Tel 0396 87225 *5 miles*
Castle Ward   Strangford Tel 0396 86204 *15 miles*

Portaferry	Portaferry Hotel	63%	£75
Tel 02477 28231 Fax 02477 28999			**HR**
10 The Strand Portaferry Co Down BT22 1PE			Map 1 D2

Formed out of an 18th-century terrace on the seafront, where the ferry crosses the neck of Strangford Lough, the Portaferry has been substantially remodelled over recent years to create a delightful small hotel run with a winning combination of charm and professionalism by John and Marie Herlihy. Public areas include a tweedy bar and several tastefully decorated little lounges sporting pictures of the surrounding area by local artists. Light, airy bedrooms come with lightwood furniture and matching floral bedcovers and curtains, neat bathrooms with huge bath sheets. No dogs. *Rooms 14. Closed 24 & 25 Dec.* ᴀᴍᴇʀɪᴄᴀɴᴇxᴘʀᴇss *Access, Diners, Visa.*

Restaurant	£65

The secret of Anne Truesdale's cooking is the use of the best local produce in dishes that are essentially simple, although not without interest. Lamb from the mountains of Mourne and Ulster beef feature but it's seafood that takes pride of place with amazingly plump scallops from the Lough (pan-fried with garlic and bacon perhaps or baked in white wine and cheese), Murlough Bay mussels, prawns from Portavogie, Ardglass crab (in filo pastry with tomato and basil sauce), goujons of monkfish (with fresh lime sauce), salmon (wild Irish in season) and lobsters from their own tanks. Vegetables, often organically grown, are well handled too. At lunchtime there is a fairly extensive bar menu that is also served in the dining room except on Sundays, when there is a fixed-price menu. *Seats 80. L 12.30-2.30 D 7-9. Set L (Sun only) £12.50. Closed 25 & 26 Dec.*

Portballintrae	**Bayview Hotel**	58%	£65

Tel 02657 31453   Fax 02657 32360

<table>
<tr><td></td><td>H</td></tr>
</table>

2 Bayhead Road Portballintrae nr Bushmills Co Antrim BT57 8RZ | Map 1 C1

Overlooking the tiny harbour and the bay, the long pebbledash
hotel building stands half a mile from the main A2 coastal route.
Functions and conferences (up to 150) are quite big business, but
residents have their own sitting room, and there's also a convivial
bar. Bedrooms include one semi-suite with a small sitting room
area and generally have modern bathrooms. No dogs. *Rooms 16.*
Indoor swimming pool, sauna, solarium, snooker. Access, Visa.

Portrush	**Ramore**	★	£55

Tel 0265 824313

R

The Harbour Portrush Co Antrim BT56 8VM | Map 1 C1

The sheer cosmopolitan buzz of this waterside restaurant, with its
sleek, chic black-and-chrome decor, smoothly operating open
kitchen flanked by huge baskets of freshly baked breads and
serried ranks of highly professional staff, is apt to take the
uninitiated by surprise. It's trendier than one might expect to find
in Portrush town and a tribute to the remarkable style of chef
George McAlpin and the family team that their bright, airy
restaurant continues to attract flocks of enthusiastic diners from
throughout Ireland and beyond. Local seafood still predominates,
but a keen feeling for the mood of the moment imbues the
cooking with unusual immediacy in starters like tempura prawns
(Dublin Bay prawns fried in spiced batter with pepper salsa and
garlic parsley butter) or Italian summer salad (cos, rocket, Parma
ham, avocado, cherry tomatoes, boiled eggs and croutons topped
off with shavings of fresh Parmesan); the wide variety of modestly
priced main dishes (collops of peppered fillet steak, supreme
of duck, rack of Irish lamb) includes a handful of interesting
'complete dishes' such as a local version of paella or Thai chicken
(succulent chargrilled breast on a bed of oriental vegetables with
a sesame and mushroom soya vinaigrette and frites) – remarkable
value at £6.95. Desserts are a speciality: there is always a hot
soufflé on the list – perhaps hot fresh fruit and Grand Marnier –
and daily blackboard specials like an excellent tangy lemon tart.
Very good coffee, served with petits fours. *Seats 60. D only
6.30-10.30 (lunchtime wine bar downstairs). Closed Sun & Mon,
2 weeks Feb, Christmas/New Year. Access, Visa.*

Portrush	**Place of Interest**

Dunluce Castle *3 miles*

Templepatrick	**Templeton Hotel**	66%	£100

Tel 084 94 32984   Fax 084 94 33406

H

882 Antrim Road Templepatrick Ballyclare Co Antrim BT39 0AH | Map 1 D2

An eye-catching modern hotel a mile from the M2 and handy for
Belfast airport. Spacious bedrooms are equipped with the expected
up-to-date amenities, and the four Executive rooms have
additionally mini-bars and jacuzzis. Day rooms take various
decorative themes – sleek black and gold for the cocktail bar,
Scandinavian for the banqueting hall (catering for up to 350),
echoes of medieval knights in the restaurant. 24hr room service.
Free parking for 125 cars. *Rooms 20. Garden. Closed 25 Dec.
Access, Diners, Visa.*

Quick Reference Lists

Quick Reference Lists

Accommodation under £65 for 2

(Restaurants with Rooms are indicated by RR)

Republic of Ireland

Co Cork, Ahakista **Hillcrest House**
Co Cork, Castletownshend **Bow Hall**
Co Cork, Cork **Flemings** (RR)
Co Cork, Cork **Forte Travelodge**
Co Cork, Cork **Seven North Mall**
Co Cork, Goleen Harbour **Herons Cove Restaurant** (RR)
Co Cork, Kinsale **The Old Bank House**
Co Cork, Kinsale **Old Presbytery** (RR)
Co Donegal, Dunkineely **Castle Murray House**
Co Dublin, Dublin **Aberdeen Lodge**
Co Dublin, Dublin **Anglesea Town House**
Co Dublin, Dublin **Ariel House**
Co Dublin, Dublin **Clarence Hotel**
Co Dublin, Dublin **Glenveagh Town House**
Co Dublin, Dublin **Jurys Christchurch Inn**
Co Dublin, Dublin **Merrion Hall**
Co Dublin, Dublin **Stauntons on the Green**
Co Dublin, Dun Laoghaire **Chestnut Lodge**
Co Dublin, Howth **Howth Lodge Hotel**
Co Dublin, Swords **Forte Travelodge**
Co Galway, Galway **Jurys Galway Inn**
Co Galway, Moycullen **Cloonnabinnia House Hotel**
Co Galway, Spiddal **Bridge House Inn**
Co Kerry, Dingle **Doyle's Seafood Bar & Townhouse** (RR)
Co Kerry, Kenmare **Hawthorn House**
Co Kerry, Killarney **Kathleen's Country House**
Co Kilkenny, Kilkenny **Lacken House** (RR)
Co Kilkenny, Maddoxtown **Blanchville House**
Co Laois, Mountrath **Roundwood House**
Co Leitrim, Carrick-on-Shannon **Hollywell House**
Co Limerick, Adare **Woodlands House Hotel**
Co Limerick, Limerick **Jackson's Turret**
Co Louth, Ardee **The Gables** (RR)
Co Offaly, Birr **Dooly's Hotel**
Co Sligo, Collooney **Glebe House** (RR)
Co Tipperary, Glen of Aherlow **Aherlow House**
Co Waterford, Waterford **Prendiville's Restaurant/Guesthouse** (RR)
Co Wexford, Newbay **Newbay Country House**
Co Wicklow, Blessington **Downshire House**

Northern Ireland

Co Antrim, Portballintrae **Bayview Hotel**
Co Londonderry, Aghadowey **Greenhill House**
Co Londonderry, Garvagh **MacDuff's Restaurant, Blackheath House** (RR)

Restaurants with rooms

Republic of Ireland

Co Cork, Cork **Flemings**
Co Cork, Goleen Harbour **Herons Cove Restaurant**
Co Cork, Kinsale **Old Presbytery**
Co Cork, Youghal **Aherne's Seafood Restaurant**
Co Dublin, Dublin **Grey Door**
Co Kerry, Dingle **Doyle's Seafood Bar & Townhouse**
Co Kerry, Killarney **Foley's Townhouse**
Co Kildare, Athy **Tonlegee House**
Co Kilkenny, Kilkenny **Lacken House**
Co Louth, Ardee **The Gables**
Co Sligo, Collooney **Glebe House**
Co Waterford, Waterford **Prendiville's Restaurant/Guesthouse**

Northern Ireland

Co Londonderry, Garvagh **MacDuff's Restaurant, Blackheath House**

Beautifully Situated Establishments

Food is only recommended at establishments marked with an R

Republic of Ireland

Co Clare, Ballyvaughan **Gregans Castle** (HR)
Co Clare, Newmarket-on-Fergus **Dromoland Castle** (HR)
Co Cork, Ahakista **Hillcrest House** (A)
Co Cork, Ballylickey **Ballylickey Manor House** (H)
Co Cork, Ballylickey **Larchwood House** (R)
Co Cork, Ballylickey **Sea View Hotel** (HR)
Co Cork, Castletownshend **Bow Hall** (H)
Co Cork, Durrus **Blairs Cove House Restaurant** (R)
Co Cork, Goleen Harbour **Herons Cove Restaurant** (RR)
Co Cork, Innishannon **Innishannon House Hotel** (H)
Co Cork, Kanturk **Assolas Country House** (AR)
Co Cork, Mallow **Longueville House** (HR)
Co Cork, Shanagarry **Ballymaloe House** (AR)
Co Donegal, Dunkineely **Castle Murray House** (HR)
Co Donegal, Fahan **Restaurant St John's** (R)
Co Donegal, Rathmullan **Rathmullan House** (H)
Co Donegal, Rossnowlagh **Smugglers Creek Inn** (P)
Co Dublin, Howth **Deer Park Hotel** (H)
Co Galway, Ballyconneely **Erriseask House** (HR)
Co Galway, Ballynahinch **Ballynahinch Castle** (H)
Co Galway, Cashel **Cashel House** (H)
Co Galway, Clifden **Abbeyglen Castle** (H)
Co Galway, Clifden **Ardagh Hotel** (HR)
Co Galway, Clifden **Rock Glen Manor** (H)
Co Galway, Letterfrack **Rosleague Manor** (HR)
Co Galway, Oughterard **Currarevagh House** (AR)
Co Galway, Renvyle **Renvyle House** (H)
Co Kerry, Beaufort **Dunloe Castle** (H)
Co Kerry, Caherdaniel **Derrynane Hotel** (HR)
Co Kerry, Caragh Lake **Hotel Ard-na-Sidhe** (H)

Co Kerry, Caragh Lake **Caragh Lodge** (A)
Co Kerry, Dingle **Dingle Skellig Hotel** (H)
Co Kerry, Kenmare **Park Hotel Kenmare**
Co Kerry, Kenmare **Sheen Falls Lodge** (HR)
Co Kerry, Killarney **Aghadoe Heights Hotel** (HR)
Co Kerry, Killarney **Cahernane Hotel** (HR)
Co Kerry, Killarney **Hotel Europe** (H)
Co Kerry, Parknasilla **Great Southern** (H)
Co Kildare, Maynooth **Moyglare Manor** (HR)
Co Kildare, Straffan **Kildare Hotel** (HR)
Co Kilkenny, Inistioge **The Motte** (R)
Co Kilkenny, Thomastown **Mount Juliet Hotel** (HR)
Co Limerick, Adare **Adare Manor** (H)
Co Monaghan, Scotshouse **Hilton Park** (H)
Co Roscommon, Hodson Bay **Hodson Bay Hotel** (H)
Co Sligo, Riverstown **Coopershill House** (AR)
Co Sligo, Rosses Point **The Moorings** (R)
Co Tipperary, Dundrum **Dundrum House** (H)
Co Tipperary, Glen of Aherlow **Aherlow House** (H)
Co Waterford, Waterford **Waterford Castle** (HR)
Co Wexford, Ferrycarrig Bridge **Ferrycarrig Hotel** (H)
Co Wexford, Gorey **Marlfield House** (HR)
Co Wicklow, Delgany **Glenview Hotel** (H)
Co Wicklow, Dunlavin **Rathsallagh House** (AR)
Co Wicklow, Laragh **Mitchell's of Laragh** (R)
Co Wicklow, Rathnew **Hunter's Hotel** (HR)
Co Wicklow, Wicklow **Old Rectory** (AR)

Northern Ireland

Co Antrim, Ballymena **Galgorm Manor** (HR)

Establishments with Sporting Facilities

Fishing

Republic of Ireland

Co Clare, Newmarket-on-Fergus **Dromoland Castle**
Co Cork, Ballylickey **Ballylickey Manor House**
Co Cork, Castlelyons **Ballyvolane House**
Co Cork, Innishannon **Innishannon House Hotel**
Co Cork, Kanturk **Assolas Country House**
Co Cork, Kinsale **Blue Haven Hotel**
Co Cork, Mallow **Longueville House**
Co Donegal, Rossnowlagh **Sand House**
Co Dublin, Killiney **Court Hotel**
Co Galway, Ballynahinch **Ballynahinch Castle**
Co Galway, Cashel **Cashel House**
Co Galway, Cashel **Zetland House**
Co Galway, Clifden **Rock Glen Manor**
Co Galway, Letterfrack **Rosleague Manor**
Co Galway, Moycullen **Cloonnabinnia House Hotel**
Co Galway, Oughterard **Currarevagh House**
Co Galway, Renvyle **Renvyle House**
Co Kerry, Beaufort **Dunloe Castle**
Co Kerry, Caragh Lake **Hotel Ard-na-Sidhe**
Co Kerry, Caragh Lake **Caragh Lodge**
Co Kerry, Kenmare **Dromquinna Manor Hotel**
Co Kerry, Kenmare **Sheen Falls Lodge**

Co Kerry, Killarney **Aghadoe Heights Hotel**
Co Kerry, Killarney **Cahernane Hotel**
Co Kerry, Killarney **Hotel Europe**
Co Kerry, Killarney **Randles Court Hotel**
Co Kerry, Parknasilla **Great Southern**
Co Kildare, Straffan **Kildare Hotel**
Co Kilkenny, Thomastown **Mount Juliet Hotel**
Co Leitrim, Carrick-on-Shannon **Hollywell House**
Co Limerick, Adare **Adare Manor**
Co Mayo, Ballina **Mount Falcon Castle**
Co Mayo, Cong **Ashford Castle**
Co Mayo, Crossmolina **Enniscoe House**
Co Mayo, Newport **Newport House**
Co Monaghan, Scotshouse **Hilton Park**
Co Offaly, Birr **Dooly's Hotel**
Co Roscommon, Hodson Bay **Hodson Bay Hotel**
Co Sligo, Ballymote **Temple House**
Co Sligo, Collooney **Markree Castle**
Co Sligo, Riverstown **Coopershill House**
Co Tipperary, Dundrum **Dundrum House**
Co Tipperary, Kilcoran **Kilcoran Lodge**

Northern Ireland

Co Antrim, Ballymena **Galgorm Manor**
Co Antrim, Bushmills **Bushmills Inn**
Co Antrim, Dunadry **Dunadry Inn**

Golf

Republic of Ireland

Co Cavan, Ballyconnell **Slieve Russell Hotel**
Co Clare, Newmarket-on-Fergus **Clare Inn Hotel**
Co Clare, Newmarket-on-Fergus **Dromoland Castle**
Co Cork, Shanagarry **Ballymaloe House**
Co Dublin, Howth **Deer Park Hotel**
Co Kerry, Kenmare **Park Hotel Kenmare**
Co Kerry, Killarney **Randles Court Hotel**
Co Kildare, Straffan **Kildare Hotel**
Co Kilkenny, Thomastown **Mount Juliet Hotel**
Co Mayo, Cong **Ashford Castle**
Co Monaghan, Carrickmacross **Nuremore Hotel**
Co Monaghan, Scotshouse **Hilton Park**
Co Tipperary, Dundrum **Dundrum House**
Co Waterford, Waterford **Waterford Castle**
Co Wicklow, Dunlavin **Rathsallagh House**

Indoor Swimming Pools

Republic of Ireland

Co Cavan, Ballyconnell **Slieve Russell Hotel**
Co Clare, Bunratty **Fitzpatricks Shannon Shamrock**
Co Clare, Newmarket-on-Fergus **Clare Inn Hotel**
Co Cork, Cork **Fitzpatrick Silver Springs**
Co Cork, Cork **Jurys Hotel**
Co Cork, Cork **Rochestown Park Hotel**

Co Cork, Kinsale **Actons Hotel**
Co Donegal, Rathmullan **Rathmullan House**
Co Dublin, Dublin **Berkeley Court**
Co Dublin, Dublin **Jurys Hotel and Towers**
Co Dublin, Dublin **Marine Hotel**
Co Dublin, Dublin Airport **Forte Crest**
Co Dublin, Howth **Howth Lodge Hotel**
Co Dublin, Killiney **Fitzpatrick's Castle**
Co Galway, Galway **Corrib Great Southern Hotel**
Co Galway, Galway **Great Southern**
Co Galway, Oughterard **Connemara Gateway Hotel**
Co Kerry, Beaufort **Dunloe Castle**
Co Kerry, Dingle **Dingle Skellig Hotel**
Co Kerry, Killarney **Aghadoe Heights Hotel**
Co Kerry, Killarney **Hotel Europe**
Co Kerry, Killarney **Great Southern**
Co Kerry, Killarney **Killarney Park Hotel**
Co Kerry, Killarney **Torc Great Southern**
Co Kerry, Parknasilla **Great Southern**
Co Kildare, Castledermot **Kilkea Castle**
Co Kildare, Straffan **Kildare Hotel**
Co Kilkenny, Kilkenny **Newpark Hotel**
Co Kilkenny, Thomastown **Mount Juliet Hotel**
Co Limerick, Adare **Adare Manor**
Co Limerick, Limerick **Castletroy Park Hotel**
Co Limerick, Limerick **Greenhills Hotel**
Co Limerick, Limerick **Jurys Hotel**
Co Limerick, Limerick **Limerick Inn**
Co Louth, Dundalk **Ballymascanlon House**
Co Mayo, Ballina **Downhill Hotel**
Co Monaghan, Carrickmacross **Nuremore Hotel**
Co Roscommon, Hodson Bay **Hodson Bay Hotel**
Co Sligo, Sligo **Sligo Park**
Co Tipperary, Kilcoran **Kilcoran Lodge**
Co Waterford, Waterford **Jurys Hotel**
Co Waterford, Waterford **Tower Hotel**
Co Waterford, Waterford **Waterford Castle**
Co Wexford, Rosslare **Great Southern**
Co Wexford, Rosslare **Kelly's Strand Hotel**
Co Wicklow, Dunlavin **Rathsallagh House**

Northern Ireland

Co Antrim, Dunadry **Dunadry Inn**
Co Antrim, Portballintrae **Bayview Hotel**
Co Down, Comber **La Mon House**
Co Down, Holywood **Culloden Hotel**
Co Down, Newcastle **Slieve Donard Hotel**

Outdoor Swimming Pools

Republic of Ireland

Co Cork, Ballylickey **Ballylickey Manor House**
Co Cork, Cork **Jurys Hotel**
Co Cork, Shanagarry **Ballymaloe House**
Co Dublin, Dublin **Jurys Hotel and Towers**
Co Galway, Clifden **Abbeyglen Castle**
Co Galway, Renvyle **Renvyle House**
Co Kerry, Caherdaniel **Derrynane Hotel**
Co Kerry, Parknasilla **Great Southern**
Co Wexford, Rosslare **Kelly's Strand Hotel**

Leisure Centres

Republic of Ireland

Co Cavan, Ballyconnell **Slieve Russell Hotel**
Co Clare, Bunratty **Fitzpatricks Shannon Shamrock**
Co Cork, Cork **Fitzpatrick Silver Springs**
Co Cork, Cork **Jurys Hotel**
Co Cork, Cork **Rochestown Park Hotel**
Co Cork, Kinsale **Actons Hotel**
Co Dublin, Howth **Howth Lodge Hotel**
Co Dublin, Killiney **Fitzpatrick's Castle**
Co Kerry, Killarney **Aghadoe Heights Hotel**
Co Kerry, Killarney **Great Southern**
Co Kerry, Parknasilla **Great Southern**
Co Kildare, Straffan **Kildare Hotel**
Co Kilkenny, Kilkenny **Newpark Hotel**
Co Kilkenny, Thomastown **Mount Juliet Hotel**
Co Limerick, Limerick **Castletroy Park Hotel**
Co Limerick, Limerick **Greenhills Hotel**
Co Limerick, Limerick **Jurys Hotel**
Co Limerick, Limerick **Limerick Inn**
Co Louth, Dundalk **Ballymascanlon House**
Co Mayo, Ballina **Downhill Hotel**
Co Monaghan, Carrickmacross **Nuremore Hotel**
Co Sligo, Sligo **Sligo Park**
Co Tipperary, Kilcoran **Kilcoran Lodge**
Co Waterford, Waterford **Tower Hotel**
Co Wexford, Rosslare **Great Southern**

Northern Ireland

Co Antrim, Dunadry **Dunadry Inn**
Co Down, Comber **La Mon House**

Riding

Republic of Ireland

Co Clare, Newmarket-on-Fergus **Clare Inn Hotel**
Co Clare, Newmarket-on-Fergus **Dromoland Castle**
Co Galway, Cashel **Cashel House**
Co Galway, Renvyle **Renvyle House**
Co Kerry, Beaufort **Dunloe Castle**
Co Kerry, Kenmare **Sheen Falls Lodge**
Co Kerry, Killarney **Hotel Europe**
Co Kerry, Killarney **Randles Court Hotel**
Co Kerry, Parknasilla **Great Southern**
Co Kilkenny, Thomastown **Mount Juliet Hotel**
Co Limerick, Adare **Adare Manor**
Co Mayo, Cong **Ashford Castle**
Co Tipperary, Dundrum **Dundrum House**
Co Tipperary, Glen of Aherlow **Aherlow House**
Co Tipperary, Kilcoran **Kilcoran Lodge**
Co Wexford, Foulksmills **Horetown House**

Northern Ireland

Co Antrim, Ballymena **Galgorm Manor**
Co Down, Annalong **Glassdrumman Lodge**

Squash

Republic of Ireland

Co Cavan, Ballyconnell **Slieve Russell Hotel**
Co Cork, Cork **Jurys Hotel**
Co Dublin, Killiney **Fitzpatrick's Castle**
Co Kildare, Straffan **Kildare Hotel**
Co Louth, Dundalk **Ballymascanlon House**
Co Mayo, Ballina **Downhill Hotel**
Co Monaghan, Carrickmacross **Nuremore Hotel**
Co Wexford, Rosslare **Kelly's Strand Hotel**

Northern Ireland

Co Antrim, Dunmurry **Forte Crest Belfast**
Co Down, Holywood **Culloden Hotel**

Tennis

Republic of Ireland

Co Cavan, Ballyconnell **Slieve Russell Hotel**
Co Clare, Ennis **Auburn Lodge**
Co Clare, Newmarket-on-Fergus **Clare Inn Hotel**
Co Clare, Newmarket-on-Fergus **Dromoland Castle**
Co Cork, Cork **Arbutus Lodge**
Co Cork, Cork **Fitzpatrick Silver Springs**
Co Cork, Kanturk **Assolas Country House**
Co Cork, Shanagarry **Ballymaloe House**
Co Donegal, Rathmullan **Rathmullan House**
Co Donegal, Rossnowlagh **Sand House**
Co Dublin, Dublin **Marine Hotel**
Co Dublin, Killiney **Fitzpatrick's Castle**
Co Galway, Ballynahinch **Ballynahinch Castle**
Co Galway, Cashel **Cashel House**
Co Galway, Cashel **Zetland House**
Co Galway, Clifden **Abbeyglen Castle**
Co Galway, Clifden **Rock Glen Manor**
Co Galway, Letterfrack **Rosleague Manor**
Co Galway, Oughterard **Connemara Gateway Hotel**
Co Galway, Oughterard **Currarevagh House**
Co Galway, Renvyle **Renvyle House**
Co Kerry, Beaufort **Dunloe Castle**
Co Kerry, Caragh Lake **Caragh Lodge**
Co Kerry, Dingle **Dingle Skellig Hotel**
Co Kerry, Kenmare **Dromquinna Manor Hotel**
Co Kerry, Kenmare **Park Hotel Kenmare**
Co Kerry, Kenmare **Sheen Falls Lodge**
Co Kerry, Killarney **Aghadoe Heights Hotel**
Co Kerry, Killarney **Cahernane Hotel**
Co Kerry, Killarney **Hotel Europe**
Co Kerry, Killarney **Great Southern**
Co Kerry, Killarney **Torc Great Southern**
Co Kerry, Parknasilla **Great Southern**
Co Kildare, Castledermot **Kilkea Castle**
Co Kildare, Maynooth **Moyglare Manor**
Co Kildare, Straffan **Kildare Hotel**
Co Kilkenny, Kilkenny **Newpark Hotel**
Co Kilkenny, Thomastown **Mount Juliet Hotel**
Co Limerick, Adare **Dunraven Arms**

Co Limerick, Limerick **Castletroy Park Hotel**
Co Limerick, Limerick **Greenhills Hotel**
Co Limerick, Limerick **Jurys Hotel**
Co Limerick, Limerick **Limerick Inn**
Co Louth, Dundalk **Ballymascanlon House**
Co Mayo, Ballina **Downhill Hotel**
Co Mayo, Ballina **Mount Falcon Castle**
Co Mayo, Cong **Ashford Castle**
Co Monaghan, Carrickmacross **Nuremore Hotel**
Co Roscommon, Hodson Bay **Hodson Bay Hotel**
Co Sligo, Sligo **Sligo Park**
Co Tipperary, Dundrum **Dundrum House**
Co Waterford, Waterford **Jurys Hotel**
Co Waterford, Waterford **Waterford Castle**
Co Wexford, Ferrycarrig Bridge **Ferrycarrig Hotel**
Co Wexford, Gorey **Marlfield House**
Co Wexford, Rosslare **Great Southern**
Co Wexford, Rosslare **Kelly's Strand Hotel**
Co Wicklow, Blessington **Downshire House**
Co Wicklow, Dunlavin **Rathsallagh House**
Co Wicklow, Rathnew **Tinakilly House**

Northern Ireland

Co Down, Annalong **Glassdrumman Lodge**
Co Down, Holywood **Culloden Hotel**
Co Down, Newcastle **Slieve Donard Hotel**

Restaurants with Private Dining Rooms

Republic of Ireland

Co Carlow, Leighlinbridge **Lord Bagenal Inn** (40)
Co Clare, Ballyvaughan **Gregans Castle** (40)
Co Clare, Bunratty **MacCloskey's** (22)
Co Clare, Newmarket-on-Fergus **Dromoland Castle** (60)
Co Cork, Ahakista **Shiro** (8)
Co Cork, Baltimore **Chez Youen** (50)
Co Cork, Carrigtwohill **Niblicks Restaurant** (70)
Co Cork, Castletownshend **Mary Ann's Bar & Restaurant** (14)
Co Cork, Cork **Arbutus Lodge** (25)
Co Cork, Cork **Clifford's** (50)
Co Cork, Cork **Flemings** (36)
Co Cork, Cork **Lovetts** (24)
Co Cork, Dunworley **Dunworley Cottage** (20)
Co Cork, Goleen Harbour **Herons Cove Restaurant** (24)
Co Cork, Kanturk **Assolas** (20)
Co Cork, Kinsale **Man Friday** (35)
Co Cork, Mallow **Longueville House** (20)
Co Cork, Oysterhaven **Oystercatcher** (20)
Co Cork, Shanagarry **Ballymaloe House** (30)
Co Donegal, Fahan **St John's** (22)
Co Donegal, Greencastle **Kealy's** (25)
Co Donegal, Rathmullan **Rathmullan House** (20)
Co Dublin, Blackrock **Ayumi-Ya** (25)
Co Dublin, Dublin **Chapter One** (40)
Co Dublin, Dublin **Chicago Pizza Pie Factory** (25)
Co Dublin, Dublin **The Chili Club** (16)
Co Dublin, Dublin **Commons Restaurant** (26)
Co Dublin, Dublin **Cooke's Café** (40)
Co Dublin, Dublin **Le Coq Hardi** (34)

Co Dublin, Dublin **Les Frères Jacques** (40)
Co Dublin, Dublin **George's Bistro & Piano Bar** (50)
Co Dublin, Dublin **Good World** (20)
Co Dublin, Dublin **Grey Door** (70)
Co Dublin, Dublin **Hibernian Hotel** (25)
Co Dublin, Dublin **Imperial Chinese Restaurant** (70)
Co Dublin, Dublin **Ivy Court** (26)
Co Dublin, Dublin **Kilkenny Kitchen** (40)
Co Dublin, Dublin **Locks** (30)
Co Dublin, Dublin **Le Mistral** (40)
Co Dublin, Dublin **Old Dublin Restaurant** (16)
Co Dublin, Dublin **Pasta Fresca** (25)
Co Dublin, Dublin **Patrick Guilbaud** (30)
Co Dublin, Dublin **Roly's Bistro** (65)
Co Dublin, Dublin **Senor Sassi's** (30)
Co Dublin, Dublin **Shalimar** (55)
Co Dublin, Dublin **La Stampa** (40)
Co Dublin, Dublin **Stephen's Hall Hotel** (40)
Co Dublin, Dublin **Tosca** (15)
Co Dublin, Dublin **Zen** (14)
Co Dublin, Dun Laoghaire **Restaurant Na Mara** (36)
Co Dublin, Howth **Adrian's** (36)
Co Dublin, Howth **King Sitric** (22)
Co Dublin, Malahide **Bon Appétit** (24)
Co Dublin, Malahide **Roches Bistro** (36)
Co Dublin, Skerries **Red Bank Restaurant** (10)
Co Dublin, Swords **Le Chateau** (20)
Co Dublin, Swords **Old Schoolhouse** (20)
Co Galway, Ballyconneely **Erriseask House** (20)
Co Galway, Cashel **Cashel House** (10)
Co Galway, Clifden **O'Grady's Seafood Restaurant** (12)
Co Galway, Letterfrack **Rosleague Manor** (10)
Co Galway, Moycullen **Drimcong House Restaurant** (32)
Co Galway, Tuam **Cre na Cille** (30)
Co Kerry, Caherdaniel **Loaves & Fishes** (12)
Co Kerry, Dingle **Beginish Restaurant** (18)
Co Kerry, Dingle **Half Door** (20)
Co Kerry, Kenmare **The Horseshoe** (30)
Co Kerry, Kenmare **The Old Bank House** (25)
Co Kerry, Kenmare **Park Hotel Kenmare** (30)
Co Kerry, Kenmare **Sheen Falls Lodge** (24)
Co Kerry, Killarney **Aghadoe Heights Hotel** (70)
Co Kerry, Killarney **Cahernane Hotel** (14)
Co Kerry, Killarney **Foley's Townhouse** (25)
Co Kerry, Killorglin **Nick's Restaurant** (35)
Co Kildare, Maynooth **Moyglare Manor** (50)
Co Kildare, Straffan **Kildare Hotel** (50)
Co Kilkenny, Kilkenny **Kilkenny Kitchen** (65)
Co Kilkenny, Kilkenny **Lacken House** (20)
Co Kilkenny, Thomastown **Mount Juliet Hotel** (40)
Co Limerick, Adare **Adare Manor** (25)
Co Limerick, Adàre **Dunraven Arms** (35)
Co Limerick, Adare **Mustard Seed** (30)
Co Limerick, Limerick **Restaurant de La Fontaine** (45)
Co Louth, Carlingford **Jordan's Bar & Restaurant** (16)
Co Mayo, Cong **Ashford Castle, Connaught Room** (40)
Co Mayo, Newport **Newport House** (35)
Co Meath, Mullingar **Crookedwood House** (35)
Co Meath, Navan **Ardboyne Hotel** (50)
Co Sligo, Boyle **Cromleach Lodge** (20)
Co Sligo, Collooney **Markree Castle** (30)
Co Sligo, Rosses Point **The Moorings** (45)
Co Waterford, Waterford **Dwyer's Restaurant** (10)
Co Waterford, Waterford **Prendiville's Restaurant/Guesthouse** (20)
Co Waterford, Waterford **Waterford Castle** (26)
Co Westmeath, Glasson **Glasson Village Restaurant** (12)
Co Westmeath, Kinnegad **The Cottage** (26)
Co Wexford, Ballyhack **Neptune Restaurant** (30)
Co Wexford, Carne **Lobster Pot** (30)

Co Wexford, Foulksmills **Horetown House** (30)
Co Wexford, Gorey **Marlfield House** (20)
Co Wicklow, Dunlavin **Rathsallagh House** (15)
Co Wicklow, Enniskerry **Curtlestown House** (25)
Co Wicklow, Enniskerry **Enniscree Lodge** (10)
Co Wicklow, Laragh **Mitchell's of Laragh** (50)
Co Wicklow, Rathnew **Hunter's Hotel** (20)
Co Wicklow, Rathnew **Tinakilly House** (40)
Co Wicklow, Roundwood **Roundwood Inn** (32)

Northern Ireland

Co Antrim, Ballymena **Galgorm Manor** (14)
Co Antrim, Belfast **Antica Roma** (70)
Co Antrim, Belfast **Bengal Brasserie** (50)
Co Antrim, Belfast **Manor House** (50)
Co Antrim, Belfast **Nick's Warehouse** (45)
Co Antrim, Belfast **Strand Restaurant** (25)
Co Antrim, Belfast **Welcome Restaurant** (30)
Co Antrim, Carnlough **Londonderry Arms** (150)
Co Down, Annalong **Glassdrumman Lodge** (20)
Co Down, Holywood **Culloden Hotel** (50)
Co Londonderry, Garvagh **MacDuff's Restaurant, Blackheath House** (12)
Co Londonderry, Londonderry **Beech Hill House Hotel** (30)

Sunday Opening

(L) and (D) refer to Lunch or Dinner *only* **opening**

Republic of Ireland

Co Carlow, Leighlinbridge **Lord Bagenal Inn**
Co Cavan, Blacklion **MacNean Bistro**
Co Cavan, Butlersbridge **Derragarra Inn**
Co Clare, Ballyvaughan **Gregans Castle**
Co Clare, Ballyvaughan **Monks Pub**
Co Clare, Ennis **The Cloister**
Co Clare, Newmarket-on-Fergus **Dromoland Castle**
Co Cork, Ahakista **Shiro** (D)
Co Cork, Ballylickey **Sea View Hotel**
Co Cork, Baltimore **Chez Youen**
Co Cork, Carrigtwohill **Niblicks Restaurant** (L)
Co Cork, Castletownshend **Mary Ann's Bar & Restaurant** (L)
Co Cork, Cork **Bully's**
Co Cork, Cork **Flemings**
Co Cork, Cork **Isaacs** (D)
Co Cork, Cork **Quay Co-Op**
Co Cork, Dunworley **Dunworley Cottage**
Co Cork, Goleen Harbour **Herons Cove Restaurant**
Co Cork, Kanturk **Assolas Country House** (D)
Co Cork, Kinsale **1601**
Co Cork, Kinsale **Blue Haven Hotel** (D)
Co Cork, Kinsale **Man Friday** (D)
Co Cork, Kinsale **Max's Wine Bar**
Co Cork, Mallow **Longueville House**
Co Cork, Oysterhaven **The Oystercatcher** (D)
Co Cork, Shanagarry **Ballymaloe House**
Co Cork, Youghal **Aherne's Seafood Restaurant**
Co Donegal, Dunkineely **Castle Murray House**
Co Donegal, Greencastle **Kealy's Seafood Bar**
Co Donegal, Rathmullan **Rathmullan House**
Co Donegal, Rossnowlagh **Smugglers Creek Inn**
Co Dublin, Blackrock **Ayumi-Ya** (D)

Co Dublin, Dublin **Ashtons**
Co Dublin, Dublin **Chapter One** (D)
Co Dublin, Dublin **Chicago Pizza Pie Factory**
Co Dublin, Dublin **Cooke's Café**
Co Dublin, Dublin **Davy Byrnes**
Co Dublin, Dublin **Furama Chinese Restaurant**
Co Dublin, Dublin **The Goat**
Co Dublin, Dublin **Good World**
Co Dublin, Dublin **Gotham Café**
Co Dublin, Dublin **Hibernian Hotel**
Co Dublin, Dublin **Imperial Chinese Restaurant**
Co Dublin, Dublin **Kielys**
Co Dublin, Dublin **Kitty O'Shea's Bar**
Co Dublin, Dublin **Little Caesar's Pizza**
Co Dublin, Dublin **Oisins** (D)
Co Dublin, Dublin **The Old Stand**
Co Dublin, Dublin **Roly's Bistro**
Co Dublin, Dublin **Ryans of Parkgate Street**
Co Dublin, Dublin **Senor Sassi's** (D)
Co Dublin, Dublin **Shalimar**
Co Dublin, Dublin **The Station House** (L)
Co Dublin, Dublin **Tosca**
Co Dublin, Dublin **The Westbury**
Co Dublin, Dublin **The Yacht** (L)
Co Dublin, Dublin **Yellow House** (L)
Co Dublin, Dublin **Zen**
Co Dublin, Howth **Adrian's**
Co Dublin, Malahide **Eastern Tandoori** (D)
Co Dublin, Monkstown **Mr Hung's**
Co Dublin, Skerries **Red Bank Restaurant** (L)
Co Dublin, Stillorgan **China-Sichuan Restaurant**
Co Dublin, Stillorgan **The Mill House**
Co Dublin, Stillorgan **Stillorgan Orchard**
Co Dublin, Swords **Le Chateau**
Co Galway, Aughrim **Aughrim Schoolhouse Restaurant** (L)
Co Galway, Cashel **Cashel House**
Co Galway, Clifden **Ardagh Hotel** (D)
Co Galway, Clifden **Destry Rides Again**
Co Galway, Clifden **O'Grady's Seafood Restaurant**
Co Galway, Galway **Casey's Westwood Restaurant & Bars**
Co Galway, Kilcolgan **Moran's Oyster Cottage**
Co Galway, Letterfrack **Rosleague Manor**
Co Galway, Oughterard **Currarevagh House** (D)
Co Galway, Spiddal **Boluisce Seafood Bar**
Co Kerry, Ballyferriter **Tigh an Tobair (The Well House)**
Co Kerry, Caherdaniel **Derrynane Hotel**
Co Kerry, Caherdaniel **Loaves & Fishes** (D)
Co Kerry, Cahirciveen **The Point Bar**
Co Kerry, Dingle **Beginish Restaurant**
Co Kerry, Dingle **Half Door**
Co Kerry, Dingle **The Islandman**
Co Kerry, Dingle **Lord Baker's Bar & Restaurant**
Co Kerry, Kenmare **The Horseshoe**
Co Kerry, Kenmare **The Old Bank House** (D)
Co Kerry, Kenmare **Park Hotel Kenmare**
Co Kerry, Kenmare **Sheen Falls Lodge**
Co Kerry, Killarney **Aghadoe Heights Hotel**
Co Kerry, Killarney **Cahernane Hotel** (D)
Co Kerry, Killarney **Foley's Townhouse**
Co Kerry, Killorglin **Nick's Restaurant** (D)
Co Kerry, Waterville **The Huntsman**
Co Kerry, Waterville **Smugglers Inn**
Co Kildare, Castledermot **Kilkea Castle**
Co Kildare, Maynooth **Moyglare Manor**
Co Kildare, Straffan **Kildare Hotel**
Co Kilkenny, Inistioge **The Motte** (D)
Co Kilkenny, Kilkenny **Kilkenny Kitchen** (L)
Co Kilkenny, Thomastown **Mount Juliet Hotel**
Co Laois, Mountrath **Roundwood House**

Co Leitrim, Dromahair **Stanford's Village Inn**
Co Limerick, Adare **Adare Manor**
Co Limerick, Adare **Dunraven Arms**
Co Limerick, Limerick **Castletroy Park Hotel** (L)
Co Louth, Carlingford **Jordan's Bar & Restaurant**
Co Louth, Carlingford **P J O'Hare's Anchor Bar**
Co Mayo, Ballina **Mount Falcon Castle** (D)
Co Mayo, Cong **Ashford Castle, Connaught Room** (D)
Co Mayo, Newport **Newport House** (D)
Co Meath, Dunderry **Dunderry Lodge Restaurant** (L)
Co Meath, Mullingar **Crookedwood House** (L)
Co Meath, Navan **Ardboyne Hotel**
Co Sligo, Boyle **Cromleach Lodge** (D)
Co Sligo, Collooney **Glebe House** (D)
Co Sligo, Riverstown **Coopershill House** (D)
Co Sligo, Rosses Point **The Moorings**
Co Sligo, Sligo **Truffles Restaurant** (D)
Co Tipperary, Birdhill **Matt the Thresher**
Co Waterford, Waterford **Waterford Castle**
Co Westmeath, Glasson **Glasson Village Restaurant** (L)
Co Wexford, Ballyhack **Neptune Restaurant**
Co Wexford, Carne **Lobster Pot** (D)
Co Wexford, Foulksmills **Horetown House** (L)
Co Wexford, Gorey **Marlfield House**
Co Wicklow, Bray **Tree of Idleness** (D)
Co Wicklow, Delgany **Wicklow Arms**
Co Wicklow, Dunlavin **Rathsallagh House** (D)
Co Wicklow, Enniskerry **Curtlestown House** (L)
Co Wicklow, Enniskerry **Enniscree Lodge**
Co Wicklow, Greystones **The Hungry Monk**
Co Wicklow, Laragh **Mitchell's of Laragh**
Co Wicklow, Rathnew **Hunter's Hotel**
Co Wicklow, Rathnew **Tinakilly House**
Co Wicklow, Roundwood **Roundwood Inn** (L)
Co Wicklow, Wicklow **Old Rectory** (D)

Northern Ireland

Co Antrim, Ballymena **Galgorm Manor**
Co Antrim, Belfast **Bengal Brasserie** (D)
Co Antrim, Belfast **Manor House**
Co Antrim, Belfast **Strand Restaurant**
Co Antrim, Belfast **Villa Italia** (D)
Co Antrim, Belfast **Welcome Restaurant** (D)
Co Antrim, Carnlough **Londonderry Arms**
Co Down, Annalong **Glassdrumman Lodge** (D)
Co Down, Helen's Bay **Deanes on the Square** (L)
Co Down, Holywood **Culloden Hotel**
Co Down, Portaferry **Portaferry Hotel**
Co Londonderry, Londonderry **Beech Hill House Hotel**

National Cuisines

Republic of Ireland

Co Dublin, Dublin **Furama Chinese Restaurant** – Chinese
Co Dublin, Dublin **Good World** – Chinese
Co Dublin, Dublin **Imperial Chinese Restaurant** – Chinese
Co Dublin, Dublin **Zen** – Chinese
Co Dublin, Monkstown **Mr Hung's** – Chinese
Co Dublin, Stillorgan **China-Sichuan Restaurant** – Chinese

Co Cork, Kinsale **Chez Jean-Marc** – French
Co Dublin, Dublin **Le Coq Hardi** – French

Co Dublin, Dublin **L'Ecrivain** – French
Co Dublin, Dublin **Les Freres Jacques** – French
Co Dublin, Dublin **Hibernian Hotel Restaurant** – French
Co Dublin, Dublin **Le Mistral** – French
Co Dublin, Dublin **Patrick Guilbaud** – French
Co Dublin, Dublon **The Westbury** – French
Co Dublin, Malahide **Bon Appétit** – French
Co Dublin, Malahide **Roches Bistro** – French
Co Dublin, Swords **Le Chateau** – French
Co Limerick, Limerick **Restaurant de La Fontaine** – French

Co Wicklow, Bray **Tree of Idleness** – Greek

Co Dublin, Dublin **Rajdoot** – Indian
Co Dublin, Dublin **Shalimar** – Indian
Co Dublin, Malahide **Eastern Tandoori** – Indian

Co Dublin, Dalkey **Il Ristorante** – Italian
Co Dublin, Dublin **Kapriol** – Italian
Co Dublin, Dublin **Pasta Fresca** – Italian
Co Dublin, Dublin **Little Caesar's Pizza** – Italian
Co Dublin, Dublin **Pizzeria Italia** – Italian
Co Dublin, Dublin **Il Primo** – Italian

Co Cork, Ahakista **Shiro** – Japanese
Co Dublin, Blackrock **Ayumi-Ya** – Japanese
Co Dublin, Dublin **Ayumi-Ya Japanese Steakhouse** – Japanese

Co Dublin, Dublin **Chapter One** – Russian/Scandinavian
Co Dublin, Dublin **Old Dublin** – Russian/Scandinavian

Co Dublin, Dublin **The Chili Club** – Thai
Co Dublin, Dublin **Langkawi Malaysian Restaurant** – South East Asian

Northern Ireland

Co Antrim, Belfast **Manor House** – Chinese
Co Antrim, Belfast **Welcome Restaurant** – Chinese

Co Down, Annalong **Glassdrumman Lodge** – French

Co Antrim, Belfast **Bengal Brasserie** – Indian

Co Antrim, Belfast **Antica Roma** – Italian
Co Antrim, Belfast **Speranza** – Italian
Co Antrim, Belfast **Villa Italia** – Italian

Restaurants offering a good vegetarian menu

Republic of Ireland

Co Carlow, Leighlinbridge **Lord Bagenal Inn**
Co Cork, Ahakista **Shiro**
Co Cork, Cork **Isaacs**
Co Cork, Cork **Quay Co-Op**
Co Cork, Kanturk **Assolas Country House**
Co Donegal, Rossnowlagh **Smugglers Creek Inn**
Co Dublin, Blackrock **Ayumi-Ya**
Co Dublin, Dublin **L'Ecrivain**
Co Dublin, Dublin **101 Talbot**
Co Galway, Moycullen **Drimcong House Restaurant**
Co Waterford, Waterford **Waterford Castle**

Northern Ireland

Co Antrim, Belfast **Manor House**
Co Down, Holywood **Culloden Hotel**

Good Restaurants for Seafood

Republic of Ireland

Co Cork, Ballylickey **Larchwood House**
Co Cork, Baltimore **Chez Youen**
Co Cork, Cork **Dan Lowrey's Seafood Tavern**
Co Cork, Cork **Lovetts**
Co Cork, Durrus **Blairs Cove House Restaurant**
Co Cork, Goleen Harbour **Herons Cove Restaurant**
Co Cork, Kanturk **Assolas Country House**
Co Cork, Kinsale **Blue Haven Hotel**
Co Cork, Kinsale **Chez Jean-Marc**
Co Cork, Kinsale **Man Friday**
Co Cork, Youghal **Aherne's Seafood Restaurant**
Co Donegal, Dunkineely **Castle Murray House**
Co Donegal, Fahan **Restaurant St John's**
Co Donegal, Greencastle **Kealy's Seafood Bar**
Co Donegal, Rossnowlagh **Smugglers Creek Inn**
Co Dublin, Dublin **Furama Chinese Restaurant**
Co Dublin, Dublin **Lobster Pot**
Co Dublin, Dublin **Periwinkle Seafood Bar**
Co Dublin, Dun Laoghaire **Restaurant Na Mara**
Co Dublin, Howth **King Sitric**
Co Galway, Clifden **Ardagh Hotel**
Co Galway, Clifden **O'Grady's Seafood Restaurant**
Co Galway, Roundstone **O'Dowd's Seafood Bar & Restaurant**
Co Galway, Spiddal **Boluisce Seafood Bar**
Co Kerry, Caherdaniel **Derrynane Hotel**
Co Kerry, Caherdaniel **Loaves & Fishes**
Co Kerry, Cahirciveen **Brennan's Restaurant**
Co Kerry, Dingle **Beginish Restaurant**
Co Kerry, Dingle **Doyle's Seafood Bar & Townhouse**
Co Kerry, Dingle **Half Door**
Co Kerry, Dingle **Lord Baker's Bar & Restaurant**
Co Kerry, Killarney **Aghadoe Heights Hotel**
Co Kerry, Killarney **Gaby's Seafood Restaurant**
Co Kerry, Killorglin **Nick's Restaurant**
Co Kilkenny, Inistioge **The Motte**
Co Sligo, Rosses Point **The Moorings**
Co Tipperary, Birdhill **Matt the Thresher**
Co Tipperary, Cashel **Chez Hans**
Co Wexford, Ballyhack **Neptune Restaurant**
Co Wexford, Carne **Lobster Pot**

Northern Ireland

Co Antrim, Portrush **Ramore**
Co Down, Portaferry **Portaferry Hotel**

Outstanding Desserts

Republic of Ireland

Co Cavan, Blacklion **MacNean Bistro**
Co Clare, Newmarket-on-Fergus **Dromoland Castle**
Co Cork, Cork **Arbutus Lodge**
Co Cork, Cork **Clifford's**
Co Cork, Durrus **Blairs Cove House Restaurant**
Co Cork, Kanturk **Assolas Country House**
Co Cork, Kinsale **Chez Jean-Marc**

Co Cork, Youghal **Aherne's Seafood Restaurant**
Co Donegal, Dunkineely **Castle Murray House**
Co Donegal, Fahan **St John's**
Co Donegal, Greencastle **Kealy's Seafood Bar**
Co Dublin, Dublin **L'Ecrivain**
Co Dublin, Dublin **Ernie's**
Co Dublin, Dublin **Le Mistral**
Co Dublin, Dublin **Patrick Guilbaud**
Co Dublin, Swords **Old Schoolhouse**
Co Galway, Ballyconneely **Erriseask House**
Co Galway, Moycullen **Drimcong House Restaurant**
Co Galway, Tuam **Cre na Cille**
Co Kerry, Caherdaniel **Loaves & Fishes**
Co Kerry, Dingle **Beginish Restaurant**
Co Kerry, Dingle **Half Door**
Co Kerry, Kenmare **Park Hotel Kenmare**
Co Kerry, Kenmare **Sheen Falls**
Co Kildare, Castledermot **Kilkea Castle**
Co Kilkenny, Inistioge **The Motte**
Co Limerick, Adare **Dunraven Arms**
Co Limerick, Adare **Mustard Seed**
Co Mayo, Cong **Ashford Castle, Connaught Room**
Co Mayo, Newport **Newport House**
Co Meath, Dunderry **Dunderry Lodge Restaurant**
Co Sligo, Boyle **Cromleach Lodge**
Co Waterford, Waterford **Dwyer's Restaurant**
Co Wicklow, Laragh **Mitchell's of Laragh**
Co Wicklow, Rathnew **Tinakilly House**

Northern Ireland

Co Antrim, Belfast **Antica Roma**
Co Antrim, Portrush **Ramore**
Co Down, Holywood **Sullivans**
Co Londonderry, Garvagh **MacDuff's Restaurant, Blackheath House**
Co Londonderry, Londonderry **Beech Hill House Hotel**

Restaurants offering a Good Cheeseboard

Republic of Ireland

Co Carlow, Leighlinbridge **Lord Bagenal Inn**
Co Cavan, Blacklion **MacNean Bistro**
Co Clare, Ballyvaughan **Gregans Castle**
Co Clare, Newmarket-on-Fergus **Dromoland Castle**
Co Cork, Ballydehob **Annie's Restaurant**
Co Cork, Carrigaline **Pew's Bistro**
Co Cork, Castletownshend **Mary Ann's Bar & Restaurant**
Co Cork, Cork **Arbutus Lodge**
Co Cork, Cork **Clifford's**
Co Cork, Cork **Crawford Gallery Café**
Co Cork, Cork **Flemings**
Co Cork, Cork **Jacques**
Co Cork, Cork **Lovetts**
Co Cork, Cork **O'Keeffe's**
Co Cork, Dunworley **Dunworley Cottage**
Co Cork, Durrus **Blairs Cove House Restaurant**
Co Cork, Goleen Harbour **Herons Cove Restaurant**
Co Cork, Kanturk **Assolas Country House**
Co Cork, Kinsale **Blue Haven Hotel**
Co Cork, Kinsale **Chez Jean-Marc**

Co Cork, Kinsale **Old Presbytery**
Co Cork, Mallow **Longueville House**
Co Cork, Oysterhaven **The Oystercatcher**
Co Cork, Shanagarry **Ballymaloe House**
Co Cork, Youghal **Aherne's Seafood Restaurant**
Co Donegal, Dunkineely **Castle Murray House**
Co Donegal, Fahan **Restaurant St John's**
Co Donegal, Rathmullan **Rathmullan House**
Co Donegal, Rossnowlagh **Smugglers Creek Inn**
Co Dublin, Blackrock **Clarets**
Co Dublin, Dublin **Chapter One**
Co Dublin, Dublin **Le Coq Hardi**
Co Dublin, Dublin **L'Ecrivain**
Co Dublin, Dublin **Ernie's**
Co Dublin, Dublin **The Goat**
Co Dublin, Dublin **Hibernian Hotel**
Co Dublin, Dublin **Kilkenny Kitchen**
Co Dublin, Dublin **Kitty O'Shea's Bar**
Co Dublin, Dublin **Lobster Pot**
Co Dublin, Dublin **Old Dublin Restaurant**
Co Dublin, Dublin **Il Primo**
Co Dublin, Dublin **La Stampa**
Co Dublin, Dublin **Stephen's Hall Hotel**
Co Dublin, Dublin **Ta Se Mohogani Gaspipes**
Co Dublin, Dublin **Yellow House**
Co Dublin, Howth **King Sitric**
Co Dublin, Malahide **Bon Appetit**
Co Dublin, Malahide **Roches Bistro**
Co Dublin, Skerries **Red Bank Restaurant**
Co Galway, Ballyconneely **Erriseask House**
Co Galway, Cashel **Cashel House**
Co Galway, Galway **Casey's Westwood Restaurant & Bars**
Co Galway, Moycullen **Drimcong House Restaurant**
Co Galway, Oughterard **Currarevagh House**
Co Galway, Roundstone **O'Dowd's Seafood Bar & Restaurant**
Co Kerry, Ballyferriter **Tigh an Tobair (The Well House)**
Co Kerry, Caherdaniel **Derrynane Hotel**
Co Kerry, Caherdaniel **Loaves & Fishes**
Co Kerry, Dingle **Beginish Restaurant**
Co Kerry, Dingle **Doyle's Seafood Bar & Townhouse**
Co Kerry, Dingle **Half Door**
Co Kerry, Kenmare **The Old Bank House**
Co Kerry, Kenmare **Park Hotel Kenmare**
Co Kerry, Kenmare **Sheen Falls Lodge**
Co Kerry, Killarney **Cahernane Hotel**
Co Kerry, Killarney **Foley's Townhouse**
Co Kerry, Killarney **Gaby's Seafood Restaurant**
Co Kerry, Killarney **Strawberry Tree**
Co Kerry, Killorglin **Nick's Restaurant**
Co Kerry, Waterville **The Huntsman**
Co Kerry, Waterville **Smugglers Inn**
Co Kildare, Athy **Tonlegee House**
Co Kilkenny, Inistioge **The Motte**
Co Kilkenny, Kilkenny **Kilkenny Kitchen**
Co Kilkenny, Kilkenny **Lacken House**
Co Kilkenny, Thomastown **Mount Juliet Hotel**
Co Limerick, Adare **Adare Manor**
Co Limerick, Adare **Dunraven Arms**
Co Limerick, Adare **Mustard Seed**
Co Limerick, Limerick **Restaurant de La Fontaine**
Co Louth, Carlingford **Jordan's Bar & Restaurant**
Co Mayo, Ballina **Mount Falcon Castle**
Co Mayo, Cong **Ashford Castle, Connaught Room**
Co Mayo, Newport **Newport House**
Co Meath, Mullingar **Crookedwood House**
Co Sligo, Collooney **Glebe House**
Co Sligo, Riverstown **Coopershill House**
Co Sligo, Rosses Point **The Moorings**
Co Sligo, Sligo **Truffles Restaurant**

Co Waterford, Waterford **Prendiville's Restaurant/Guesthouse**
Co Westmeath, Glasson **Glasson Village Restaurant**
Co Wexford, Gorey **Marlfield House**
Co Wicklow, Dunlavin **Rathsallagh House**
Co Wicklow, Enniskerry **Curtlestown House**
Co Wicklow, Enniskerry **Enniscree Lodge**
Co Wicklow, Laragh **Mitchell's of Laragh**
Co Wicklow, Roundwood **Roundwood Inn**

Northern Ireland

Co Antrim, Belfast **Roscoff**
Co Antrim, Portrush **Ramore**
Co Down, Helen's Bay **Deanes on the Square**
Co Londonderry, Garvagh **MacDuff's Restaurant, Blackheath House**
Co Londonderry, Londonderry **Beech Hill House Hotel**

Restaurants with an Outstanding Wine List

Republic of Ireland

Co Carlow, Leighlinbridge **Lord Bagenal Inn**
Co Clare, Newmarket-on-Fergus **Dromoland Castle**
Co Cork, Cork **Arbutus Lodge**
Co Cork, Kinsale **Blue Haven Hotel**
Co Dublin, Dublin **Le Coq Hardi**
Co Dublin, Dublin **Patrick Guilbaud**
Co Dublin, Howth **King Sitric**
Co Dublin, Malahide **Bon Appétit**
Co Kerry, Kenmare **Park Hotel**
Co Kerry, Kenmare **Sheen Falls Lodge**
Co Kerry, Killarney **Cahernane Hotel**
Co Kerry, Killarney **Gaby's Seafood Restaurant**
Co Kerry, Killorglin **Nick's Restaurant**
Co Kerry, Waterville **The Huntsman**
Co Kildare, Maynooth **Moyglare Manor**
Co Mayo, Newport **Newport House**
Co Wicklow, Bray **Tree of Idleness**
Co Wicklow, Greystones **The Hungry Monk**

Restaurants offering a good range of wines by the glass

Republic of Ireland

Co Cavan, Butlersbridge **Derragarra Inn**
Co Clare, Newmarket-on-Fergus **Dromoland Castle**
Co Cork, Castletownshend **Mary Ann's Bar & Restaurant**
Co Cork, Dunworley **Dunworley Cottage**
Co Cork, Durrus **Blairs Cove House Restaurant**
Co Cork, Kinsale **Blue Haven Hotel**
Co Donegal, Culdaff **McGuinness's**
Co Donegal, Fahan **Restaurant St John's**
Co Dublin, Dalkey **Il Ristorante**
Co Dublin, Dublin **Davy Byrnes**
Co Dublin, Dublin **The Goat**

Co Dublin, Dublin **Il Primo**
Co Dublin, Dublin **Stephen's Hall Hotel**
Co Dublin, Howth **Adrian's**
Co Dublin, Howth **King Sitric**
Co Galway, Clifden **Destry Rides Again**
Co Kerry, Dingle **Beginish Restaurant**
Co Kerry, Dingle **Doyle's Seafood Bar & Townhouse**
Co Kerry, Dingle **Half Door**
Co Kerry, Dingle **Lord Baker's Bar & Restaurant**
Co Kerry, Kenmare **The Old Bank House**
Co Kerry, Killarney **Foley's Townhouse**
Co Kerry, Killarney **Gaby's Seafood Restaurant**
Co Kildare, Castledermot **Kilkea Castle**
Co Kilkenny, Inistioge **The Motte**
Co Louth, Carlingford **Jordan's Bar & Restaurant**
Co Meath, Ceanannas Mor **O'Shaughnessy's**
Co Meath, Dunderry **Dunderry Lodge Restaurant**
Co Sligo, Sligo **McGettigan's**
Co Wicklow, Enniskerry **Enniscree Lodge**
Co Wicklow, Greystones **The Hungry Monk**
Co Wicklow, Roundwood **Roundwood Inn**

Northern Ireland

Co Antrim, Belfast **Nick's Warehouse**
Co Antrim, Belfast **Roscoff**
Co Antrim, Portrush **Ramore**
Co Down, Annalong **Glassdrumman Lodge**

Family-friendly Establishments

Republic of Ireland

Co Clare, Ballyvaughan **Monks Pub**
Co Clare, Ennis **The Cloister**
Co Cork, Ahakista **Ahakista Bar**
Co Cork, Baltimore **Bushe's Bar**
Co Cork, Bantry **Anchor Tavern**
Co Cork, Cork **An Spailpin Fanac**
Co Cork, Cork **Flemings**
Co Cork, Crookhaven **O'Sullivan's**
Co Cork, Crosshaven **Cronin's Bar**
Co Cork, Dunworley **Dunworley Cottage**
Co Cork, Goleen Harbour **Herons Cove Restaurant**
Co Cork, Kinsale **Blue Haven Hotel**
Co Cork, Kinsale **The Dock Bar**
Co Cork, Shanagarry **Ballymaloe House**
Co Donegal, Culdaff **McGuinness's**
Co Donegal, Dunkineely **Castle Murray House**
Co Donegal, Rossnowlagh **Sand House**
Co Donegal, Rossnowlagh **Smugglers Creek Inn**
Co Dublin, Dublin **Chicago Pizza Pie Factory**
Co Dublin, Dublin **Dillons Restaurant**
Co Dublin, Dublin **The Goat**
Co Dublin, Dublin **Kilkenny Kitchen**
Co Dublin, Dublin **101 Talbot**
Co Dublin, Dublin **The Station House**
Co Galway, Galway **Brennans Yard**
Co Galway, Galway **Corrib Great Southern Hotel**
Co Galway, Moycullen **Cloonnabinnia House Hotel**
Co Galway, Moycullen **Drimcong House Restaurant**
Co Galway, Oughterard **Connemara Gateway Hotel**
Co Galway, Renvyle **Renvyle House**
Co Kerry, Beaufort **Dunloe Castle**

Co Kerry, Caherdaniel **Derrynane Hotel**
Co Kerry, Cahirciveen **The Point Bar**
Co Kerry, Caragh Lake **Caragh Lodge**
Co Kerry, Dingle **Dingle Skellig Hotel**
Co Kerry, Killarney **Foley's Townhouse**
Co Kildare, Naas **Manor Inn**
Co Kilkenny, Kilkenny **Kilkenny Kitchen**
Co Kilkenny, Kilkenny **Newpark Hotel**
Co Laois, Mountrath **Roundwood House**
Co Limerick, Limerick **Jurys Hotel**
Co Mayo, Ballina **Downhill Hotel**
Co Meath, Mullingar **Crookedwood House**
Co Offaly, Birr **Tullanisk**
Co Sligo, Rosses Point **The Moorings**
Co Sligo, Sligo **McGettigan's**
Co Sligo, Tubbercurry **Killoran's Traditional Restaurant**
Co Waterford, Dunmore East **The Ship**
Co Waterford, Waterford **Jack Meade's Bar**
Co Waterford, Waterford **Jury's**
Co Wexford, Rosslare **Great Southern**
Co Wexford, Rosslare **Kelly's Strand Hotel**

Northern Ireland

Co Antrim, Belfast **Speranza**
Co Antrim, Belfast International Airport **Novotel**
Co Antrim, Dunadry **Dunadry Inn**
Co Down, Comber **La Mon House**

No-smoking Restaurants
or restaurants with a no-smoking room

Republic of Ireland

Co Cork, Cork **Gingerbread House**
Co Cork, Kinsale **Max's Wine Bar**
Co Donegal, Fahan **Restaurant St John's**
Co Donegal, Greencastle **Kealy's Seafood Bar**
Co Dublin, Dublin **Good World**
Co Galway, Ballyconneely **Erriseask House**
Co Galway, Letterfrack **Rosleague Manor**
Co Galway, Oughterard **Currarevagh House**
Co Kildare, Maynooth **Moyglare Manor**
Co Louth, Carlingford **Jordan's Bar & Restaurant**
Co Mayo, Ballina **Mount Falcon Castle**
Co Mayo, Newport **Newport House**
Co Sligo, Boyle **Cromleach Lodge**
Co Sligo, Riverstown **Coopershill House**
Co Wexford, Carne **Lobster Pot**
Co Wicklow, Wicklow **Old Rectory**

Northern Ireland

Co Down, Annalong **Glassdrumman Lodge**
Co Down, Holywood **Bay Tree**
Co Londonderry, Garvagh **MacDuff's Restaurant, Blackheath House**

Establishments
listed in
county order

REPUBLIC OF IRELAND ENTRIES LISTED IN COUNTY ORDER

HR = Hotel with recommended Restaurant open to public H = Hotel RR = Restaurant with Rooms R = Restaurant open to public P = Pub
AR = Other Accommodation with recommended Restaurant A = other Accommodation
See Starred Restaurants and map on page 13 for ★ and ↑ restaurant listings.
Some hotels are ungraded due to their categorisation as a Private House Hotel or Inns without public rooms (see Quick Reference Lists); the former are usually de luxe B&B establishments and their restaurant may not generally be open to non-residents. Restaurants with Rooms are also ungraded.
Other hotels (for example the *Europa Hotel* in Belfast) may be currently undergoing substantial renovation work that may radically change the hotel's grading when completed.
Restaurants without prices are generally of an informal, snackier nature.

Location	Establishment	Cat	Room Price	%	Food Price	Rooms	Conf	Banq	Beaut Sit	Family Friendly	Leis Cntr	Swim Pool	Golf	Address

Co Carlow

Location	Establishment	Cat	Room Price	%	Food Price	Rooms	Conf	Banq	Beaut Sit	Family Friendly	Leis Cntr	Swim Pool	Golf	Address
Leighlinbridge	Lord Bagenal Inn	R			£45									Leighlinbridge

Co Cavan

Location	Establishment	Cat	Room Price	%	Food Price	Rooms	Conf	Banq	Beaut Sit	Family Friendly	Leis Cntr	Swim Pool	Golf	Address
Ballyconnell	Slieve Russell Hotel	H	£120	78%		120	800	450		Family	yes	yes	yes	Ballyconnell
Blacklion	MacNean Bistro	R			£40									Blacklion
Butlersbridge	Derragarra Inn	P												Butlersbridge

Co Clare

Location	Establishment	Cat	Room Price	%	Food Price	Rooms	Conf	Banq	Beaut Sit	Family Friendly	Leis Cntr	Swim Pool	Golf	Address
Ballyvaughan	Gregans Castle	HR	£88	71%	£75	22			yes					Ballyvaughan
Ballyvaughan	Monks Pub	P								Family				The Quay Ballyvaughan
Bunratty	Fitzpatricks Shannon Shamrock	H	£137	60%		115	200	200			yes	yes		Bunratty
Bunratty	MacCloskey's	R			£70									Bunratty House Mews Bunratty
Ennis	Auburn Lodge	H	£84	61%		100		400		Family				Galway Road Ennis
Ennis	The Cloister	P												Abbey Street Ennis

Location	Establishment	Cat	£	%	£								Address
Ennis	Old Ground Hotel	H	£99	66%		58	250	180					Ennis
Ennis	West County Inn	H	£77	59%		100	200	500		Family			Clare Road Ennis
New Quay	Linnane's Bar	P											New Quay Burrin
Newmarket-on-Fergus	Clare Inn Hotel	H	£99	64%		121	400	350			yes		Dromoland Newmarket-on-Fergus
Newmarket-on-Fergus	Dromoland Castle	HR†	£252	79%		73	450	450			yes		Newmarket-on-Fergus
Shannon	Oakwood Arms Hotel	H	£88	63%		76	200	250	yes				Shannon
Shannon Airport	Great Southern	H	£110	64%	£115	115	170	140					Shannon Airport Shannon

Co Cork

Location	Establishment	Cat	£	%	£								Address
Ahakista	Ahakista Bar	P											Ahakista
Ahakista	Hillcrest House	A	£31							Family			Ahakista
Ahakista	Shiro	R★			£80								Ahakista
Ballydehob	Annie's Restaurant	R			£55	4					yes		Main Street Ballydehob
Ballydehob	Levis Bar	P											Corner House Main Street Ballydehob
Ballylickey	Ballylickey Manor House	A	£110	67%		5					yes		Ballylickey Bantry Bay
Ballylickey	Larchwood House	R			£60						yes		Pearsons Bridge Ballylickey
Ballylickey	Sea View Hotel	HR	£100	70%	£55	17	35			Family	yes		Ballylickey nr Bantry
Baltimore	Bushe's Bar	P											Baltimore
Baltimore	Chez Youen	R			£75								The Pier Baltimore
Baltimore	McCarthy's Bar	P											The Square Baltimore
Bantry	Anchor Tavern	P								Family			New Street Bantry
Cape Clear Island	Paddy Bourke's	P								Family			Cape Clear Island
Carrigaline	Pew's Bistro	R			£55								Main Street Carrigaline
Carrigtwohill	Niblicks Restaurant	R			£38								Fota Island Golf Club Carrigtwohill
Castlelyons	Ballyvolane House	A	£80		£80	6		25					Castlelyons
Castletownbere	MacCarthy's	P											Town Square Castletownbere
Castletownshend	Bow Hall	H	£50			3			yes				Castletownshend
Castletownshend.	Mary Ann's Bar & Restaurant	R			£50								Castletownshend nr Skibbereen
Cork	An Spailpin Fanac	P											28-29 South Main Street Cork
Cork	Arbutus Lodge	HR★	£72	70%	£80	20	120	180		Family			Montenotte Cork
Cork	Bully's	R			£25								40 Paul Street Cork
Cork	Clifford's	R★			£70								18 Dyke Parade Cork
Cork	Crawford Gallery Cafe	R			£45								Emmet Place Cork

Location	Establishment	Cat	Room Price	%	Food Price	Rooms	Conf	Banq	Beaut Sit	Family Friendly	Leis Cntr	Swim Pool	Golf	Address
Cork	Dan Lowrey's Seafood Tavern	P												13 MacCurtain Street Cork
Cork	Fitzpatrick Silver Springs	H	£89	65%		110	800	750			yes	yes		Tivoli Cork
Cork	Flemings	RR	£55		£55	4								Silver Grange House Tivoli Cork
Cork	Forte Travelodge	H	£42			40								Jnct South Ring Road/Kinsale R Cork Airport nr Cork Blackash
Cork	Gingerbread House	R												Frenchchurch Street Cork
Cork	Imperial Hotel	H	£121	66%		101	600	350						South Mall Cork
Cork	Isaacs	R			£35									48 MacCurtain Street Cork
Cork	Ivory Tower Restaurant	R			£55									35 Princes Street Cork
Cork	Jacques	R			£55									9 Phoenix Street Cork
Cork	Jurys Hotel	H	£133	66%		185	700	520				yes		Western Road Cork
Cork	Lovetts	R			£72									Churchyard Lane off Well Road
Cork	Metropole Hotel	H	£85	58%		108	500	300						Maccurtain Street Cork
Cork	Morrisons Island Hotel	H	£119	69%		40	15	15						Morrisons Quay Cork
Cork	O'Keeffe's	R			£65									23 Washington Street West Cork
Cork	Quay Co-Op	P												24 Sullivan's Quay Cork
Cork	Reidy's Wine Vaults	P												Lancaster Place Western Road Cork
Cork	Rochestown Park Hotel	H	£85	67%		63	150	150				yes		Rochestown Road Douglas Cork
Cork	Seven North Mall	H	£60			5								7 North Mall Cork
Crookhaven	O'Sullivan's	P								Family				Crookhaven
Crosshaven	Cronin's Bar	P								Family				Crosshaven
Dunworley	Dunworley Cottage	R			£60					Family				Butlerstown Clonakilty Dunworley
Durrus	Blairs Cove House Restaurant	R			£60				yes					Blairs Cove Durrus nr Bantry
East Ferry	Marlogue Inn	P												East Ferry Marina East Ferry Cobh
Glengarriff	The Blue Loo	P												Main Street Glengarriff
Goleen Harbour	Herons Cove Restaurant	RR	£33		£35	3			yes	Family				Goleen Harbour
Innishannon	Innishannon House Hotel	H	£95	63%		13	200	150	yes					Innishannon
Kanturk	Alley Bar	P							yes					Strand Street Kanturk
Kanturk	Assolas Country House	AR*	£104	72%		9	20	20						Kanturk
Kanturk	The Vintage	P			£65									O'Brien Street Kanturk
Kinsale	Actons Hotel	H	£100	60%		57	400	300				yes	yes	Pier Road Kinsale

Kinsale	Blue Haven Hotel	HR	£84			10		Family		3 Pearse Street Kinsale
Kinsale	The Bulman Bar	R↑						Family		Summer Cove Kinsale
Kinsale	Chez Jean-Marc	P			£55					Lower O'Connell Street Kinsale
Kinsale	The Dock Bar	R			£55			Family		Castlepark Kinsale
Kinsale	Man Friday	R			£40					Scilly Kinsale
Kinsale	Max's Wine Bar	H	£52			9				Main Street Kinsale
Kinsale	The Old Bank House	RR	£38			6				Pearse Street Kinsale
Kinsale	Old Presbytery	A	£80			7				Cork Street Kinsale
Kinsale	Scilly House	P		65%			25			Scilly Kinsale
Kinsale	1601	P								Pearse Street Kinsale
Kinsale	The Spaniard Inn	HR↑	£110			16	20	Family		Scilly Kinsale
Mallow	Longueville House	R	£65	72%						Mallow
Oysterhaven	The Oystercatcher	P	£65					yes		Oysterhaven nr Kinsale
Rathpeacon	Country Squire Inn	P								Mallow Road Rathpeacon
Schull	TJ Newman's	P								Main Street Schull
Shanagarry	Ballymaloe House	AR*	£120	66%		30		yes	Family	yes	Shanagarry
Timoleague	Dillon's	P			£80			Family		Mill Street Timoleague
Youghal	Aherne's Seafood Restaurant	RR	£67		£60	10		Family		163 North Main Street Youghal

Co Donegal

Culdaff	McGuinness's	HR	£44	69%	£55	10		Family		Culdaff Inishaven
Dunkineely	Castle Murray House	R			£55		25	Family		Dunkineely
Fahan	Restaurant St John's	R			£45					Fahan Innishowen
Greencastle	Kealy's Seafood Bar	P								Greencastle
Portsalon	Rita's	P						Family		The Pier Portsalon Letterkenny
Rathmullan	Rathmullan House	H	£121	62%	£60	23	20	yes	Family	Rathmullan nr Letterkenny
Rossnowlagh	Smugglers Creek Inn	P			£35			yes	Family	Rossnowlagh
Rossnowlagh	Sand House	H	£88	69%		40	75		Family	Rossnowlagh

Co Dublin

Blackrock	Ayumi-Ya	R		£40					Newtownpark Ave Blackrock

Location	Establishment	Cat	Room Price	%	Food Price	Rooms	Conf	Banq	Beaut Sit	Family Friendly	Leis Cntr	Swim Pool	Golf	Address
Blackrock	Clarets	R†			£70									63 Main Street Blackrock
Dalkey	The Queens	P												Castle Street Dalkey
Dalkey	Il Ristorante	R			£60									108 Coliemore Road Dalkey
Dublin 1	Chapter One	R			£70									18/19 Parnell Square
Dublin 1	Gresham Hotel	H	£140	64%	£32	200	325	200		Family				Upper O'Connell Street
Dublin 1	101 Talbot	R												101 Talbot Street
Dublin 1	Royal Dublin Hotel	H	£99	63%		117	250	230						40 Upper O'Connell Street
Dublin 2	Ayumi-Ya Japanese Steakhouse	R			£40									132 Lower Baggot Street
Dublin 2	Bleeding Horse	P												24 Upper Camden Street
Dublin 2	Blooms Hotel	H	£121	60%		86	30							Anglesea Street
Dublin 2	Central Hotel	H	£139	57%		70	80	70						1-5 Exchequer Street
Dublin 2	Chicago Pizza Pie Factory	R			£60					Family				St Stephen's Green
Dublin 2	The Chili Club	R												1 Anns Lane
Dublin 2	Clarence Hotel	H	£50	60%		66	60	60						6/8 Wellington Quay
Dublin 2	Commons Restaurant	R			£85									85-86 St Stephen's Green
Dublin 2	Cooke's Cafe	R†			£65									14 South William Street
Dublin 2	Davenport Hotel	H	£177	76%		120	300	400						Merrion Square
Dublin 2	Davy Byrnes	P												21 Duke Street
Dublin 2	Dillons Restaurant	R			£70					Family				21 Suffolk Street
Dublin 2	Doheny & Nesbitt	P			£80									5 Lower Baggot Street
Dublin 2	L'Ecrivain	R			£70									112 Lower Baggot Street
Dublin 2	Les Frères Jacques	R												74 Dame Street
Dublin 2	George's Bistro & Piano Bar	R												29 South Frederick Street
Dublin 2	Georgian House	H	£83	56%		33								20 Lower Baggot Street
Dublin 2	Good World	R			£40									18 South Great George's Street
Dublin 2	Gotham Cafe	R												8 South Anne Street
Dublin 2	Grey Door	RR	£99		£50	7								22 Upper Pembroke Street
Dublin 2	Imperial Chinese Restaurant	R			£40									13 Wicklow Street
Dublin 2	Kapriol	R			£64									45 Lower Camden Street
Dublin 2	Kilkenny Kitchen	R								Family				Nassau Street

Area	Name	Type	Price	%	Price2	No.1	No.2	No.3	Notes	Address
Dublin 2	Little Caesar's Pizza	R								5 Chatham House Balfe Street
Dublin 2	Le Mistral	R★	£146	66%	£80	74	150	120		16 Harcourt Street
Dublin 2	Mont Clare Hotel	H								Merrion Square
Dublin 2	National Museum Cafe	R	£68			5				Kildare Street
Dublin 2	Number 31	A								31 Leeson Close off Lower Leeson St
Dublin 2	O'Dwyer's	P								Mount Street
Dublin 2	Osins	R	£95							31 Upper Camden Street
Dublin 2	The Old Stand	P								37 Exchequer Street
Dublin 2	Pasta Fresca	R	£30							2-4 Chatham Street
Dublin 2	Patrick Guilbaud	R★†	£100							46 James Place off Lower Baggot Street
Dublin 2	The Pembroke	P								31 Lower Pembroke Street
Dublin 2	Periwinkle Seafood Bar	R								South William Street
Dublin 2	Pizzeria Italia	R	£25			23				Temple Bar
Dublin 2	Il Primo	R	£45							16 Montague Street
Dublin 2	Rajdoot	R	£48							26 Clarendon Street Westbury Centre
Dublin 2	Shalimar	R	£50							17 South Great George's Street
Dublin 2	Shelbourne Hotel	H	£223	74%		164	500	300	Family	St Stephen's Green
Dublin 2	Stag's Head	P								1 Dame Court
Dublin 2	La Stampa	R	£55							35 Dawson Street
Dublin 2	Stauntons on the Green	A	£62			30				83 St Stephen's Green South
Dublin 2	Stephen's Hall Hotel	HR	£143	65%	£45	37				14-17 Lower Leeson Street
Dublin 2	Toners Pub	P								139 Lower Baggot Street
Dublin 2	Tosca	R								20 Suffolk Street
Dublin 2	The Westbury	HR	£180	79%	£85	203	300	200		Off Grafton Street
Dublin 3	The Yacht	P								73 Clontarf Road
Dublin 4	Aberdeen Lodge	A	£60			16				53/55 Park Avenue Ailesbury Road
Dublin 4	Anglesea Town House	A	£60			7				63 Anglesea Road
Dublin 4	Ariel House	A	£63			28				52 Lansdowne Road Ballsbridge
Dublin 4	Berkeley Court	H	£191	76%		207	400	275	yes	Lansdowne Road
Dublin 4	Burlington Hotel	H	£154	70%		450	1000	1000		Upper Leeson Street
Dublin 4	Le Coq Hardi	R★	£95							35 Pembroke Road Ballsbridge
Dublin 4	Doyle Montrose Hotel	H	£106	65%		179	90			Stillorgan Road
Dublin 4	Doyle Tara Hotel	H	£106	61%		114	200	165		Merrion Road

Location	Establishment	Cat	Room Price	%	Food Price	Rooms	Conf	Banq	Beaut Sit	Family Friendly	Leis Cntr	Swim Pool	Golf	Address
Dublin 4	Ernie's	R			£80									Mulberry Gardens Donnybrook
Dublin 4	Furama Chinese Restaurant	R			£75									88 Donnybrook Road
Dublin 4	Glenveagh Town House	A	£50		£55	11								31 Northumberland Road
Dublin 4	Hibernian Hotel	HR	£135	70%		30	40	55						Eastmoreland Place Ballsbridge
Dublin 4	Jurys Hotel and Towers	H	£162	76%		400	850	600				yes		Pembroke Road Ballsbridge
Dublin 4	Kielys	P												22-24 Donnybrook Road Donnybrook
Dublin 4	Kitty O'Shea's Bar	R												23-25 Upper Grand Canal Street
Dublin 4	Langkawi Malaysian	R	£40											46 Upper Street
Dublin 4	Lobster Pot	P												9 Ballsbridge Terrace
Dublin 4	McCormack's Merrion Inn	A			£70									188 Merrion Road
Dublin 4	Merrion Hall	A	£45			15								54-56 Merrion Road
Dublin 4	Raglan Lodge	A	£77			7								10 Raglan Road Ballsbridge
Dublin 4	Roly's Bistro	R			£50					Family				7 Ballsbridge Terrace
Dublin 4	Sachs Hotel	H	£98	62%		20	170	150						19 Morehampton Road Donnybrook
Dublin 4	Senor Sassi's	R			£58									146 Upper Leeson Street
Dublin 5	The Station House	P								Family				3-5 Station Road Raheny
Dublin 6	Ashtons	P												Clonskeagh
Dublin 6	Ivy Court	Rt			£55									88 Rathgar Road
Dublin 6	Zen	R			£45									89 Upper Rathmines Road
Dublin 7	Ta Se Mohogani Gaspipes	R			£45									17 Manor Street Stoneybatter
Dublin 8	Hotel Conrad	H	£217	75%		191	300							Earlsfort Terrace
Dublin 8	Jurys Christchurch Inn	H	£56	55%		183		250						Christchurch Place
Dublin 8	Locks	R			£85									1 Windsor Terrace Portobello
Dublin 8	Old Dublin Restaurant	R			£60									90-91 Francis Street
Dublin 8	Ryans of Parkgate Street	P												28 Parkgate Street
Dublin 9	The Brian Boru	P												5 Prospect Road Glasnevin
Dublin 9	Kavanagh's	P												Prospect Square Glasnevin
Dublin 13	Marine Hotel	H	£84	64%		26	150	200		Family		yes		Sutton Cross
Dublin 14	The Goat	P												Goatstown
Dublin 14	Yellow House	P												Willbrook Road Rathfarnham
Dublin Airport	Forte Crest	H	£129	57%		192	200	150				yes		Collinstown Dublin Airport

Location	Establishment	Cat	£	%	£						Address
Dun Laoghaire	Chestnut Lodge	A	£45			4					2 Vesey Place Monkstown
Dun Laoghaire	Restaurant Na Mara	R			£75						1 Harbour Road
Dun Laoghaire	Royal Marine Hotel	H	£85	64%		104	700	400			Marine Road
Howth	Abbey Tavern	P									Howth
Howth	Adrian's	R			£50				yes		3 Abbey Street Howth
Howth	Deer Park Hotel	H	£67	64%		50	140	100			Howth
Howth	Howth Lodge Hotel	H	£63	65%		46	200	200			Howth
Howth	King Sitric	R			£70				yes	yes	East Pier Harbour Road Howth
Killiney	Court Hotel	H	£97	68%		86	300	300			Killiney Bay Killiney
Killiney	Fitzpatrick's Castle	H	£147	68%		85	550	400	yes	yes	Killiney
Kilmoon	Snail Box	P									Kilmoon
Malahide	Bon Appetit	R			£80						9 St James Terrace Malahide
Malahide	Eastern Tandoori	R			£40						1 New Street Malahide
Malahide	Grand Hotel	H	£90	66%		100	900	600			Malahide
Monkstown	Mr Hung's	R			£55						12 New Street Malahide
Skerries	Red Bank Restaurant	R			£64						5A The Crescent Monkstown
Stillorgan	China-Sichuan Restaurant	R			£60						7 Church Street Skerries
Stillorgan	The Mill House	P			£50						4 Lower Kilmacud Road Stillorgan
Stillorgan	Stillorgan Orchard	P									Lower Kilmacud Road Stillorgan
Swords	Le Chateau	R			£55						Stillorgan
Swords	Forte Travelodge	H	£42			40					River Mall Main Street Swords
Swords	Old Schoolhouse	R			£50						N1 Dublin/Belfast Road Swords Bypass
											Coolbanagher Swords

Co Galway

Location	Establishment	Cat	£	%	£				Address
Aughrim	Aughrim Schoolhouse	R			£45				Aughrim nr Ballinasloe
Ballyconneely	Erriseask House	HR	£72	64%	£60	13		yes	Ballyconneely Clifden Connemara
Ballynahinch	Ballynahinch Castle	H	£104	71%		28	25	yes	Recess Ballynahinch
Barna	Donnelly's of Barna	P							Barna
Cashel	Cashel House	HR	£135	76%	£70	32		yes	Cashel
Cashel	Zetland House	H	£109	65%		20			Cashel

Location	Establishment	Cat	Room Price	%	Food Price	Rooms	Conf	Banq	Beaut Sit	Family Friendly	Leis Cntr	Swim Pool	Golf	Address
Clifden	Abbeyglen Castle	H	£99	60%	£55	40	230	200	yes					Sky Road Clifden
Clifden	Ardagh Hotel	HR	£75	60%	£40	21			yes					Ballyconneely Road Clifden
Clifden	Destry Rides Again	R												Clifden
Clifden	E J King's	P												The Square Clifden
Clifden	O'Grady's Seafood Restaurant	R			£50									Market Street Clifden
Clifden	Rock Glen Manor	H	£90	61%		29			yes					Roundstowe Road Clifden
Galway	Ardilaun House	H	£94	66%		90	400	250						Taylors Hill Galway
Galway	Brennans Yard	H	£70	64%		24								Lower Merchants Road Galway
Galway	Casey's Westwood Restaurant	R			£60					Family				Dangan Upper Newcastle Galway
Galway	Corrib Great Southern Hotel	H	£123	68%		180	850	700		Family		yes		Dublin Road Galway
Galway	Glenlo Abbey	H	£115	66%		43	48	75						Bushy Park Galway
Galway	Great Southern	H	£113	69%		116	450	350				yes		Eyre Square Galway
Galway	Jurys Galway Inn	H	£61	55%		128								Quay Street Galway
Kilcolgan	Moran's Oyster Cottage	P												The Weir Kilcolgan
Letterfrack	Rosleague Manor	HR	£90	72%		20			yes	Family				Letterfrack Connemara
Moycullen	Cloonnabinnia House Hotel	H	£55	61%		14				Family				Ross Lake Moycullen
Moycullen	Drimcong House Restaurant	R*			£60					Family				Moycullen
Oughterard	Connemara Gateway Hotel	H	£105	65%		64	100	150				yes		Oughterard
Oughterard	Currarevagh House	AR	£89	65%	£50	15			yes					Oughterard Connemara
Oughterard	Sweeny's Oughterard House	H	£98	59%		21								Oughterard
Renvyle	Renvyle House	H	£118	64%		64	120	150	yes	Family				Renvyle
Roundstone	O'Dowd's Seafood Bar	P			£45									Roundstone
Spiddal	Boluisce Seafood Bar	R												Spiddal Village Connemara
Spiddal	Bridge House Inn	H	£65			14								Spiddal
Tuam	Cre na Cille	R			£50									High Street Tuam

Co Kerry

Location	Establishment	Cat	Room Price	%	Food Price	Rooms	Conf	Banq	Beaut Sit	Family Friendly	Leis Cntr	Swim Pool	Golf	Address
Annascaul	Dan Foley's	P												Annascaul

Town	Establishment											Address
Ballyferriter	Long's Pub	P										Ballyferriter Village
Ballyferriter	Tigh an Tobair (Well House)	R										Ballyferriter
Beaufort	Dunloe Castle	H	£96	71%		120	300	200	yes	Family	yes	Beaufort nr Killarney
Caherdaniel	Derrynane Hotel	HR	£66	62%	£44	75			yes			Caherdaniel
Caherdaniel	Loaves & Fishes	R			£55							Caherdaniel nr Derrynane
Cahirciveen	Brennan's Restaurant	R			£55					Family		13 Main Street Cahirciveen
Cahirciveen	The Point Bar	P				20			yes			Renard Point Cahirciveen
Caragh Lake	Hotel Ard-na-Sidhe	H	£96	70%		10			yes	Family		Caragh Lake nr Killorglin
Caragh Lake	Caragh Lodge	A	£99	65%	£55				yes	Family		Caragh Lake nr Killorglin
Dingle	Beginish Restaurant	R										Green Street Dingle
Dingle	Dick Mack's	P										Green Lane Dingle
Dingle	Dingle Skellig Hotel	H	£86	61%		115	120		yes	Family	yes	Dingle
Dingle	Doyle's Seafood Bar & T'house	RR	£59		£62	8						4 John Street Dingle
Dingle	Greenmount House	A	£70			8						Greenmount Dingle
Dingle	Half Door	R			£55							John Street Dingle
Dingle	The Islandman	P										Main Street Dingle
Dingle	James Flahive	P										The Quay Dingle
Dingle	Lord Baker's Bar & Restaurant	R			£60							Main Street Dingle
Dingle	O'Flaherty's	P										Bridge Street Dingle
Kenmare	Dromquinna Manor Hotel	H	£70	60%		28			yes			Blackwater Bridge
Kenmare	The Horseshoe	R	£30		£32							3 Main Street Kenmare
Kenmare	The Old Bank House	R			£70	5						Main Street Kenmare
Kenmare	Packies	R			£45							Henry Street Kenmare
Kenmare	Park Hotel Kenmare	HR*	£264	87%		50	50	30	yes		yes	Kenmare
Kenmare	Purple Heather	R			£90							Henry Street Kenmare
Kenmare	Sheen Falls Lodge	HR*	£230	87%	£90	40	120		yes	yes		Kenmare
Killarney	Aghadoe Heights Hotel	HR†	£136	70%	£100	60	100		yes	yes	yes	Aghadoe Killarney
Killarney	Cahernane Hotel	HR	£110	66%	£65	52	130		yes			Muckross Road Killarney
Killarney	Dingles Restauraunt	R			£45							40 New Street Killarney
Killarney	Hotel Europe	H	£96	72%		205	500	600	yes		yes	Killorglin Road Fossa Killarney
Killarney	Foley's Townhouse	RR	£70		£60	12	25	95		Family		23 High Street Killarney
Killarney	Gaby's Seafood Restaurant	R			£60							27 High Street Killarney
Killarney	Great Southern	H	£129	69%		183	1000	650			yes	Killarney
Killarney	Kathleen's Country House	A	£55			17						Tralee Road Killarney
Killarney	Killarney Towers Hotel	H	£90	57%		157					yes	College Square Killarney

Location	Establishment	Cat	Room Price	%	Food Price	Rooms	Conf	Banq	Beaut Slt	Family Friendly	Leis Cntr	Swim Pool	Golf	Address
Killarney	Killarney Park Hotel	H	£110	73%		55	150	160				yes		Kenmare Place Killarney
Killarney	Randles Court Hotel	H	£120			37		130					yes	Muckross Road Killarney
Killarney	Strawberry Tree	R			£77								yes	24 Plunkett Street Killarney
Killarney	Torc Great Southern	H	£91	63%		96						yes		Park Road Killarney
Killarney	Yer Man's Pub	P												24 Plunkett Street Killarney
Killorglin	Nick's Restaurant	R			£65									Lower Bridge Street Killorglin
Parknasilla	Great Southern	H	£156	72%		83	80	70	yes			yes		Parknasilla Sneem
Tralee	Ballyseede Castle Hotel	H	£85	60%		15	180	80						Tralee
Waterville	The Huntsman	P												Waterville
Waterville	Smugglers Inn	P												Waterville

Co Kildare

Location	Establishment	Cat	Room Price	%	Food Price	Rooms	Conf	Banq	Beaut Slt	Family Friendly	Leis Cntr	Swim Pool	Golf	Address
Athy	Tonlegee House	RR	£58		£55	5								Athy
Castledermot	Kilkea Castle	HR	£178	70%	£75	45	200	200				yes		Kilkea Castledermot
Maynooth	Moyglare Manor	HR	£110	77%	£70	17	40	70	yes					Moyglare Maynooth
Moone	Moone High Cross Inn	P												Bolton Hill Moone
Naas	Fletcher's	P												Commercial House Naas
Naas	Manor Inn	P								Family				Main Street Naas
Newbridge	Hotel Keadeen	H	£80	68%		37	500	600						Ballymany Newbridge
Straffan	Kildare Hotel	HR	£245	87%	£100	45	70	44	yes		yes	yes	yes	Straffan

Co Kilkenny

Location	Establishment	Cat	Room Price	%	Food Price	Rooms	Conf	Banq	Beaut Slt	Family Friendly	Leis Cntr	Swim Pool	Golf	Address
Castlewarren	Langton's	P												Castlewarren
Inistioge	The Motte	R			£60				yes					Inistioge
Kilkenny	Caislean Ui Cuain	P												2 High Street Kilkenny
Kilkenny	Kilkenny Kitchen	R								Family				Kilkenny Design Centre Castle Street Kilkenny
Kilkenny	Lacken House	RR	£55		£60	8	12							Dublin Road Kilkenny

Town	Name	Type	Price	%	Price2	No.	No.	No.					Address
Kilkenny	Langton's	P											69 John Street Kilkenny
Kilkenny	Newpark Hotel	H	£94	58%		60	600	350		Family	yes	yes	Castlecomer Road Kilkenny
Kilkenny	Shem's	P											61 John Street Kilkenny
Kilkenny	Tynan's	P											Bridge House 2 Johns Bridge Kilkenny
Maddoxtown	Blanchville House	A	£50			6	30						Dunbell Maddoxtown
Thomastown	Mount Juliet Hotel	HR	£195	84%	£75	32	50	140	yes		yes	yes	Mount Juliet Thomastown

Co Laois

Abbeyleix	Morrisseys	P											Main Street Abbeyleix
Mountrath	Roundwood House	AR	£64	58%	£60	6	12			Family	yes		Mountrath

Co Leitrim

Carrick-on-Shannon	Hollywell House	A	£46			3							Liberty Hill Carrick-on-Shannon
Dromahair	Stanford's Village Inn	P											Dromahair

Co Limerick

Abbeyfeale	The Cellar	P											Abbeyfeale
Adare	Adare Manor	HR†	£220	81%	£85	64		220				yes	Adare
Adare	Dunraven Arms	HR	£125	72%	£55	43	300	250					Adare
Adare	Mustard Seed	R†			£60								Main Street Adare
Adare	Woodlands House Hotel	H	£50	60%		32	350	270					Adare
Castleconnell	Bradshaw's Bar	P											Castleconnell
Limerick	Castletroy Park Hotel	HR	£140	74%	£65	107	400	300			yes		Dublin Road Limerick
Limerick	Greenhills Hotel	H	£111	62%		60	600	400			yes		Ennis Road Limerick
Limerick	Jackson's Turrett	A	£36			4							Clancy Strand Limerick
Limerick	Jurys Hotel	H	£116	68%		100	200	130		Family	yes	yes	Ennis Road Limerick
Limerick	Restaurant de La Fontaine	R			£60								12 Upper Gerald Griffin Street
Limerick	Limerick Inn	H	£115	68%		153	600	800				yes	Ennis Road Limerick
Limerick	Two Mile Inn	H	£78	63%		125	350	300			yes		Ennis Road Limerick

Location	Establishment	Cat	Room Price	%	Food Price	Rooms	Conf	Banq	Beaut Sit	Family Friendly	Leis Cntr	Swim Pool	Golf	Address
Co Longford														
Moydow	The Vintage	P												Moydow
Co Louth														
Ardee	The Gables	RR	£34		£60	5								Dundalk Road Ardee
Blackrock	Brake Tavern	P			£55									Main Street Blackrock nr Dundalk
Carlingford	Jordan's Bar & Restaurant	R				7								Carlingford
Carlingford	P J O'Hare's Anchor Bar	P												Carlingford
Dundalk	Ballymascanlon House	H	£75	59%		36	250	300		yes		yes		Ballymascanlon Dundalk
Co Mayo														
Ballina	Downhill Hotel	H	£86	65%	£50	50	500	450		Family	yes	yes		Ballina
Ballina	Mount Falcon Castle	AR	£72	60%		10								Ballina
Cong	Ashford Castle	HR†	£256	88%	£110	83	40	140					yes	Cong
Crossmolina	Enniscoe House	A	£88	63%		6								Castlehill nr Crossmolina Ballina
Newport	Newport House	HR	£120	67%	£70	20								Newport
Co Meath														
Ceanannas Mor	O'Shaughnessy's	P												Market Street Ceanannas Mor nr Kells
Dunderry	Dunderry Lodge Restaurant	R			£75									Dunderry Navan
Mullingar	Crookedwood House	R			£55					Family				Crookedwood Mullingar
Navan	Ardboyne Hotel	HR	£75	60%	£55	27	700	400						Dublin Road Navan
Skryne	O'Connell's Pub	P												Skryne nr Tara

Co Monaghan

Town	Establishment	Type	£	%	£								Location
Carrickmacross	Nuremore Hotel	H	£120	72%		69	300	500	yes		yes	yes	Carrickmacross
Scotshouse	Hilton Park	A	£111	62%		5					yes	yes	Scotshouse nr Clones

Co Offaly

Town	Establishment	Type	£	%	£								Location
Birr	Dooly's Hotel	H	£50	60%		18				Family			Birr
Birr	Tullanisk	A	£76			7							Birr

Co Roscommon

Town	Establishment	Type	£	%	£								Location
Athleague	Fitzmaurice's Tavern	P	£90			46							Athleague
Hodson Bay	Hodson Bay Hotel	H	£90	65%			500	400	yes		yes		Hodson Bay nr Athlone

Co Sligo

Town	Establishment	Type	£	%	£								Location
Ballisodare	The Thatch	P											Ballisodare
Ballymote	Temple House	A	£70	61%		5							Ballymote
Boyle	Cromleach Lodge	HR*	£118	78%	£75	10							Ballindoon Castlebaldwin nr Boyle
Colloney	Glebe House	RR	£30		£45	4							Colloney
Colloney	Markree Castle	H	£97	61%		15	40	100					Colloney
Drumcliffe	Yeats Tavern	P											Drumcliffe
Riverstown	Coopershill House	AR	£84	69%	£50	7			yes				Coopershill Riverstown
Rosses Point	Austie's	P											Rosses Point
Rosses Point	The Moorings	R			£45				yes	Family			Rosses Point
Sligo	Hargadon's	P											O'Connell Street Sligo
Sligo	McGettigan's	P											Connolly Street Sligo
Sligo	Sligo Park	H	£95	58%		89				Family			Pearse Road Sligo
Sligo	Truffles Restaurant	R			£22						yes	yes	The Mall Sligo
Tubbercurry	Killoran's	P								Family			Main Street Tubbercurry

Co Tipperary

Location	Establishment	Cat	Room Price	%	Food Price	Rooms	Conf	Banq	Beaut Sit	Family Friendly	Leis Cntr	Swim Pool	Golf	Address
Birdhill	Matt the Thresher	P												Birdhill
Cashel	Chez Hans	R			£70									Rockside Cashel
Cashel	Dowling's	P												Cashel
Clonmel	Clonmel Arms	H	£83	61%		31	450	400						Sarsfield Street Clonmel
Dundrum	Dundrum House	H	£84	66%		55	400	350	yes				yes	Dundrum Cashel
Glen of Aherlow	Aherlow House	H	£53	63%		10	280	220	yes					Glen of Aherlow nr Tipperary
Kilcoran	Kilcoran Lodge	H	£68	58%		23	300	220			yes	yes		Kilcoran Cahir
Killaloe	Goosers	P												Killaloe Ballina

Co Waterford

Location	Establishment	Cat	Room Price	%	Food Price	Rooms	Conf	Banq	Beaut Sit	Family Friendly	Leis Cntr	Swim Pool	Golf	Address
Cheekpoint	McAlpin's Suir Inn	P												Cheekpoint
Dunmore East	The Ship	P								Family				Dunmore East
Waterford	Dwyer's Restaurant	R			£55									8 Mary Street Waterford
Waterford	Granville Hotel	H	£79	69%		74	300	200						Waterford
Waterford	Jack Meade's Bar	P								Family				Ballycanavan Little Halfway House
Waterford	Jurys Hotel	H	£106	61%		98	700	600				yes		Ferrybank Waterford
Waterford	Prendiville's	RR	£44		£60	9								Cork Road Waterford
Waterford	Tower Hotel	H	£114	59%		141	500	600			yes	yes		The Mall Waterford
Waterford	Waterford Castle	HR	£205	76%	£80	19	16		yes			yes	yes	The Island Ballinakill Waterford
Glasson	Glasson Village Restaurant	R			£50									Glasson Athlone

Co Westmeath

Location	Establishment	Cat	Room Price	%	Food Price	Rooms	Conf	Banq	Beaut Sit	Family Friendly	Leis Cntr	Swim Pool	Golf	Address
Glasson	Grogan's	P												Glasson nr Athlone
Kinnegad	The Cottage	R												Kinnegad

Co Wexford

Town	Name	Type	£	%	£	No.	No.	No.		Family			Address
Ballyhack	Neptune Restaurant	R			£50								Ballyhack New Ross
Carne	Lobster Pot	R			£50								Carne
Ferrycarrig Bridge	Ferrycarrig Hotel	H	£90	61%		40	400	400	yes	Family			Ferrycarrig Bridge nr Wexford
Foulksmills	Horetown House	R			£50								Foulksmills
Gorey	Marlfield House	HR	£140	81%	£90	19	20	30					Gorey
Newbawn	Cedar Lodge	H	£75	62%		18	100	70	yes				Carrigbyrne Newbawn
Newbay	Newbay Country House	A	£60			6							Newbay nr Wexford
Rosslare	Great Southern	H	£87	62%		99	150	200		Family	yes	yes	Rosslare
Rosslare	Kelly's Strand Hotel	H	£84	71%		99	20			Family		yes	Rosslare
Wexford	White's Hotel	H	£69	62%		82	600	450					George Street Wexford

Co Wicklow

Town	Name	Type	£	%	£	No.	No.	No.				Address
Blessington	Downshire House	H	£63	59%		25	100	250				Blessington
Bray	Tree of Idleness	R			£65							Seafront Bray
Delgany	Glenview Hotel	H	£70	63%		42	300	200	yes			Glen of the Downs Delgany
Delgany	Wicklow Arms	P										Delgany
Dunlavin	Rathsallagh House	AR	£110	67%	£65	14	50		yes		yes	Dunlavin
Enniskerry	Curtlestown House	R			£50							Curtlestown Enniskerry
Enniskerry	Enniscree Lodge	HR	£75	59%	£60	10						Glencree Valley Enniskerry
Greystones	The Hungry Monk	R			£55							Greystones
Laragh	Mitchell's of Laragh	R			£25							The Old Schoolhouse Laragh
Rathnew	Hunter's Hotel	HR	£80	60%	£55	17	20	30		yes		Newrath Bridge Rathnew
Rathnew	Tinakilly House	HR	£110	76%	£75	29	150	100		yes		Rathnew Wicklow
Roundwood	Roundwood Inn	R			£60	5						Roundwood
Wicklow	Old Rectory	AR	£88	59%	£60						yes	Wicklow

NORTHERN IRELAND ENTRIES LISTED IN COUNTY ORDER

HR = Hotel with recommended Restaurant open to public   H = Hotel   RR = Restaurant with Rooms   R = Restaurant open to public   P = Pub
See Starred Restaurants and map on page 13 for ★ and ↑ restaurant listings.
Some hotels are ungraded due to their categorisation as a Private House Hotel or Inns without public rooms (see Quick Reference Lists); the former are usually de luxe B&B establishments and their restaurant may not generally be open to non-residents. Restaurants with Rooms are also ungraded.
Other hotels (for example the *Europa Hotel* in Belfast) may be currently undergoing substantial renovation work that may radically change the hotel's grading when completed. Restaurants without prices are generally of an informal, snackier nature.

Co Antrim

Location	Establishment	Cat	Room Price	%	Food Price	Rooms	Conf	Banq	Beaut Sit	Family Friendly	Leis Cntr	Swim Pool	Golf	Address
Ballycastle	House of McDonnell	P												21 Castle Street Ballycastle
Ballymena	Galgorm Manor	HR	£95	71%	£68	23	60	60	yes					136 Fenaghy Road Ballymena
Belfast	Antica Roma	R			£62									67-69 Botanic Avenue Belfast
Belfast	Bengal Brasserie	R			£33									339 Ormeau Road Belfast
Belfast	Crown Liquor Saloon	P												46 Great Victoria Street Belfast
Belfast	Dukes Hotel	H	£92	67%		21	130	140						65 University Street Belfast
Belfast	Europa Hotel	H	£120			184	1200	600						Great Victoria Street Belfast
Belfast	Kelly's Cellars	P												Bank Street Belfast
Belfast	Manor House	R			£40									43-47 Donegall Pass Belfast
Belfast	Nick's Warehouse	R			£45									35-39 Hill Street Belfast
Belfast	Plaza Hotel	H	£82	64%		83	100	100						15 Brunswick Street Belfast
Belfast	Roscoff	R★			£75									Lesley House Shaftesbury Square
Belfast	Speranza	R			£38					Family				16 Shaftesbury Square Belfast
Belfast	Stormont Hotel	H	£115	69%		107	500	350						587 Upper Newtownards Road
Belfast	Strand Restaurant	R			£35									12 Stranmillis Road Belfast
Belfast	Villa Italia	R			£44									39 University Road Belfast
Belfast	Welcome Restaurant	R			£40									22 Stranmillis Road Belfast
Belfast	Wellington Park	H	£90	59%		50	180	120						21 Malone Road Belfast

Location	Name	Type	Price	%	£						Address
Belfast Int'nl A'port	Novotel	H	£75	62%		108	250	180	Family		Belfast International Airport Belfast
Bushmills	Bushmills Inn	H	£74	58%		11	85	85			25 Main Street Bushmills
Carnlough	Londonderry Arms	P									20 Harbour Road Carnlough
Carnlough	The Waterfall	P									High Street Carnlough
Carrickfergus	Wind-Rose Wine Bar	R									The Marina Carrickfergus
Cushendall	PJ McCollam	P									23 Mill Street Cushendall
Dunadry	Dunadry Inn	H	£105	64%		67	350	300	Family	yes	2 Islandreagh Drive Dunadry
Dunmurry	Forte Crest Belfast	H	£98	67%		82	450	350			300 Kingsway Dunmurry
Larne	Magheramorne House	H	£66	63%		22	180	180			59 Shore Road Magheramorne Larne
Portballintrae	Bayview Hotel	H	£65	58%		16	150	150		yes	2 Bayhead Road Portballintrae
Portrush	Ramore	R*			£55						The Harbour Portrush
Templepatrick	Templeton Hotel	H	£100	66%		20	400	350			882 Antrim Road Templepatrick Ballyclare

Co Down

Location	Name	Type	Price	%	£						Address
Annalong	Glasdrumman Lodge	HR	£95	69%	£60	10	16	60			85 Mill Road Annalong
Comber	La Mon House	H	£85	59%		38	1100	450	Family	yes	The Mills 41 Gransha Road Comber
Crawfordsburn	Old Inn	H	£85			34	150	90			15 Main Street Crawfordsburn
Helen's Bay	Deanes on the Square	R†			£58						7 Station Square Helen's Bay
Holywood	Bay Tree	R									118 High St Audley Court H'wood
Holywood	Culloden Hotel	HR	£140	72%	£65	91	500	300		yes	142 Bangor Craigavad Rd H'wood
Holywood	Sullivans	R			£55						Sullivan Place Holywood
Newcastle	Slieve Donard Hotel	H	£99	63%		110	1000	440		yes	Downs Road Newcastle
Portaferry	Portaferry Hotel	HR	£75	63%	£65	14	30	80			10 The Strand Portaferry

Co Fermanagh

Location	Name	Type	Address
Enniskillen	Blakes of the Hollow	P	6 Church Street Enniskillen

Co Londonderry

Location	Establishment	Cat	Room Price	%	Food Price	Rooms	Conf	Banq	Beaut Sit	Family Friendly	Leis Cntr	Swim Pool	Golf	Address
Aghadowey	Greenhill House	H	£40			6								24 Greenhill Road Aghadowey
Garvagh	MacDuff's Restaurant, Blackheath House	RR	£55		£50	5								112 Killeague Road Garvagh
Londonderry	Beech Hill House Hotel	HR†	£85	59%	£50	17								32 Ardmore Road Londonderry
Londonderry	Everglades Hotel	H	£78	59%		52	350	250						Prehen Road Londonderry

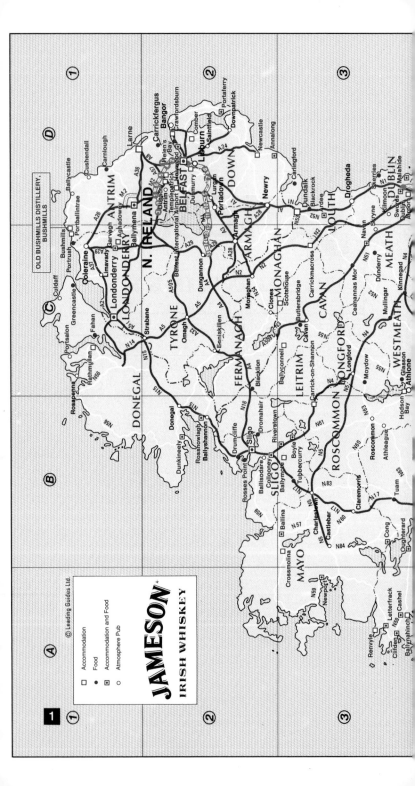

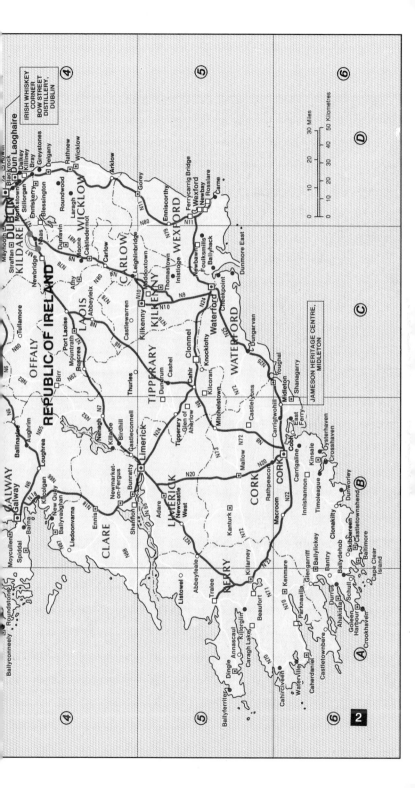

N3 to
TRIM 45 (28)
KELLS 62 (39)
NAVAN 46 (29)

N2 to
ASHBOURNE 21 (13)
SLANE 46 (29)
DERRY 235 (147)

Kavanagh's
Forte
Crest,
Dublin
Airport
The
Brian
Boru

N1 to
AIRPORT 10 (6)
BALBRIGGAN 32 (20)
DROGHEDA 50 (31)
DUNDALK 85 (53)
BELFAST 166 (104)

Marino

to
MALAHIDE
14 (9)

Cabra

Prison

PHIBSBOROUGH

Ta Se Mahogani
Gaspipes

Ryans

CONNOLLY STATION

PRO CATHEDRAL

CUSTOM HOUSE

TARA QUAY

Alexandra
Basin

River Liffey

HEUSTON
STA

GUINNESS
BREWERY

Kilmainham

CHRIST CHURCH
CATHEDRAL

CASTLE

CITY HALL

PEARSE STA

Ringsend

ST PATRICK
CATHEDRAL

MUSEUM

GOVERNMENT
BUILDINGS

Dolphin's
Barn

For central area, see pages 5 & 6

LANSDOWNE
ROAD
STA

Donaghagh

BALLSBRIDGE

Sandymount

Merrion
Hall

Harold's
Cross

Ranelagh

Cemetery

Sachs
Hospitals

N7 to
NAAS 34 (21)
KILKENNY 117 (73)
WATERFORD 157 (98)
LIMERICK 197 (123)
CORK 258 (161)
KILLARNEY 306 (191)

RATHMINES

Kielys

Donny
brook
Furama

RDS
SHOWGROUNDS
Ernie's

Anglesea
Town House

Zen

Milltown

Ashtons

RTE
Studios

Ivy Court

Rathgar

University
College

Kimmage

Terenure

Windy
Arbour

to N7 for
NAAS 34 (21)
KILKENNY 117 (73)
WATERFORD 157 (98)
LIMERICK 197 (123)
CORK 258 (161)
KILLARNEY 306 (191)
N81 to
BLESSINGTON 30 (19)

Club
House

Milltown
Golf Course

Rathfarnham

Club
House

Castle
Golf Course

Yellow
House

Willbrook

Goatstown
The Goat

to DUBLIN MTS

DUNDRUM

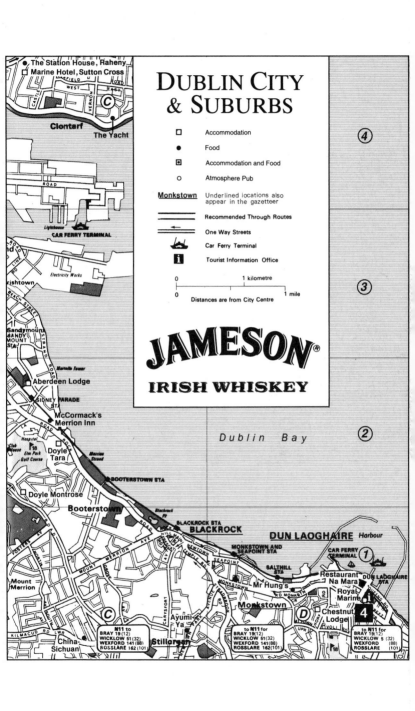

DUBLIN CITY & SUBURBS

□	Accommodation
●	Food
⊡	Accommodation and Food
○	Atmosphere Pub
<u>Monkstown</u>	Underlined locations also appear in the gazetteer
═══════	Recommended Through Routes
←──────	One Way Streets
⛴	Car Ferry Terminal
i	Tourist Information Office

0   1 kilometre

0   1 mile

Distances are from City Centre

JAMESON®
IRISH WHISKEY

The Station House, Raheny
Marine Hotel, Sutton Cross

C

Clontarf

The Yacht

Lighthouse

CAR FERRY TERMINAL

Electricity Works

ishtown

Sandymount
SANDY
MOUNT
STA.

Martello Tower

Aberdeen Lodge

SIDNEY PARADE STA.

McCormack's
Merrion Inn

Hospital
Elm Park
Golf Course

Doyle
Tara

Marine
Strand

BOOTERSTOWN STA.

Doyle Montrose

Booterstown

Blackrock Pk

BLACKROCK STA.
BLACKROCK

Dublin Bay

DUN LAOGHAIRE Harbour

CAR FERRY TERMINAL

①

MONKSTOWN AND
SEAPOINT STA.

SALTHILL STA.

Restaurant
Na Mara

DUN LAOGHAIRE
STA.

Royal
Marine

Mr Hung's

Monkstown

Chestnut
Lodge

4

Mount
Merrion

C

Ayumi
Ya

Stillorgan

China-
Sichuan

N11 to
BRAY 19(12)
WICKLOW 51(32)
WEXFORD 141(88)
ROSSLARE 162(101)

to N11 for
BRAY 19(12)
WICKLOW 51(32)
WEXFORD 141(88)
ROSSLARE 162(101)

D

to N11 for
BRAY 19(12)
WICKLOW 5 (32)
WEXFORD (88)
ROSSLARE (101)

④

③

②

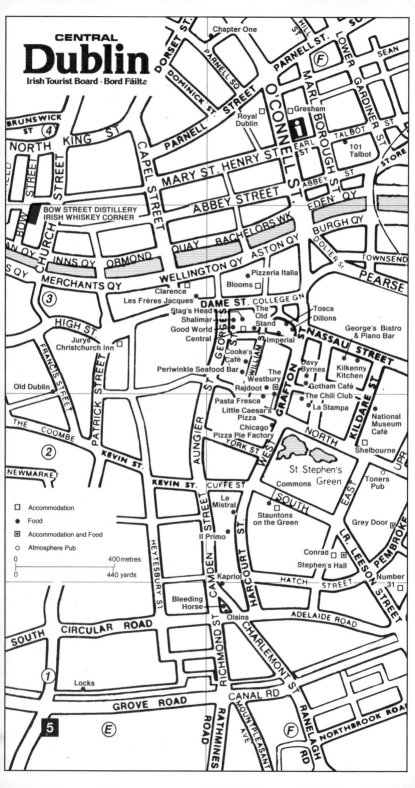

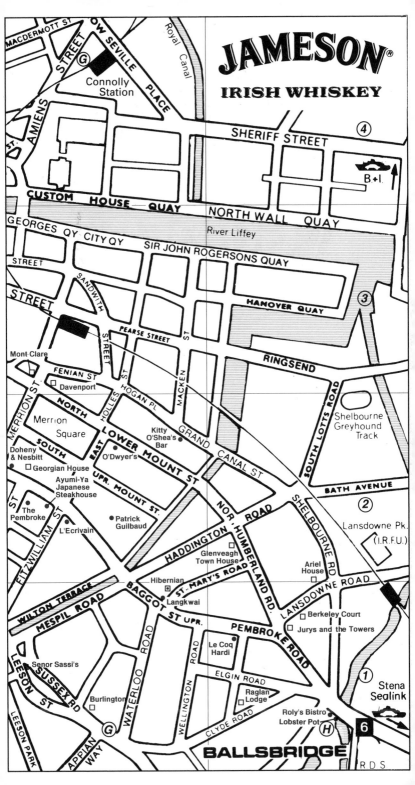

Recommended by

EGON RONAY'S GUIDES

1994

YOUR GUARANTEE
OF
QUALITY AND INDEPENDENCE

- Establishment inspections are anonymous

- Inspections are undertaken by qualified
  Egon Ronay's Guides' inspectors

- The Guides are completely independent
  in their editorial selection

- The Guides do not accept advertising,
  hospitality or payment from listed
  establishments

Hotels & Restaurants   Pubs & Inns
Just A Bite   Oriental Restaurants
. . . . And Baby Comes Too   Ireland
Paris Restaurants & Bistros   Europe

READERS' COMMENTS

Please use this sheet, and the continuation overleaf, to recommend hotels, restaurants or pubs of **really outstanding quality.**

Complaints about any of the Guide's entries will be treated seriously and passed on to our inspectorate, but we would like to remind you always to take up your complaint with the management at the time.

We regret that owing to the volume of readers' communications received each year we will be unable to acknowledge all these forms, but your comments will certainly be seriously considered.

Please post to: **Egon Ronay's Guides, 35 Tadema Road, London SW10 0PZ**

Please use an up-to-date Guide. We publish annually. (IRELAND 1994)

Name and address of establishment	Your recommendation or complaint

Readers' Comments continued

Name and address of establishment   **Your recommendation or complaint**

Your Name (BLOCK LETTERS PLEASE)

Address

READERS' COMMENTS

Please use this sheet, and the continuation overleaf, to recommend hotels,
restaurants or pubs of **really outstanding quality.**

Complaints about any of the Guide's entries will be treated seriously and
passed on to our inspectorate, but we would like to remind you always to
take up your complaint with the management at the time.

We regret that owing to the volume of readers' communications received
each year we will be unable to acknowledge all these forms, but your
comments will certainly be seriously considered.

Please post to: **Egon Ronay's Guides, 35 Tadema Road, London SW10 0PZ**

Please use an up-to-date Guide. We publish annually. (IRELAND 1994)

Name and address of establishment	Your recommendation or complaint

336

Readers' Comments continued

Name and address of establishment **Your recommendation or complaint**

_____ _____

_____ _____

_____ _____

_____ _____

_____ _____

_____ _____

_____ _____

_____ _____

_____ _____

_____ _____

_____ _____

_____ _____

_____ _____

Your Name (BLOCK LETTERS PLEASE)

_____

Address

_____

_____

_____

_____